Kay Robison

are room is

_____ yards and inches or 14 feet

9 yards 26 inches or 56 feet

27 2 inches   X 9 yd   2 in.   Long

18 ft   10 in.   X 63 yd   10 in. Wide

Row - Peterson Arithmetic

BOOK FIVE

By

HARRY GROVE WHEAT

GERALDINE KAUFFMAN

HARL R. DOUGLASS

Illustrated by

Bill Neebe and Jane Scott

ROW, PETERSON AND COMPANY

EVANSTON, ILLINOIS   WHITE PLAINS, NEW YORK

CONTENTS

Chapter 1
Adding and Subtracting

Using Arithmetic

The pupils in the fifth grade at Riverside School were telling about the uses they made of arithmetic during the summer vacation.

"I had to use arithmetic every day while I was away at camp," said Alice. "Mother sent me $8.00 each week, and I had to pay $6.50 as my share of the camp expenses."

"Well!" said Henry. "The manager of the camp gave you a dollar and fifty cents change, and you had that left. Not much arithmetic there."

"Yes, but there was," answered Alice. "I had to buy stamps, paper, envelopes, and post cards, and then I bought candy and ice cream—all with my $1.50. I had to subtract and multiply and count change."

Robert spoke up, "I use arithmetic all the time. I have a paper route. My papers cost 12¢ a week, and I collect 20¢ a week from each person who takes a paper. I deliver papers to 45 houses each morning."

"I mowed lawns for the neighbors. For some lawns I got 50¢, and for others I got 75¢. Mr. Hill gave me $1.25 to mow his lawn," said George. "I used arithmetic to keep a record of what I was making, spending, and saving. I added when I was making money, and I subtracted when I was spending money."

"I checked our grocery bills," said Grace. "Father told me that it was a good idea to check each purchase because people sometimes make mistakes. So each time I bought groceries, I checked the bill."

Using Arithmetic

"I guess I had to use arithmetic more than anyone else," said Jack Woods. "I worked as a clerk in the grocery store. Elsie was one of my best customers."

Working in the store gave Jack a lot of practice in arithmetic. Here are a few of his problems:

1. One day Elsie bought a bag of sugar for 35 cents and a box of oatmeal for 29 cents. How much should Elsie pay for the groceries? How much should Jack charge her for the groceries?

2. Another day Elsie bought a loaf of bread for 16¢. She gave Jack a quarter. How much change should he give Elsie?

Jack did not subtract to find how many cents he should give Elsie. He just counted the change. He counted it to himself as he took the money from the cash box, and he counted it aloud as he gave it to Elsie.

Count Elsie's change as Jack did.

Elsie was a careful shopper; so she counted the change to herself as Jack counted it aloud.

3. If Elsie had paid for her 16-cent loaf of bread with a half dollar, how should Jack have counted her change?

4. Mr. Brown bought a dozen eggs for 42¢. He gave Jack a dollar. Jack had no half dollars. Tell several ways in which he might have made Mr. Brown's change.

5. On the way home from delivering papers, Robert bought a pound of butter for 59¢, a quart of milk for 17¢, and a loaf of bread for 16¢. What was his bill?

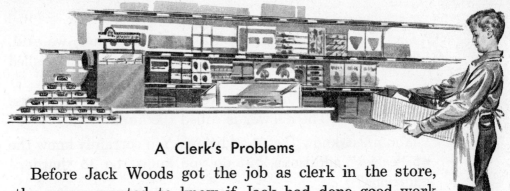

A Clerk's Problems

Before Jack Woods got the job as clerk in the store, the owner wanted to know if Jack had done good work in arithmetic. Why do you suppose the owner of the store wanted to know about that?

Every day Jack had problems in arithmetic to work, and it was a very good thing for Jack that he was able to work them correctly.

1. One day Mrs. Rankin bought the following:

6 quarts of strawberries at 25¢ a quart

25 pounds of sugar at 5¢ a pound

4 packages of jar rubbers at 10¢ a package

What did Jack have to do to find the cost of the strawberries? How did he find the cost of the sugar? of the rubbers?

What did Jack have to do to find the cost of all?

2. Mrs. Rankin gave Jack a 5-dollar bill to pay for the berries, sugar, and rubbers. Did Jack find out how much change to give Mrs. Rankin? What did he do?

3. The owner of the grocery told Jack that he had to get $9.00 for 6 baskets of peaches he had for sale. How did Jack find out how much to charge for each?

To solve everyday problems, we must be able to add, subtract, multiply, and divide correctly and quickly.

7

$$\left.\begin{array}{r}7 \\ 6 \\ 3 \\ \hline 16\end{array}\right\}\text{ addends}$$

16   *sum*

When we think numbers together, we **add**. The sign that tells us to add is called the **plus** sign. We write it like this: +.

The numbers we add are called **addends**. The answer is called the **sum**.

You must know the 81 additions. You certainly know the 45 "easier" additions, but do you know the 36 "harder" additions?

Say the answers to these addition questions:

8	7	6	6	3	9	5	5	8
9	4	7	5	8	7	9	6	8
6	2	9	7	8	8	4	6	5
6	9	4	6	5	3	9	9	8
6	8	7	4	9	8	9	7	9
8	4	7	8	3	6	9	5	6
4	5	7	7	8	3	9	9	9
7	7	9	8	7	9	8	5	2

Find the answer to any question that you do not know. You may use what you know about ten to find the answer.

Suppose you do not know the answer to $\begin{array}{r}8\\9\\\hline\end{array}$

Think: Eight and two are ten.

Two from nine is seven.

Ten and seven are seventeen.

Eight and nine are seventeen.

Now study the addition so that you will remember it. Say over and over, "Eight and nine are seventeen."

8

[Self-test]   **Reviewing Subtraction**

When we think numbers away, we **subtract**.
When we compare two numbers, we **subtract**.
We have a sign that tells us to subtract.
We call it the **minus** sign. We write it: **−**.

97	minuend
−35	subtrahend
62	remainder
	or
	difference

The number that we subtract is called the **subtrahend**. The larger number from which we subtract is called the **minuend**. The subtraction answer is called the **remainder** or **difference**.

You must know the 81 subtractions. Surely you know the 45 "easier" subtractions, but do you know the 36 "harder" subtractions?

Say the answers to these subtraction questions:

11	12	12	13	14	11	13	15	11
2	3	4	6	9	3	4	8	4

12	11	13	12	15	13	11	14	13
6	5	9	7	9	5	8	6	8

12	13	11	12	11	14	15	14	15
5	7	6	8	9	7	6	8	7

16	12	14	18	11	17	16	17	16
8	9	5	9	7	9	7	8	9

Find the answer to any question that you do not know. You may use what you know about ten to find the answer.

Suppose you do not know the answer to 17 −8.
Think: Eight from ten is two.
Two and seven are nine.
Eight from seventeen is nine.

Now study the subtraction so that you will remember it. Say over and over, "Eight from seventeen is nine."

9

Adding Tens

```
30
50
──
80
```

There are no ones to add; so we write 0 in one's place in the answer. Then we add the tens and write 8 in ten's place in the answer.

```
45
34
──
79
```

First, we add the ones and write 9 in one's place in the answer. Then we add the tens and write the ten's answer in ten's place.

```
40
58
──
98
```

There are only 8 ones; so we write 8 in one's place. Then we add the tens and write the ten's answer in ten's place.

```
75
63
───
138
```

First, we add the ones and write the 8 in its proper place. Then we add the tens: Seven and six are thirteen. Thirteen tens are 1 hundred and 3 tens; so we write 1 in hundred's place and 3 in ten's place.

We add tens the way we add ones.

Add these numbers down. Then add up to check.

	(a)	(b)	(c)	(d)	(e)	(f)	(g)	(h)	(i)
1.	32	67	60	43	44	53	86	54	80
	45	12	37	52	30	43	12	24	40
2.	56	71	52	77	63	61	51	92	84
	30	34	56	41	55	70	96	64	52
3.	50	62	33	70	78	95	60	72	45
	66	62	76	53	70	41	44	67	70
4.	87	49	92	51	23	91	80	42	30
	70	90	13	78	80	51	61	61	85

Subtracting Tens

There are no ones to subtract; so we write 0 in one's place in the answer. Then we subtract the tens and write 8 in ten's place in the answer.

First, we subtract the ones and write 5 in one's place in the answer. Then we subtract the tens and write 8 in ten's place.

There are no ones to subtract from 7; so we write 7 in one's place. Then we subtract the tens and write 7 in ten's place.

Think: Five from eight is three
Four from ten is six.

There are no ones left when we subtract 8 from 8; so we write 0 in one's place. The 0 puts our ten's answer in ten's place. Then we subtract the tens.

We subtract tens the way we subtract ones.

150
70
80
148
63
85
137
60
77
108
45
63
148
68
80

Copy and subtract:

	(a)	(b)	(c)	(d)	(e)	(f)	(g)	(h)
1.	160 90	120 70	109 35	147 82	158 75	137 84	108 86	119 64
2.	128 83	139 76	157 83	118 74	107 66	127 67	135 65	124 54
3.	169 87	178 97	143 63	138 52	149 73	106 43	115 53	119 88
4.	108 98	119 49	109 22	116 34	117 25	172 82	166 72	156 96

Adding and Subtracting Hundreds

We add hundreds the way we add tens and ones.

456	First, we add the ones. Next, we add	400
423	the tens. Last, we add the hundreds.	500
879	We write each part of the answer in its	900

proper place, using 0 when we need it.

Tell how these numbers were added:

434	403	640	600	638	788	405	638
653	502	340	400	520	600	580	520
1087	905	980	1000	1158	1388	985	1158

Copy and add:

	(a)	(b)	(c)	(d)	(e)	(f)	(g)
1.	854	643	534	850	760	856	876
	802	444	700	640	712	430	722
2.	407	780	434	529	903	502	656
	660	405	355	670	576	896	713

We subtract hundreds the way we subtract tens and ones.

975	First, we subtract the ones, next, the	1000
424	tens, last, the hundreds.	800
551	We write each part of the answer in its	200

proper place, using 0 when we need it.

Tell how these numbers were subtracted:

850	1286	1592	1086	1488	1697	1308	1500
630	432	770	543	968	997	605	600
220	854	822	543	520	700	703	900

Copy and subtract:

3.	1135	1598	1465	1370	1470	1354	1548
	902	698	903	570	930	930	835
4.	1678	1565	1679	1465	1442	1775	1234
	870	964	900	810	940	825	932

Dollars and Cents

$5.30 is read: *Five dollars and thirty cents.*

Read these amounts of money:

$6.02	$10.05	$12.65	$15.00	$80.10	$1.04
$.80	$.03	$15.60	$20.20	$75.66	$5.50

We write ten dollars and six cents like this: $10.06.

Write with figures these amounts of money:

four cents	one dollar and ten cents	forty cents
sixty dollars	six dollars and six cents	eighty dollars

How do we add and subtract dollars and cents?

$4.65	$ 8.26	$ 9.06		$10.80	$15.90	$17.85
3.20	2.73	8.12		3.50	7.00	9.25
$7.85	$10.99	$17.18		$ 7.30	$ 8.90	$ 8.60

Copy and add:

	(a)	(b)	(c)	(d)	(e)	(f)	(g)
1.	$4.45	$6.70	$6.10	$7.15	$9.05	$9.00	$6.05
	7.00	8.10	9.35	8.50	8.60	7.05	9.80
2.	$5.00	$1.90	$9.50	$9.50	$6.45	$5.10	$3.54
	5.90	9.06	6.00	8.30	5.50	9.70	7.44

Copy and subtract:

	(a)	(b)	(c)	(d)	(e)	(f)
3.	$15.75	$12.80	$13.80	$14.85	$10.95	$14.75
	7.25	8.50	7.80	9.80	8.75	7.05
4.	$16.60	$10.98	$12.08	$15.88	$15.55	$18.80
	7.00	5.45	7.05	9.06	9.52	9.50
5.	$1.50	$1.65	$1.00	$1.35	$1.75	$1.80
	.80	.90	.80	.80	.75	.90

Adding and Subtracting Thousands

How do we add thousands?

4000	3010	3200	3000	3450	5005	4500
5000	5000	5000	5286	5508	4003	5300
9000	8010	8200	8286	8958	9008	9800

Copy and add:

	(a)	(b)	(c)	(d)	(e)	(f)	(g)
1.	3000	6000	4040	2400	3426	3605	5453
	5000	2000	5030	4300	3353	3353	2103
2.	1106	4555	3326	2090	4363	5006	2650
	4780	5420	2452	7806	4524	2103	2040

How do we subtract thousands?

6000	9050	10000	10980	11258	12708	14976
4000	4050	5000	7450	4055	4703	5430
2000	5000	5000	3530	7203	8005	9546

Copy and subtract:

	(a)	(b)	(c)	(d)	(e)	(f)
3.	14996	13634	16555	11898	16768	12786
	6654	8230	9530	8234	7262	7150
4.	10870	13786	16982	13860	10904	11777
	5870	6666	7432	4000	9900	5247

Copy and add:

	(a)	(b)	(c)	(d)	(e)	(f)
5.	$50.70	$25.75	$70.10	$68.05	$10.10	$20.80
	60.25	80.20	80.05	40.90	75.65	3.15

Copy and subtract:

	(a)	(b)	(c)	(d)	(e)	(f)
6.	$125.80	$115.75	$160.85	$95.80	$110.75	$78.95
	80.50	80.25	90.80	25.70	20.70	58.15

14

Adding by Endings

<table>
<tr><td>4
3
—
7</td><td>When we see 14 and 3, we know that the sum is like the sum of 4 and 3, but with a ten.</td><td>14
3
—
17</td></tr>
<tr><td>5
4
—
9</td><td>Think: 4 and 3 are 7; so 14 and 3 are 17.

◆

Think: 5 and 4 are 9; so 25 and 4 are 29.</td><td>25
4
—
29</td></tr>
</table>

1. Study these sums. How are they alike?

6	16	26	36	46	5	15	35	45	65
2	2	2	2	2	4	4	4	4	4
8	18	28	38	48	9	19	39	49	69

2. Say the sums only:

12	14	20	22	21	32	16	24	22	31
4	3	4	6	4	6	3	4	3	4

10	11	12	13	14	12	23	14	11	10
5	6	5	6	4	7	6	5	3	6

20	21	21	22	23	23	24	22	21	24
6	5	6	7	5	4	5	4	7	3

32	34	35	45	31	34	36	35	37	26
3	5	2	4	6	4	2	3	2	3

3. Jane made 12 valentines, and she bought 6 more. How many valentines did she have in all?

4. Joe spent 44¢ for a ticket to the show and 5¢ for a bag of peanuts. How much did he spend for both?

5. June has 42¢. If she had 2 more cents, she could go to the show. How much does a ticket cost?

Adding by Endings

6	We know that 6 and 4 are 10 and that 16 is ten more than 6. So 16 and 4 are 2 tens or 20.	16
4		4
10		20
8	We know that 8 and 6 are 14 and that 18 is ten more than 8. So 18 and 6 are ten more than 14. 18 and 6 are 24.	18
6		6
14		24

1. Study these examples:

6	16	26	36	46	7	17	27	37	47
5	5	5	5	5	7	7	7	7	7
11	21	31	41	51	14	24	34	44	54

8	18	28	38	48	8	18	28	38	48
4	4	4	4	4	2	2	2	2	2
12	22	32	42	52	10	20	30	40	50

2. Say the answers:

11	13	15	14	17	14	18	19	17	15
9	8	8	9	4	6	6	5	3	5

18	12	13	17	12	19	17	13	18	21
8	8	9	6	9	4	5	7	5	9

22	24	35	35	44	38	22	24	36	24
8	8	6	8	8	5	9	7	7	6

36	42	38	39	23	24	25	25	26	27
6	9	8	5	8	9	7	8	8	5

32	33	34	36	39	39	37	35	36	33
8	8	7	8	4	8	4	9	9	9

Column Addition

Begin at the top, and add down.
Think: 6 and 7 are 13, and 3 are 16, and 5 are 21.
To check, add up.
Think: 5 and 3 are 8, and 7 are 15, and 6 are 21.

```
 6              6
 7              7
 3              3
 5              5
---            ---
21             21
```
Check

Copy and add:

	(a)	(b)	(c)	(d)	(e)	(f)	(g)	(h)	(i)	(j)
1.	7	3	6	9	1	3	7	4	8	6
	7	9	8	1	8	8	9	7	6	5
	6	6	6	8	6	2	6	8	4	9
	5	5	4	7	8	9	5	7	8	7
2.	9	9	6	5	9	4	3	2	6	7
	5	7	8	7	6	8	9	8	6	6
	8	7	8	7	6	8	9	7	7	7
	9	9	6	5	9	4	3	6	7	6
3.	7	5	9	5	9	7	9	3	7	5
	5	9	6	3	8	5	1	8	4	4
	9	6	8	7	2	9	7	6	9	5
	8	8	9	4	9	5	8	8	8	7

Copy and add. Remember to keep the columns straight.

	(a)	(b)	(c)
4.	7 + 8 + 1 + 9 + 4	7 + 4 + 6 + 2 + 5	5 + 7 + 5 + 8 + 5
5.	8 + 4 + 4 + 1 + 5	7 + 7 + 5 + 4 + 1	7 + 2 + 8 + 6 + 8
6.	9 + 2 + 7 + 4 + 7	5 + 7 + 7 + 2 + 8	5 + 7 + 2 + 7 + 6

Carrying When We Add

When we add two-place numbers and the sum of the ones is 10 or more, what do we do with the ten?

```
 78      First, add the ones: 8 and 2 are 10. Write
 42    0 in one's place and carry 1 (ten).
───      Next, add the tens: 1 (carried) and 7 are
120    8, and 4 are 12.
```

Copy and add:

	(a)	(b)	(c)	(d)	(e)	(f)	(g)	(h)	(i)
1.	67	76	92	58	46	57	95	83	87
	56	58	48	54	54	44	76	98	77
2.	89	67	77	79	87	38	89	35	98
	59	33	25	68	89	77	66	67	53

```
 78      Sometimes we carry more than 1 ten.
 57      Add the ones: 8 and 7 are 15, and 9 are 24.
 99    Write 4 in one's place and carry 2 (tens).
───      Add the tens: 2 and 7 are 9, and 5 are 14,
234    and 9 are 23.
```

Copy and add:

3.	78	89	67	57	46	47	69	68	85
	66	86	79	68	88	47	69	19	29
	56	87	46	95	37	47	69	85	58
4.	70	98	88	88	9	19	89	79	68
	69	30	47	9	89	38	8	96	48
	38	67	70	16	4	76	16	8	96

Sometimes we carry to the hundred's column.
Add the ones: 2 and 5 are 7.
Add the tens: 8 and 6 are 14. Write 4 in ten's place and carry 1 (hundred).
Add the hundreds: 1 and 2 are 3, and 4 are 7.

$$\begin{array}{r} 282 \\ 465 \\ \hline 747 \end{array}$$

Copy and add:

	(a)	(b)	(c)	(d)	(e)	(f)	(g)	(h)
1.	524	382	580	490	635	275	370	497
	294	385	378	390	293	660	570	250
2.	567	480	353	763	680	460	784	980
	590	578	680	276	846	660	765	991

Sometimes we carry twice.
Add the ones: 8 and 7 are 15. Write 5 and carry 1. Then add the tens: 1 and 2 are 3, and 7 are 10. Write 0 in ten's place and carry 1. Now add the hundreds: 1 and 5 are 6, and 4 are 10.

$$\begin{array}{r} 528 \\ 477 \\ \hline 1005 \end{array}$$

Copy and add:

	(a)	(b)	(c)	(d)	(e)	(f)	(g)	(h)
3.	389	489	698	598	498	366	165	448
	512	223	45	57	168	264	755	455
4.	987	798	745	897	781	765	487	367
	833	474	866	695	699	765	578	689
5.	416	654	646	572	682	567	375	698
	889	497	688	479	788	766	58	64

Using a Ten in Subtracting

1. Explain each example on the board.

Copy and subtract:

	(a)	(b)	(c)	(d)	(e)	(f)	(g)	(h)	(i)
2.	81	95	64	73	132	157	112	142	133
	43	77	29	56	53	68	35	66	88
3.	161	112	153	131	132	164	117	163	142
	99	87	86	54	43	75	68	87	88
4.	144	115	177	155	155	158	145	163	184
	98	78	99	66	89	69	87	79	87

Copy and subtract:

	(a)	(b)	(c)	(d)	(e)	(f)	(g)
5.	$1.72	$1.21	$1.82	$1.46	$1.15	$1.63	$1.56
	.75	.84	.96	.58	.49	.78	.88
6.	$1.35	$1.28	$1.62	$1.72	$1.83	$1.64	$1.75
	.77	.39	.78	.85	.94	.96	.88

Carrying Back

Copy and subtract:

	(a)	(b)	(c)	(d)	(e)	(f)	(g)	(h)
1.	518	629	839	748	929	646	865	670
	332	243	554	555	566	365	370	490
2.	784	851	854	562	766	757	965	846
	390	291	174	372	480	487	392	486

Sometimes we carry back 1 ten and 1 hundred.

Think

$$\begin{array}{r} 642 \\ 285 \\ \hline 357 \end{array}$$

First, subtract the ones.
Next, subtract the tens.
Last, subtract the hundreds.

$$\begin{array}{r} {}^{5}\cancel{6}\ {}^{13}\cancel{4}{}^{1}2 \\ 2\ 8\ 5 \\ \hline 3\ 5\ 7 \end{array}$$

	(a)	(b)	(c)	(d)	(e)	(f)	(g)
3.	588	972	$3.15	$12.26	$15.81	$8.23	$8.62
	199	774	1.48	7.89	6.74	2.75	.86
4.	1554	1754	1535	1656	1787	1635	1451
	878	867	768	889	999	789	899
5.	1453	1653	1578	1232	1456	1224	1657
	877	876	789	789	967	896	799

Zeros in Subtraction

$$\begin{array}{r} {}^{79}\\ \cancel{80}{}^{1}0 \\ 31\ 6 \\ \hline 48\ 4 \end{array}$$

800 is 80 tens. We use 1 of the 80 tens and have 79 left.

1. Tell how these examples were worked:

$$\begin{array}{r} {}^{5\ 9\ 9}\\ \cancel{600}{}^{1}0 \\ 435\ 1 \\ \hline 164\ 9 \end{array}\qquad \begin{array}{r} {}^{3\ 9}\\ \cancel{40}{}^{1}2 \\ 29\ 6 \\ \hline 10\ 6 \end{array}\qquad \begin{array}{r} {}^{3\ 9}\\ \cancel{40}{}^{1}06 \\ 19\ 64 \\ \hline 20\ 42 \end{array}\qquad \begin{array}{r} {}^{6\ 9\ 14}\\ \cancel{70}\ \cancel{5}{}^{1}0 \\ 24\ 9\ 1 \\ \hline 45\ 5\ 9 \end{array}$$

Copy and subtract:

	(a)	(b)	(c)	(d)	(e)	(f)	(g)
2.	100	200	500	680	902	1000	1000
	25	176	204	356	538	250	256
3.	500	507	802	600	820	3003	5002
	182	295	548	499	367	2967	1686

4. Copy and subtract:

(a)	(b)	(c)	(d)	(e)	(f)	(g)
$10.00	$6.00	$7.05	$1.00	$1.05	$1.30	$5.00
7.50	2.07	4.98	.45	.09	.80	1.10

5. Three of the examples on the board are wrong. Find the mistakes and correct them.

$$\begin{array}{r} \$7.00 \\ 1.54 \\ \hline \$6.56 \end{array}\qquad \begin{array}{r} \$8.06 \\ 5.40 \\ \hline \$3.66 \end{array}\qquad \begin{array}{r} \$10.00 \\ 3.65 \\ \hline \$6.35 \end{array}\qquad \begin{array}{r} \$5.04 \\ 2.65 \\ \hline \$3.35 \end{array}$$

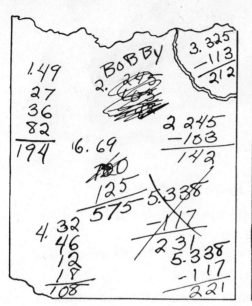

Writing Neat Papers

These arithmetic papers were written by two boys in the same class. Why is Jim's paper better than Bobby's?

Do you think it is a good plan to scratch out an example as Bobby scratched out example 2? See how neatly he crossed out example 5.

How do neat figures help you? Children often make mistakes in addition and subtraction when they do not make their figures well. Why should you write the figures in a straight column?

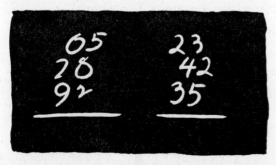

Jack's Account

1. Jack keeps his own account. In June he earned $22.50. In July he earned $25, and in August $18.75. How much did Jack earn that summer?

2. During the last two weeks in August, Jack went to Boy Scout Camp. His expenses the first week were $8.45. The second week they were $7.65. How much were his expenses for the whole time he was in camp?

3. When Jack got home, he bought a suit and an overcoat for $28.75. How much did he spend altogether for camp and new clothes?

4. How much of the money that Jack earned during the summer did he have left after he paid for his camp expenses and clothes?

5. That fall Jack's schoolbooks cost $6.75. How much money did he have left after he paid for them?

6. Jack wanted a new bicycle that cost $28.95, but he had only $14.65. His father offered to give him the amount of money he needed so that he could have his bicycle to use while the weather was nice. How much money did Jack need?

24

Copy and add:

	(a)	(b)	(c)	(d)	(e)	(f)	(g)	(h)	(i)
1.	43	27	63	50	30	94	52	84	70
	52	42	30	65	98	49	48	68	85
2.	564	247	624	178	655	895	777	684	921
	356	219	167	541	239	115	334	526	179
3.	8	8	6	14	17	82	79	18	31
	7	2	0	19	25	37	36	6	12
	6	0	7	3	66	65	68	57	8
	5	7	8	10	96	20	48	75	5
	4	9	5	6	43	54	87	66	38
4.	165	287	393	476	555	667	876	678	448
	98	102	560	457	80	155	100	51	248
	160	190	350	288	109	84	108	9	22
	446	258	49	104	18	107	96	106	10

Copy and subtract:

	(a)	(b)	(c)	(d)	(e)	(f)
5.	98	65	90	89	43	69
	28	42	30	7	8	64
6.	842	653	168	149	134	752
	512	511	77	61	129	628
7.	$9.65	$3.00	$40.34	$70.04	$46.00	$13.80
	8.15	1.23	31.38	58.50	6.06	6.76
8.	7884	4222	7004	8586	6222	5000
	1997	1057	1630	2490	5245	1648

Chapter 2
Multiplying and Dividing

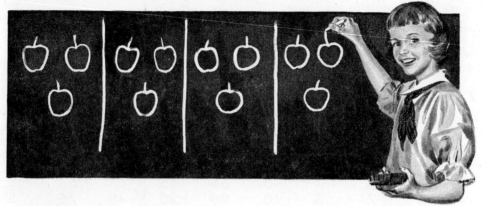

When we think equal groups together, we **multiply**. The sign (×) that tells us to multiply is called the **multiplication** sign, or **times** sign.

$$\begin{array}{r} 3 \\ \times 4 \\ \hline \end{array}$$

$$\begin{array}{r} 3 \\ \times 4 \\ \hline 12 \end{array}$$

4 × 3 =

Four threes are how many?
Four threes are twelve.

4 × 3 = 12

When we separate a group into a number of equal groups, we **divide**. When we separate an object into a number of equal parts, we **divide**.

This sign (÷) and this sign ($\overline{)}$) tell us to divide.

$3\overline{)12}$

$3\overline{)12}^{\,4}$

12 ÷ 3 =

How many 3's are in 12?
There are four 3's in 12.

12 ÷ 3 = 4

12 ÷ 3 means: **Divide 12 by 3.**

12 ÷ 3 = 4 is read: **Twelve divided by 3 is four.**

The 81 Multiplications

Here are the 81 multiplications. How many do you know? Cover the answers. Then say the answer to each question:

1 1 — 1	2 1 — 2	3 1 — 3	4 1 — 4	5 1 — 5	6 1 — 6	7 1 — 7	8 1 — 8	9 1 — 9
1 2 — 2	2 2 — 4	3 2 — 6	4 2 — 8	5 2 — 10	6 2 — 12	7 2 — 14	8 2 — 16	9 2 — 18
1 3 — 3	2 3 — 6	3 3 — 9	4 3 — 12	5 3 — 15	6 3 — 18	7 3 — 21	8 3 — 24	9 3 — 27
1 4 — 4	2 4 — 8	3 4 — 12	4 4 — 16	5 4 — 20	6 4 — 24	7 4 — 28	8 4 — 32	9 4 — 36
1 5 — 5	2 5 — 10	3 5 — 15	4 5 — 20	5 5 — 25	6 5 — 30	7 5 — 35	8 5 — 40	9 5 — 45
1 6 — 6	2 6 — 12	3 6 — 18	4 6 — 24	5 6 — 30	6 6 — 36	7 6 — 42	8 6 — 48	9 6 — 54
1 7 — 7	2 7 — 14	3 7 — 21	4 7 — 28	5 7 — 35	6 7 — 42	7 7 — 49	8 7 — 56	9 7 — 63
1 8 — 8	2 8 — 16	3 8 — 24	4 8 — 32	5 8 — 40	6 8 — 48	7 8 — 56	8 8 — 64	9 8 — 72
1 9 — 9	2 9 — 18	3 9 — 27	4 9 — 36	5 9 — 45	6 9 — 54	7 9 — 63	8 9 — 72	9 9 — 81

9×6

4×7

2×8

7×7

5×8

8×9

Swing
the lasso

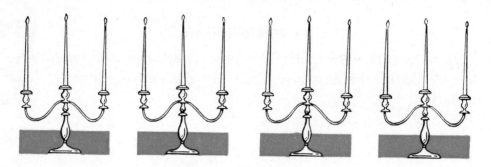

The 81 Divisions

[Self-test]

Here are the 81 divisions. Study them.

$$1\overline{)1}^{\,1} \quad 1\overline{)2}^{\,2} \quad 1\overline{)3}^{\,3} \quad 1\overline{)4}^{\,4} \quad 1\overline{)5}^{\,5} \quad 1\overline{)6}^{\,6} \quad 1\overline{)7}^{\,7} \quad 1\overline{)8}^{\,8} \quad 1\overline{)9}^{\,9}$$

$$2\overline{)2}^{\,1} \quad 2\overline{)4}^{\,2} \quad 2\overline{)6}^{\,3} \quad 2\overline{)8}^{\,4} \quad 2\overline{)10}^{\,5} \quad 2\overline{)12}^{\,6} \quad 2\overline{)14}^{\,7} \quad 2\overline{)16}^{\,8} \quad 2\overline{)18}^{\,9}$$

$$3\overline{)3}^{\,1} \quad 3\overline{)6}^{\,2} \quad 3\overline{)9}^{\,3} \quad 3\overline{)12}^{\,4} \quad 3\overline{)15}^{\,5} \quad 3\overline{)18}^{\,6} \quad 3\overline{)21}^{\,7} \quad 3\overline{)24}^{\,8} \quad 3\overline{)27}^{\,9}$$

$$4\overline{)4}^{\,1} \quad 4\overline{)8}^{\,2} \quad 4\overline{)12}^{\,3} \quad 4\overline{)16}^{\,4} \quad 4\overline{)20}^{\,5} \quad 4\overline{)24}^{\,6} \quad 4\overline{)28}^{\,7} \quad 4\overline{)32}^{\,8} \quad 4\overline{)36}^{\,9}$$

$$5\overline{)5}^{\,1} \quad 5\overline{)10}^{\,2} \quad 5\overline{)15}^{\,3} \quad 5\overline{)20}^{\,4} \quad 5\overline{)25}^{\,5} \quad 5\overline{)30}^{\,6} \quad 5\overline{)35}^{\,7} \quad 5\overline{)40}^{\,8} \quad 5\overline{)45}^{\,9}$$

$$6\overline{)6}^{\,1} \quad 6\overline{)12}^{\,2} \quad 6\overline{)18}^{\,3} \quad 6\overline{)24}^{\,4} \quad 6\overline{)30}^{\,5} \quad 6\overline{)36}^{\,6} \quad 6\overline{)42}^{\,7} \quad 6\overline{)48}^{\,8} \quad 6\overline{)54}^{\,9}$$

$$7\overline{)7}^{\,1} \quad 7\overline{)14}^{\,2} \quad 7\overline{)21}^{\,3} \quad 7\overline{)28}^{\,4} \quad 7\overline{)35}^{\,5} \quad 7\overline{)42}^{\,6} \quad 7\overline{)49}^{\,7} \quad 7\overline{)56}^{\,8} \quad 7\overline{)63}^{\,9}$$

$$8\overline{)8}^{\,1} \quad 8\overline{)16}^{\,2} \quad 8\overline{)24}^{\,3} \quad 8\overline{)32}^{\,4} \quad 8\overline{)40}^{\,5} \quad 8\overline{)48}^{\,6} \quad 8\overline{)56}^{\,7} \quad 8\overline{)64}^{\,8} \quad 8\overline{)72}^{\,9}$$

$$9\overline{)9}^{\,1} \quad 9\overline{)18}^{\,2} \quad 9\overline{)27}^{\,3} \quad 9\overline{)36}^{\,4} \quad 9\overline{)45}^{\,5} \quad 9\overline{)54}^{\,6} \quad 9\overline{)63}^{\,7} \quad 9\overline{)72}^{\,8} \quad 9\overline{)81}^{\,9}$$

Cover the answers. Now say the answer to each division question above. How many do you know?

Practice

Say the answer to each multiplication question, but do not guess.

8	4	5	7	9	6	6	5	8
×7	×7	×8	×7	×4	×9	×6	×6	×4

9	9	8	7	9	6	6	8	7
×6	×7	×9	×8	×8	×7	×8	×8	×9

Find the answer to any question that you did not know. Then study that multiplication so that you will remember it.

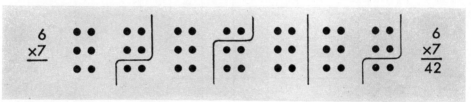

Say the answer to each division question below. Do not guess.

8)56	9)45	6)54	9)63	8)48	8)64	7)63	9)72
9)54	9)81	7)49	8)40	7)56	8)72	7)42	9)36
6)30	7)28	6)42	4)36	6)48	8)32	5)45	3)27

Find the answer to any question that you did not know. Then study that division so that you will remember it.

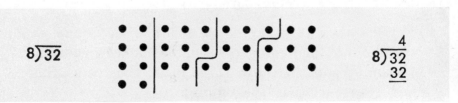

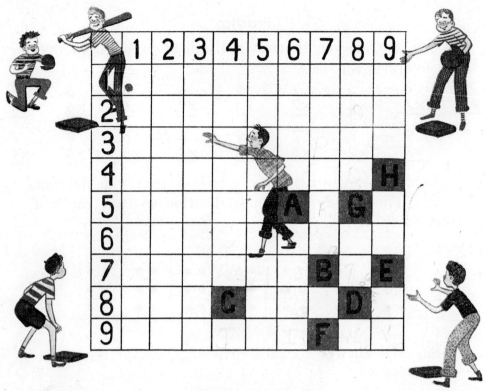

Arithmetic Baseball

Choose sides so that the class is divided into two teams. Each player on the team at bat takes his turn. A player on the other team is the pitcher. The pitcher points to a block, such as A. The player at bat may give the answers in this way:

Six fives are thirty.   *Five sixes are thirty.*
Sixes in thirty, five.   *Fives in thirty, six.*

If the player at bat makes a mistake, he is out. If he gives all four answers correctly, he makes one run for his team. When there are three outs, the teams change sides. The teacher is the umpire.

Baseball with Products

As in the game just described, the class should choose sides. Each player on the team at bat takes his turn, and a player on the other team acts as the pitcher. In this game, also, each completely correct answer counts one run, and the team at bat has three outs.

The pitcher tosses a product, say 48. The player at bat must answer in this way:

Six eights are forty-eight.
Eight sixes are forty-eight.
Sixes in forty-eight, eight.
Eights in forty-eight, six.

$$\begin{array}{r} 8 \\ \times 6 \\ \hline 48 \end{array} \qquad \begin{array}{r} 6 \\ \times 8 \\ \hline 48 \end{array} \qquad 6\overline{)48} \atop \underline{48} \qquad 8\overline{)48} \atop \underline{48}$$

The answers do not have to be in this order, but they must be completely correct to count 1 run. Any mistake means 1 out, and when there are 3 outs, the teams change sides.

Here are some useful products:

In the twenties: 20 21 24 25 27 28
In the thirties: 30 32 35 36
In the forties: 40 42 45 48 49
In the fifties: 54 56
In the sixties: 63 64
In the seventies: 72
In the eighties: 81

When Do We Multiply?

Mr. Wagner was ordering some apple trees and peach trees from the catalogue that the nursery sent him. He asked Bill to find the total cost for him.

1. How much will 1 Grimes Golden at 65¢, 1 Delicious at 85¢, and 1 Jonathan at 49¢ cost altogether?

$ .65
.85
.49
———
$1.99

To find the total cost of the apple trees, Bill added 65¢, 85¢, and 49¢. He found that the total cost would be $1.99.

2. Now find the total cost of 3 Elberta Peach trees at 89¢ each.

$ .89
3
———
$2.67

Again Bill had to find the total cost. He could have added 89¢, 89¢, and 89¢, but he just multiplied 89¢ by 3 to save time.

Sometimes we add to find the total amount, and sometimes we multiply to find the total amount. When do we add to find the total amount? When do we multiply to find the total amount?

Make up problems, using the pictures, to show that you know when to add and when to multiply to find the total amount.

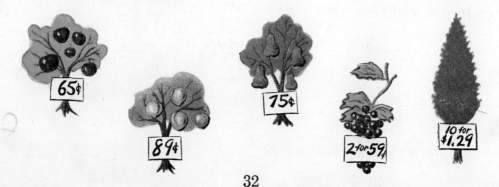

How Do We Multiply?

1. Jane and her mother bought 2 crates of cherries at the fruit stand. There were 24 boxes of cherries in each crate. How many boxes of cherries did they buy?

To find the answer, we multiply 24 by 2. We multiply the ones first: Two 4's are 8. Write 8 in one's place in the answer. Then multiply the tens: Two 2's are 4. Write 4 in ten's place.

They bought 48 boxes of cherries.

$$\begin{array}{r} 24 \\ \times 2 \\ \hline 48 \end{array}$$

2. There are 144 pieces of chalk in each box. How many pieces are there in 2 boxes?

Multiply the ones: Two 4's are 8.
Multiply the tens: Two 4's are 8.
Multiply the hundreds: Two 1's are 2.
There are 288 pieces in the 2 boxes.

$$\begin{array}{r} 144 \\ \times 2 \\ \hline 288 \end{array}$$

The number we multiply is the **multiplicand,** and the number we multiply by is the **multiplier.** The answer is the **product**.

$$\begin{array}{r} 423 \ \textit{multiplicand} \\ \times 3 \ \textit{multiplier} \\ \hline 1269 \ \textit{product} \end{array}$$

Copy and multiply:

	(a)	(b)	(c)	(d)	(e)	(f)	(g)	(h)	(i)
3.	63	73	11	82	41	51	32	61	71
	2	3	8	4	9	8	3	5	7
4.	93	92	91	82	83	74	51	62	81
	3	4	5	3	3	2	7	4	8
5.	621	811	821	711	831	532	624	522	513
	4	7	3	5	3	3	2	4	3

Zeros in Multiplication

$$\begin{array}{r} 50 \\ 2 \\ \hline 100 \end{array}$$

Since there are **no ones** to multiply by 2, we write 0 in one's place in the answer. Then we multiply the tens: Two 5's are 10. Ten 10's are 100; so we write 0 in ten's place and 1 in hundred's place.

$$\begin{array}{r} 403 \\ 3 \\ \hline 1209 \end{array}$$

Multiply the ones first: Three 3's are 9. Write 9 in one's place. Next multiply the tens. There are **no tens** to multiply by 3; so we write 0 in ten's place. Then we multiply the hundreds: Three 4's are 12. 12 hundreds are 1 thousand and 2 hundreds. We write 2 in hundred's place and 1 in thousand's place.

Tell how these numbers were multiplied:

500	502	520	400	403	430	740	901
4	4	4	3	3	3	2	9
2000	2008	2080	1200	1209	1290	1480	8109

Copy and multiply:

	(a)	(b)	(c)	(d)	(e)	(f)	(g)	(h)	(i)
1.	70	90	80	90	60	70	80	40	50
	8	6	7	9	7	6	5	9	7
2.	701	710	800	630	604	640	810	810	602
	8	8	4	3	2	2	8	7	4
3.	120	103	401	501	420	530	901	910	700
	4	3	9	8	4	3	9	8	7
4.	643	703	411	720	322	202	820	413	230
	2	3	4	4	2	4	3	2	3

Problems

Read each problem carefully. What does the question ask you to find? Must you add, subtract, or multiply to find the answer to the question?

1. Jane bought 3 packages of post cards when she went to the city to visit her aunt. There were 12 post cards in each package. How many post cards did she buy?

2. The girls in the Camp Fire group have made 27 place cards for the Camp Fire dinner, but they need 50 place cards in all. How many place cards do they still have to make?

3. May got 6 birthday cards the day before her birthday, 27 on her birthday, and 9 the day after. How many birthday cards did she get in all?

4. The fifth-grade girls sold 235 tickets for their play. The boys sold 309. How many more tickets did the boys sell than the girls? How many tickets did they sell altogether?

5. To decide how many quarts of fruit to can this fall, Grace and her mother want to know how many quarts they used last winter. They canned 215 quarts last year and have 37 quarts left. How many quarts did they use last winter?

6. Jimmy Brown lives 24 miles from the city. How many miles would he travel in going to the city and back home again?

7. Jane had 47 shells in her collection before Jack brought her 18 more from Florida. How many shells did Jane have then?

PRACTICE

179
-84

230
X3

17
46
29

362
-108

201
X6

35

Carrying in Multiplying

Jack visited his uncle's ranch. He watched the men clip the sheep.

1. A new man clipped the wool from 216 sheep in one day. How many sheep can he clip in 5 days?

First, we multiply the ones: Five 6's are 30. We write 0 and carry 3. Next, we multiply the tens: Five 1's are 5, and 3 (carried) are 8. We write 8 in ten's place. Then we multiply the hundreds: Five 2's are 10.

$$\begin{array}{r} 216 \\ 5 \\ \hline 1080 \end{array}$$

$8 \times 5 + 4 = 44$ *Think:* Eight 5's are 40, and 4 are 44.

Think each of the following:

2.	$7 \times 8 + 6$	$3 \times 7 + 2$	$8 \times 2 + 4$	$6 \times 7 + 3$
3.	$4 \times 6 + 3$	$2 \times 9 + 1$	$9 \times 2 + 5$	$8 \times 4 + 7$
4.	$6 \times 6 + 5$	$9 \times 4 + 5$	$3 \times 5 + 2$	$9 \times 9 + 7$
5.	$8 \times 5 + 7$	$7 \times 3 + 6$	$6 \times 4 + 5$	$5 \times 6 + 4$
6.	$5 \times 7 + 3$	$6 \times 8 + 2$	$8 \times 6 + 4$	$7 \times 7 + 1$
7.	$6 \times 9 + 3$	$9 \times 6 + 6$	$9 \times 8 + 8$	$5 \times 5 + 4$
8.	$9 \times 3 + 2$	$4 \times 8 + 2$	$5 \times 9 + 3$	$8 \times 7 + 5$

9. Another man clipped the wool from 271 sheep in one day. How many sheep can he clip in 5 days?

$$\begin{array}{r} 271 \\ \underline{5} \\ 1355 \end{array}$$

10. A third man clipped the wool from 286 sheep in one day. How many sheep can he clip in 5 days?

$$\begin{array}{r} 286 \\ \underline{5} \\ 1430 \end{array}$$

11. The clipped wool from one sheep weighs about 8 lb. About how much will the wool from 216 sheep weigh? from 271 sheep? from 286 sheep?

12. Tell how these numbers were multiplied:

415	408	432	525	619	551
6	8	8	4	7	8
2490	3264	3456	2100	4333	4408

Copy and multiply:

	(a)	(b)	(c)	(d)	(e)	(f)	(g)	(h)	(i)
13.	315	413	514	106	712	918	204	709	306
	4	6	7	9	6	2	9	5	8
14.	641	381	971	350	621	342	341	631	651
	8	9	9	8	5	4	9	7	4
15.	561	235	863	546	469	578	982	973	578
	7	6	7	8	4	6	8	6	3

16. Some of the examples on the board are wrong. Find each mistake and correct it.

845	606	905	785
4	7	4	4
3280	422	3620	2922

Multiplying Dollars and Cents

Jack and Jim wanted to learn to play badminton; so they had to order rackets and birds.

1. Jack ordered 2 sets of birds. How much did they cost at $1.29 a set?

We multiply dollars and cents the way we multiply other numbers, but we must write dollars and cents in their proper places. Where do we put the point in our answer?

2. Jack also ordered a racket for each of them. How much did the 2 rackets cost at $2.72 each?

3. There was a better racket that sold for $3.79. How much would 2 of these cost?

4. If Jack had ordered the racket for $2.72 and Jim had ordered the racket for $3.79, how much would these 2 rackets have cost?

```
  $1.29
      2
  $2.58


  $2.72
      2
  $5.44


  $3.79
      2
  $7.58
```

Copy and multiply:

	(a)	(b)	(c)	(d)	(e)	(f)	(g)
5.	$1.50 8	$1.27 4	$2.46 5	$3.89 6	$4.56 3	$9.75 5	$.35 9
6.	$8.64 8	$9.15 7	$7.25 6	$5.65 7	$4.86 8	$7.36 9	$.42 8

Practice

Copy and add. Check your work.

	(a)	(b)	(c)	(d)	(e)	(f)	(g)	(h)	(i)	(j)
1.	8	17	8	78	6	8	7	45	9	28
	9	79	8	88	4	43	0	17	8	19
	7	88	6	46	7	19	9	66	0	36
	6	45	0	57	8	62	8	80	7	48
	5	56	4	25	6	87	5	58	6	5

Copy and multiply. Check your answers.

2.	96	80	77	58	47	91	39	68	76	86
	7	5	6	8	9	9	7	9	8	7

3.	245	387	503	630	800	755	780	909	877	919
	9	8	8	8	9	7	7	9	9	8

Copy, subtract, and check.

	(a)	(b)	(c)	(d)	(e)	(f)	(g)	(h)
4.	8512	5000	5006	1830	4900	8704	1240	8500
	2278	2985	1874	497	4347	3536	780	930

In row **5**, add; in **6**, subtract; in **7**, multiply.

	(a)	(b)	(c)	(d)	(e)	(f)
5.	$1.75	$5.00	$6.40	$3.84	$12.40	$10.80
	4.35	.80	.57	4.75	8.60	5.60
	4.08	6.15	.08	.92	20.10	4.37
	3.62	3.98	1.76	1.08	7.00	3.80
6.	$20.00	$12.60	$10.00	$8.32	$7.30	$5.82
	8.75	5.86	2.98	5.86	4.96	3.90
7.	$3.78	$5.65	$8.30	$8.08	$4.05	$5.90
	4	6	7	8	9	6

Multiplying by a Two-Place Number

1. The school store sold 24 boxes of pencils during September. There were 12 pencils in each box. How many pencils were sold in September?

```
 24
 12
 48
 24
288
```

First, we multiply by ones. So we multiply 24 by the 2 in 12. The product is 48. Where do we write the 48?

Next, we multiply by tens. So we multiply by the 1 in 12. The product is 24 (tens). We write 4 in ten's place under the 1 that we multiplied by because we are multiplying by 1 ten.

```
 82
 12
164
 82
984
```

2. A pilot flies his airplane about 82 hours a month. How many hours does he fly in a year?

3. The children took 32 boxes of rolls when they went on a picnic. If there were 12 rolls in each box, how many rolls did they take?

4. They also took 12 cases of soda. If there were 12 bottles in each case, how many bottles of soda were there in all?

Copy and multiply:

	(a)	(b)	(c)	(d)	(e)	(f)	(g)	(h)	(i)	(j)
5.	82	73	64	81	93	62	51	43	44	11
	11	13	12	24	33	24	56	33	22	86
6.	18	48	64	83	92	53	42	11	72	81
	11	11	21	33	43	13	23	38	32	45

Multiplying by Tens

1. "How many apple trees do you have?" asked Joe. "There are 20 rows with 12 trees in each row," said his uncle.

To find how many apple trees there are, we multiply 12 by 20.

There are no ones to multiply by. So we write 0 in one's place in the product. The 0 shows that we are ready to multiply tens. Now when we multiply by 2 (tens), we can start writing our ten's answer in ten's place.

```
  12
  20
 ---
 240
```

2. Tell how these numbers were multiplied:

85	74	63	52	45	38	66	56
10	20	30	40	50	60	70	80
850	1480	1890	2080	2250	2280	4620	4480

Copy and multiply:

	(a)	(b)	(c)	(d)	(e)	(f)	(g)	(h)	(i)
3.	72	67	83	85	77	48	37	98	84
	30	60	50	90	40	70	80	20	10
4.	78	54	68	59	47	98	68	98	76
	50	60	40	70	80	30	20	10	90
5.	38	67	55	26	99	48	88	75	28
	90	70	60	80	40	50	20	80	10

Multiplying with Carrying

1. There are 24 hours in a day. How many hours were in February, 1948? in February, 1950?

When our multiplier is a two-place number, we multiply by the ones first. This product is 216. Then we multiply by the tens. What is the product of 24 multiplied by 20?

We call 216 and 480 **partial products** because each of them is only a part of the product. Now we add the partial products.

In the second partial product, we often do not write the zero in one's place. We must be sure that we start writing our ten's answer in ten's place. We write it directly under the tens we are multiplying by.

```
  24
  29
 ───
 216
 480
 ───
 696

Check

  29
  24
 ───
 116
  58
 ───
 696
```

Copy these examples and multiply. Check each answer.

	(a)	(b)	(c)	(d)	(e)	(f)	(g)	(h)	(i)
2.	35	48	29	39	45	80	77	52	90
	24	63	48	59	75	59	37	69	32
3.	27	53	71	68	38	74	69	88	55
	85	38	49	24	67	42	97	85	64

Study the example in the box. Then copy the examples below and multiply. Check each answer.

```
  275
   25
 ────
 1375
  550
 ────
 6875
```

	(a)	(b)	(c)	(d)	(e)	(f)
4.	142	184	379	180	406	600
	53	48	26	59	24	16
5.	746	950	742	819	764	816
	61	37	84	90	81	19

Zeros in Multiplication

1. There are seats for 60 people on the big bus. There are seats for how many people on 20 busses?

First, we multiply by ones. There are **no ones** in 20. We write 0 in one's place in the product. Then we multiply by tens; so we multiply 60 by the 2 in 20.

```
  60
  20
----
1200
```

Study the next example. There is a zero in one's place in both the multiplicand and the multiplier. Do we have any ones to multiply 260 by? What do we write in one's place in the product? Next, we multiply 260 by the 3 (tens) in 30.

```
 260
  30
----
7800
```

In the third example we have a zero in ten's place in the multiplicand and a zero in one's place in the multiplier. Study the example and tell how we multiply 106 by 20.

```
 106
  20
----
2120
```

2. Explain how these examples were worked:

```
  80        80        800        64        640        604
   7        70         70         4         40         40
----      ----     -------      ----     ------     ------
 560      5600      56,000      256      25,600      24,160
```

Copy and multiply:

	(a)	(b)	(c)	(d)	(e)	(f)	(g)	(h)	(i)
3.	40	30	60	50	80	70	90	70	50
	80	90	70	70	30	70	80	90	60
4.	650	840	760	840	190	280	390	470	560
	40	30	50	70	60	80	50	60	60
5.	106	308	209	406	505	406	305	408	606
	50	40	50	80	90	70	80	60	90

Shopping

Janet has a problem to work. She has to figure the cost of her grocery bill.

Find the cost:
8 lb. ham at 85¢ a pound
2 lb. butter at 69¢ a pound
4 doz. eggs at 45¢ a dozen

$$\begin{array}{r} \$\ .85 \\ 8 \\ \hline \$6.80 \end{array}$$

Janet said, "First, I find the cost of each item. The cost of the ham is 85¢ multiplied by 8, or $6.80. I find the cost of each of the other items in the same way. Then I add to find the **total** cost, which is $9.98."

$$\begin{array}{r} \$6.80 \\ 1.38 \\ 1.80 \\ \hline \$9.98 \end{array}$$

Work Janet's problem to see if she did her work right. Be sure to check your own work as you find each amount.

Grapes per basket	39¢	Plums per basket	65¢
Hens (dressed) per lb.	43¢	Butter per lb.	80¢
Breakfast Bacon per lb.	56¢	Country Ham per lb.	55¢
Sweet Potatoes per lb.	6¢	Irish Potatoes per lb.	5¢
Eggs per dozen	45¢	Beans (Navy) per lb.	9¢

Finding Costs

At the prices given above, find the cost of these purchases:

1. 4 lb. breakfast bacon
2. 5 doz. eggs
3. 4 baskets grapes
4. 3 lb. dressed hen
5. 2 lb. butter
6. 3 lb. breakfast bacon

7. 2 baskets grapes
8. 4 baskets plums
9. 8 lb. country ham
10. 12 lb. Irish potatoes
11. 6 lb. sweet potatoes
12. 4 lb. navy beans

13. 2 baskets grapes
   3 doz. eggs
   4 lb. breakfast bacon
   12 lb. sweet potatoes

14. 3 lb. navy beans
   6 lb. Irish potatoes
   6 lb. sweet potatoes
   1 doz. eggs

15. 7 lb. country ham
   2 lb. butter
   3 doz. eggs
   1 basket plums

16. 1 basket grapes
   1 basket plums
   5 lb. dressed hen
   12 lb. Irish potatoes

17. 2 doz. eggs
   4 lb. dressed hen
   2 lb. breakfast bacon
   1 lb. butter
   3 lb. navy beans

18. 6 lb. country ham
   3 lb. breakfast bacon
   5 lb. dressed hen
   2 lb. butter
   4 lb. sweet potatoes

More about Zero

1. Jack's father drives a bus 304 miles each day. How far does he drive the bus in 24 days?

```
 304
  24
1216
```

First, multiply by ones. Multiply 304 by 4 in 24. Think: Four 4's are 16. Write 6 in one's place and carry 1 (ten). Think: There are **no tens** in 304 to multiply by 4. But since we had 1 to carry, we write 1 in ten's place. Think: Four 3's are 12 (hundreds). Write 2 in hundred's place and 1 in thousand's place.

```
 304
  24
1216
 608
7296
```

Next, multiply by tens. Multiply 304 by 2 in 24. Think: Two 4's are 8. Write 8 in ten's place under the 2 in the multiplier, 24. Think: There are no tens in 304 to multiply by 2; so write 0 in hundred's place. Think: Two 3's are 6. Write 6 in thousand's place.

Add the partial products.

```
$ .14          54
  54        $ .14
  56        2 16
  70          5 4
$7.56       $7.56
```

2. Mr. Hanes bought 54 gallons of fuel oil at 14¢ a gallon. How much did the fuel oil cost?

How do we multiply dollars and cents?

Copy and multiply:

	(a)	(b)	(c)	(d)	(e)	(f)	(g)
3.	440	880	209	666	700	290	555
	62	27	91	48	49	37	65
4.	175	396	480	300	509	136	707
	18	35	67	83	27	39	29
5.	$1.26	$3.84	$5.20	$2.08	$4.60	$8.72	$3.80
	15	26	60	48	48	39	19

Finding Costs

Find out from your grocer the prices he charges for each of the following:

Eggs per doz. *Butter per lb.*

Chickens per lb. *Hams per lb.*

Bacon per lb. *Steak per lb.*

Chuck roast per lb. *Sugar per lb.*

Rib roast per lb. *Potatoes per lb.*

Now find the cost of each purchase:

1. 3 doz. eggs
  10 lb. potatoes
  4 lb. bacon
  5 lb. sugar
  3 lb. chuck roast

2. 3 lb. bacon
  7 lb. ham
  3 lb. chicken
  2 doz. eggs
  2 lb. butter

3. 2 lb. steak
  9 lb. ham
  5 lb. chicken
  6 lb. rib roast
  4 doz. eggs

4. 5 lb. potatoes
  10 lb. sugar
  3 lb. steak
  6 lb. chuck roast
  5 lb. bacon

5. 2 lb. butter
  3 doz. eggs
  15 lb. sugar
  8 lb. ham
  4 lb. bacon

6. 10 lb. potatoes
  4 lb. steak
  10 lb. sugar
  3 doz. eggs
  5 lb. chuck roast

Solving Problems

Jack Woods had a problem like this:

~~~~~~

Find the cost: 3 lb. butter at 42¢ per lb.

2 doz. eggs at 38¢ per doz.

5 lb. sugar at 6¢ per lb.

2 pk. potatoes at 40¢ per pk.

7 lb. ham at 35¢ per lb.

Amount given clerk: $10.00   *How much change?*

~~~~~~

Jack said, "I often had problems like this to solve when I was working in the grocery store last summer.

"First, I find the cost of each item. Thus, 3 pounds of butter at 42 cents a pound cost 42¢ times 3, or $1.26. Next, I find the cost of the other items. Then I add to find the cost of all. The total cost is $5.57.

"Last, I subtract $5.57 from $10.00 to find how much change the customer should get."

Work the problem to see if Jack multiplied and added and subtracted correctly.

```
 $.42
    3
$1.26
```

```
$1.26
  .76
  .30
  .80
 2.45
$5.57
```

```
$10.00
  5.57
$ 4.43
```

1. Find the cost of this playground equipment:

10 baseballs at $1.85 each

6 bats at $1.37 each

18 gloves at $1.37 each

2. Find the cost of these toys:

4 express trucks at $1.29 each

3 speed boats at 87¢ each

2 auto transports at $1.89 each

Making Change

"Of course," said Jack, "I did not find the change by subtracting."

"Did you count it the way our grocer does when he makes change?" asked Ellen.

"Surely," answered Jack. "If a customer owed 57¢ and gave me a dollar, I counted his change like this:

"57 and 3 are 60, and 10 are 70, and 5 are 75, and 25 are a dollar. Or I would just say 57¢—60, 70, 75, and $1.00."

"Suppose a customer owed $5.57 and gave you $10.00. How would you count the change?" asked George.

"Like this," answered Jack. "$5.57 and 3 are $5.60, and 10 are $5.70, and 5 are $5.75, and 25 are $6.00, and 1 are $7.00, and 1 are $8.00, and 1 are $9.00, and 1 are $10.00."

The amount of change would be $4.43 when counted. If you want to find the amount in working a problem, you can subtract $5.57 from $10.00. You will find that the amount is the same, $4.43.

3¢
10¢
5¢
25¢
43¢
$.03
.10
.05
.25
1.00
1.00
1.00
1.00
$4.43

1. How much change should you get back if you bought $3.65 worth of groceries and gave the clerk $5.00?

2. How much change should you get back from a 10-dollar bill if the total cost of the things you bought was $6.38?

3. How much change should you get back if you bought $9.68 worth of groceries and paid for them with a 10-dollar bill? Count the change.

Finding Costs

Find the amount of each purchase and the amount of change received.

1. 15 dozen pencils
   12 dozen pencil tablets
   10 boxes white chalk
   4 boxes colored chalk
   2 dozen art brushes

   Amount given clerk: $30.00
   How much change?

2. 2 globes
   6 outline maps
   3 dozen art gum
   4 dozen erasers
   20 packages writing paper

   Amount given clerk: $80.00
   How much change?

3. 30 dozen pencils
   12 dozen penholders
   2 globes
   4 outline maps
   25 boxes white chalk
   6 boxes colored chalk
   10 dozen pencil tablets

   Amount given clerk: $80.00
   How much change?

4. 2 dozen art brushes
   5 boxes colored chalk
   24 boxes white chalk
   3 dozen erasers
   4 dozen ink erasers
   24 dozen pencil tablets
   36 dozen pencils

   Amount given clerk: $60.00
   How much change?

Why Do We Divide?

1. Mr. Brown and Ted picked 12 bushels of apples to put in the cellar for winter use. Mr. Brown has 3 big boxes ready for the apples. How many bushels will they put into each box if they put the same number of bushels in each?

Jane said, "We must find how many bushels there are in each of 3 equal groups; so we divide 12 by 3. They will put 4 bushels into each box because there are four 3's in 12."

2. Mr. Brown and Ted picked 12 more bushels of apples. They want to send the same number of bushels to each of 4 persons. How many bushels should they send to each person?

3. Mr. Brown and Ted put the 12 bushels of apples into boxes. Each box held 4 bushels. How many boxes did they fill?

Bill said, "They will fill 3 boxes because there are three 4's in 12."

How Do We Divide?

1. John has 48 rabbits. He made 2 new pens for them. He plans to put the same number of rabbits in each pen. How many should he put in each pen?

$$\frac{24}{2)\overline{48}}$$

We can use **short division** to work this problem. When we use short division, we write only the answer.

$$\begin{array}{r} 24 \\ 2)\overline{48} \\ \underline{4} \\ 8 \\ \underline{8} \end{array}$$

First, we divide the tens. How many 2's are in 4? Write 2 in the quotient above 4.

Next, we divide the ones. How many 2's are in 8? Write 4 in the quotient above 8.

John should put 24 rabbits in each pen.

---

2. Helen was given a box of salt-water taffy to share equally with Alice, Jerry, and Susan. There were 124 pieces in the box. Helen found 4 smaller boxes to put the shares in. How many pieces of taffy should she put into each box?

$$\text{divisor } 4)\overline{124} \text{ dividend}$$
(with *31 quotient* above)

The number we divide is called the **dividend**.
The number we divide by is called the **divisor**.
The answer is called the **quotient**.

Copy and divide:

	(a)	(b)	(c)	(d)	(e)	(f)
3.	3)96	4)1688	5)455	2)108	2)848	3)1599
4.	6)246	9)4599	8)1688	2)486	7)1477	3)669

52

We Learn about Dividing

1. Jim had 24 pictures of airplanes. He pasted 6 pictures on each page of his scrapbook. How many pages did he use?

2. Ann had 240 butterflies in her collection. She pinned them on a large cardboard. She put 8 butterflies in each row. How many rows of butterflies did she have?

3. Four girls took 2400 Christmas seals to sell. They divided the seals equally among themselves. How many seals did each girl have to sell?

4. The football stadium holds 24,000 people. One sixth of the seats are reserved for the students. How many seats are reserved for the students?

We divide tens, hundreds, and thousands the way we divide ones.

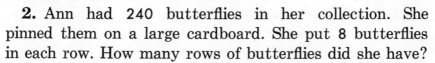

$$\begin{array}{r} 4 \\ 6\overline{)24} \\ 24 \end{array} \qquad \begin{array}{r} 30 \\ 8\overline{)240} \\ 24 \\ \hline 0 \end{array} \qquad \begin{array}{r} 600 \\ 4\overline{)2400} \\ 24 \\ \hline 00 \end{array} \qquad \begin{array}{r} 4000 \\ 6\overline{)24000} \\ 24 \\ \hline 000 \end{array}$$

Copy and divide:

	(a)	(b)	(c)	(d)	(e)	(f)
5.	8)320	9)810	8)720	7)630	9)540	6)420
6.	9)4500	5)3000	7)4900	9)2700	8)3200	7)5600
7.	8)64000	9)18000	5)15000	6)36000	8)40000	9)54000

Sharing

It is Betty's turn to take taffy apples to the club meeting. There are 18 members; so Betty needs 18 taffy apples. Two of her friends will help her make them.

"Each of us should make the same number," suggested Grace. "Each of us should make one third of them."

"How many should I make?" asked Sue.

"Six, of course," said Grace. "One third of 18 is 6. We divide 18 by 3 to find one third of it."

1. How do we find one fifth of a number of things? one half? one eighth? one fourth?

2. Find these parts of numbers:

$\frac{1}{2}$ of 24 $\frac{1}{3}$ of 96 $\frac{1}{8}$ of 72 $\frac{1}{6}$ of 54 $\frac{1}{7}$ of 49

$\frac{1}{4}$ of 204 $\frac{1}{5}$ of 255 $\frac{1}{9}$ of 270 $\frac{1}{2}$ of 126 $\frac{1}{3}$ of 276

3. Mrs. Cotten offered to take 240 cookies to the bake sale. Jane asked if she might make half of them. How many cookies should Jane make?

4. Ann has 186 bird pictures to share. If she gives one half of them away, how many pictures will she keep?

Dividing Dollars and Cents

1. How much should Harry's father pay each month if he buys a $48 radio and pays for it in 6 equal payments?

$$\begin{array}{r} \$8 \\ 6\overline{)\$48} \\ \underline{48} \end{array}$$

2. Mr. Dent bought a radio for $48 and paid for it at the rate of $8 a month. In how many months did he have the radio paid for?

$$\begin{array}{r} 6 \\ \$8\overline{)\$48} \\ \underline{48} \end{array}$$

3. The nine members of the Good Cheer Club decided that $2.70 would be enough to spend for food to fill a Thanksgiving basket for a needy family. Each will give the same amount. How much will each give?

$$\begin{array}{r} \$.30 \\ 9\overline{)\$2.70} \\ \underline{27} \\ 0 \end{array}$$

4. The pupils in our room paid $1.68 for milk today. If the pupils paid 8¢ for each bottle of milk, how many bottles of milk did they buy?

How do we divide cents by cents?
We think of $1.68 as 168 cents.
Then we divide 168 by 8.

$$\begin{array}{r} 21 \\ 8¢\overline{)168¢} \\ \underline{16} \\ 8 \\ \underline{8} \end{array}$$

---

5. Eight of us will buy Grandmother a $16.80 present and share the cost equally. What will each of us pay?

$$\begin{array}{r} \$2.10 \\ 8\overline{)\$16.80} \\ \underline{16} \\ 8 \\ \underline{8} \\ 0 \end{array}$$

6. At a sale Mrs. Rich paid $3.50 for 5 pairs of socks for Jim. How much did she pay for each pair if they cost the same amount?

7. Ann had $3.60 to buy 6 dozen oranges for a school picnic. What price per dozen can she pay for the oranges?

	1	2	3	4	5	6	7	8	9
1	1	2	3	4	5	6	7	8	9
2	2	4	6	8	10	12	14	16	18
3	3	6	9	12	15	18	21	24	27
4	4	8	12	16	20	24	28	32	36
5	5	10	15	20	25	30	35	40	45
6	6	12	18	24	30	36	42	48	54
7	7	14	21	28	35	42	49	56	63
8	8	16	24	32	40	48	56	64	72
9	9	18	27	36	45	54	63	72	81

Multiplication and Division Table

We can use the table to find the answer to a multiplication or a division question that we cannot answer. Suppose the question is: **Seven eights are how many?** Move your pencil down the column at the left until you come to 7. Then move your pencil along the 7 row until you come to the 8 column. At that point is the answer. You know that **seven eights are fifty-six.**

Suppose the question is: **How many 8's in 56?** Move your pencil down the column at the left until you come to 8. Then move your pencil along the 8 row until you come to 56. Now look at the top row of figures and see in which column 56 is. You know that there are **seven eights in fifty-six.**

For practice find these answers:

$$\begin{array}{ccccccccc} 8 & 7 & 9 & 8 & 9 \\ \times 8 & \times 8 & \times 4 & \times 9 & \times 7 & 9\overline{)63} & 7\overline{)56} & 8\overline{)72} & 9\overline{)54} \end{array}$$

Using the Table for Dividing

Pauline has saved 38 pennies. She is going to take them to the bank and exchange them for nickels to put in her nickel saver. How many nickels should she get for her pennies?

The question is: **How many 5's are in 38?**

Of course, you know, but suppose that Pauline does not know. She can run her pencil down the column at the left until she comes to 5. Then she can move her pencil along the 5 row until she comes to 38. But there is no 38 in the 5 row; so Pauline stops at the number in the 5 row that is nearest 38, but less than 38. That number is 35. Now she can see that 35 is in column 7.

Pauline should get 7 nickels and have 3 pennies left over.

$$\begin{array}{r} 7 \\ 5\overline{)38} \\ 35 \\ \hline 3 \end{array}$$

Find the answers and remainders:

	(a)	(b)	(c)	(d)	(e)	(f)	(g)	(h)
1.	6)38	7)45	7)50	8)60	9)70	6)56	5)47	9)44
2.	9)48	6)50	8)47	9)65	7)60	6)45	7)36	6)25
3.	7)52	6)28	7)62	7)40	7)20	8)36	9)42	8)62
4.	8)45	9)58	8)54	9)60	5)39	4)37	8)70	9)67
5.	8)65	9)75	8)75	9)80	8)68	9)78	6)59	7)59

Remainders in Dividing

The fifth-grade class is having a picnic in the city park. There are 23 girls and 25 boys.

1. "We girls want to run a relay race. We will choose two teams with the same number of players on each team. If there is an extra person, she can be the starter," said Mary.

How many girls can be on each team?

$$\begin{array}{r} 11 \\ 2\overline{)23} \\ \underline{2} \\ 3 \\ \underline{2} \\ 1 \text{ remainder} \end{array}$$

There will be 11 girls on each team with 1 left over for starter.

2. The 25 boys want to choose 3 teams for a relay race. They also must have the same number on each team. How many boys can be on each team? Will there be an extra boy?

Oral Practice in Uneven Division

1. Say all the numbers that are useful products when you divide by 6; by 7; by 8; by 9.

2. What useful product is next smaller than each of these numbers when you divide by 6?

7   16   25   11   35   41   56   49   27   51

3. What useful product is next smaller than each of these numbers when you divide by 9?

42   28   16   35   48   21   64   56   24   15

4. Say the quotient and remainder when you divide each number below by 7 and then by 8.

$$\begin{array}{r} 7 \\ 7\overline{)50} \\ 49 \\ \hline 1 \text{ remainder} \end{array}$$

15   25   29   34   41   58   60   69

5. Divide the numbers in columns *a* and *b* by 2. Divide the numbers in columns *a*, *b*, and *c* by 3, and so on. Last, divide each number by 9.

a	*b*	*c*	*d*	*e*	*f*	*g*	*h*
10	23	36	41	59	67	78	84
13	26	31	45	50	64	72	89
12	29	35	48	56	68	71	87
18	20	39	43	54	65	77	86
19	25	30	47	55	61	79	83
16	27	38	44	51	62	70	80
14	21	34	40	53	66	76	82
17	24	32	42	58	63	75	81
11	28	37	49	52	60	73	85
15	22	33	46	57	69	74	88

Steps in Division

This is the way Kenneth divides 602 by 7.

He thinks, "Any sevens in 6? No. Any 7's in 60? Yes." He knows where to start writing his answer. He writes the first figure in the quotient in ten's place above 0.

He **divides**: Sevens in 60, 8. He writes 8 in ten's place in the quotient.

He **multiplies**: Eight 7's are 56. He writes 56 under 60, and he notices that 56 is not larger than the 60 above it.

He **subtracts** 56 from 60, and writes 4. He notices that the remainder 4 is less than the divisor 7.

He **brings down** the 2 and writes it beside the 4.

He **divides** 42 by 7: Sevens in 42, 6. He writes 6 in one's place in the quotient.

He **multiplies**: Six 7's are 42. He writes 42 under 42 and notices that he has finished the division.

He has divided both the tens and the ones. First, he divided the 60 tens. Then he divided the 42 ones. His answer is 8 tens and 6 ones, or 86.

Explain how we divide $53.55 by 7.

Division with Carrying

1. Susan bought 6 little chickens for 96 cents. How much did she pay for each?

First, divide the tens. How many 6's in 9? Write 1 in ten's place above the 9. Multiply, subtract, and bring down. Next, divide the ones. How many 6's in 36? Write 6 in one's place.

Susan paid 16¢ for each little chicken.

```
    16¢
6)96¢
   6
  36
  36
```

2. After keeping the chickens for two months, she sold the 6 chickens for $2.70. How much was she paid for each?

```
      $.45
6)$2.70
   2 4
     30
     30
```

3. Susan bought 8 yards of chicken wire to build a fence around her chicken yard. She had to pay $1.44 for the wire. How much was the cost of the wire per yard?

4. During the 8 weeks that Susan kept her little chickens, she spent $1.20 for feed. How much did the chicken feed cost her each week?

```
8)$1.20
```

Zero in the Quotient

1. The fifth-grade class is giving a show in the school auditorium. They have invited the rest of the school to the show. There are 424 pupils in the other grades, but they cannot all see the show at one time. The auditorium will seat about one fourth of them at a time. How many may see the show at a time?

$$\begin{array}{r} 1 \\ 4)\overline{424} \\ \underline{4} \end{array}$$

Where shall we write the first figure of our quotient? How many 4's in 4? Write 1 in hundred's place in the quotient. Multiply 4 by 1 and write 4 under 4. Subtract. What is left when you subtract 4 from 4? Bring down the 2.

$$\begin{array}{r} 10 \\ 4)\overline{424} \\ \underline{4} \\ 2 \end{array}$$

Now divide the tens. Are there any 4's in 2? No, but we must write 0 in ten's place in the quotient. Why? Bring down the 4.

$$\begin{array}{r} 106 \\ 4)\overline{424} \\ \underline{4} \\ 24 \\ \underline{24} \end{array}$$

Now divide the ones and write the answer in one's place.

106 pupils may see the show at a time.

Copy and divide:

	(a)	(b)	(c)	(d)	(e)	(f)
2.	6)630	4)832	3)918	7)742	8)1648	9)1872
3.	5)1525	6)1842	8)8336	9)9495	7)7574	4)8232
4.	6)7842	2)8130	5)5430	8)9664	6)6252	7)7567

Reviewing Division

Steps to remember:

1. Decide where to write the first quotient figure.
2. Divide.
3. Multiply.
4. Compare the product with the partial dividend.
5. Subtract.
6. Compare the remainder with the divisor.
7. Bring down.
8. Proceed as before, beginning with Step 2.

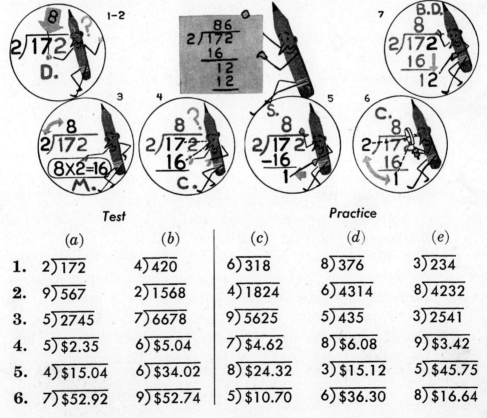

	Test		Practice		
	(a)	(b)	(c)	(d)	(e)
1.	2)172	4)420	6)318	8)376	3)234
2.	9)567	2)1568	4)1824	6)4314	8)4232
3.	5)2745	7)6678	9)5625	5)435	3)2541
4.	5)$2.35	6)$5.04	7)$4.62	8)$6.08	9)$3.42
5.	4)$15.04	6)$34.02	8)$24.32	3)$15.12	5)$45.75
6.	7)$52.92	9)$52.74	5)$10.70	6)$36.30	8)$16.64

Chapter 3
Reading and Solving Problems

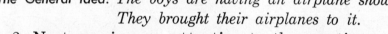

The boys brought 24 fighters and 8 bombers for their airplane show at the Boy Scout hut. How many airplanes did they bring altogether?

To solve the problem:

1. We read the problem carefully and thoughtfully to get an idea of what it is about.

The General Idea: The boys are having an airplane show. They brought their airplanes to it.

2. Next we give our attention to the question.

   a. What is the question?

The Question: How many airplanes did they bring?

   b. How do we answer the question?

The Thinking: We think the airplanes together.

   c. What process do we use?

The Process: Thinking together is addition.

3. We get ready to answer the question. We read the problem again to find the number facts that it tells.

The Facts: The boys brought 24 fighters and 8 bombers.

4. Now we solve the problem. We find the answer to the question. We use the facts to answer the question.

The Solution: 24   *The Answer:* 32 airplanes
                 8
              —   *The boys brought 32 airplanes.*
             32

The boys brought 24 fighters and 8 bombers for their airplane show at the Boy Scout hut. How many more fighters than bombers did they bring?

This problem gives us the same facts as the problem on page 64, but to answer the two questions, we use different processes. The question on page 64 makes that problem a "put-together" problem. The question above makes this problem a "compare" problem. To solve the first problem, we add. To solve the problem above, we subtract.

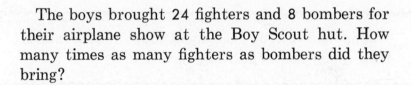

The boys brought 24 fighters and 8 bombers for their airplane show at the Boy Scout hut. How many times as many fighters as bombers did they bring?

What process must we use to answer the question?

Read the problem. Tell what process we use to answer the question. Solve the problem.

1. The boys planned to have 40 airplanes in the show. Only 32 airplanes were brought in. How many more airplanes had they planned to have in the show?

2. There are 32 airplanes in the show. One eighth of them belong to Tom. How many airplanes are Tom's?

3. There are 32 airplanes in the show. Eight of them are bombers, and the others are fighters. How many fighters are there?

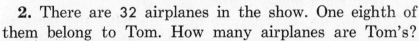

Reading and Solving Problems

Every day each of us has a few problems to solve. Some of them are in our arithmetic work. Some are in our other school work. Many more are in the things we do outside of school.

When we have a problem to solve, we have a question to answer. We decide what we must do to answer the question. There are only four things that we can do: add, subtract, multiply, or divide. We call addition, subtraction, multiplication, and division the **processes**.

The problem tells us two or more facts. From them we get the numbers that we **add**, subtract, multiply, or divide.

~~~~~~

Jane had $1.25. She spent 50¢ at the store. How much money did she have left?

~~~~~~

First, we read the problem carefully and think about it so that we know what it means. What is the problem about? What happens in the problem?

Jane had some money. She spent part of it.

Next, we find the facts that the problem tells.

Jane had $1.25. She spent 50¢.

We read the question again:

How much money did she have left?

Then we decide what we must do with the facts to answer the question. Do we add, subtract, multiply, or divide?

Does the answer that we get really answer the question that the problem asks?

66

Why Do We Add?

When something happens in a problem to give us more than we had at first, we add to find how many we have.

〰〰〰〰〰〰〰〰〰〰〰〰〰〰〰〰〰〰〰〰〰

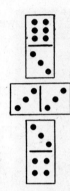

Jack had 75¢. His father gave him 50¢ for his birthday. How much did Jack have then?

Tom had 25 Savings Stamps. He bought 15 more. How many Savings Stamps did he have then?

〰〰〰〰〰〰〰〰〰〰〰〰〰〰〰〰〰〰〰〰〰

We add when we have two or more groups that are alike and want to find how many there are in all.

〰〰〰〰〰〰〰〰〰〰〰〰〰〰〰〰〰〰〰〰〰

Jim brought 6 watermelons for the party, and John brought 4. How many did both boys bring?

Jane saw 6 robins, 6 blue jays, and 8 wrens. How many birds did she see altogether?

〰〰〰〰〰〰〰〰〰〰〰〰〰〰〰〰〰〰〰〰〰

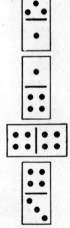

Altogether, both, and more help us to see that we add to answer the questions.

1. Mary made 24 red paper hats and 38 blue paper hats. How many paper hats did she make?

2. Jim ate his lunch at school. He got an apple for 5¢, soup for 8¢, bread and butter for 4¢, and milk for 6¢. How much did his lunch cost?

3. Jane spent 80¢ for ribbon and 28¢ for buttons. How much did she spend for both?

4. Fred had some money. He spent 75¢ for a cap and had 25¢ left. How much did he have at first?

5. Tom has 65¢. Jane has 45¢ more than Tom has. How much does Jane have?

Why Do We Subtract?

When something happens to leave fewer or less than there were at first, we subtract to find how many are left.

Why do we subtract to answer these questions?

1. Jack has saved $1.50. He buys a book of puzzles for 35¢. How much money has he left?

2. Joe had 120 chickens before he sold 36 of them. Then how many chickens did he have?

3. Mary bought a book for 72¢. She gave the clerk a dollar. How much change should she get?

We subtract to find how many are left when we take some away from a group.

Look at each picture. What happens? Tell why the picture shows taking away or subtracting.

Why Do We Subtract?

We subtract when we have two groups and want to find how many more or how many fewer there are in one group than in the other.

Why do we subtract to answer these questions?

1. Alice colored 36 Easter eggs, and Jane colored 24. How many more eggs did Alice color than Jane?

2. Jim has 30¢, and Jack has $1.00. How much more money does Jack have than Jim?

COST

3. Jim is 65 inches tall, and Jane is 56 inches tall. How much taller is Jim than Jane?

4. Alice is 10 years old, and her mother is 35 years old. How much younger is Alice than her mother?

HEIGHT

5. Jack went with his father on a trip. They drove 98 miles in the morning and 164 miles in the afternoon. How much farther did they drive in the afternoon than in the morning?

6. Jim weighs 68 pounds, and his father weighs 175 pounds. Jim's father is how much heavier than Jim?

SIZE

7. Ted wants to buy a horn for his bicycle. He saw two horns. One cost 90¢, and the other cost 75¢. What is the difference in the cost of the horns?

8. Jack spent $1.15 for his baseball cap, and Jim spent 90¢ for his. How much more did Jack's cap cost than Jim's?

When we compare numbers to find how much more or how much less one is than the other, we subtract to find the difference. We subtract to find the difference in size, amount, price, cost, length, height, or weight.

WEIGHT

More about Comparing

We subtract to find how many more we need when we know how many we want and how many we have.

Tell why we subtract to answer these questions:

1. Bill wants to buy a baseball bat that costs a dollar. He has 80¢. How much more money does he need?

2. Betty wants to color 60 Easter eggs. She has already colored 15 eggs. How many eggs does she still need to color?

3. When Helen bought her book, she gave the clerk a dollar, and he gave her 25¢ change. How much did the book cost?

4. Early this morning the thermometer read 64°. This afternoon it read 80°. How much warmer was it in the afternoon than in the morning?

We subtract to find how many are gone when we know how many there were in all and how many there are now.

5. Tom had 100 marbles in a bag. He dropped the bag and spilled the marbles in the tall grass. He found 85 marbles. How many marbles did he lose?

6. Jim's father had 64 sheep in the pasture. When Jim counted them, there were only 60. How many sheep were gone?

When we know how many there are in a whole group and how many of one kind there are, we subtract to find how many of the other kind there are.

7. Jim's father has 64 sheep. Eight of them are black, and the others are white. How many white sheep does he have?

Why Do We Multiply?

We multiply when we have several equal groups and want to know how many there are altogether.

1. Three boys **each** brought 4 watermelons to the party. How many watermelons did they bring?

We multiply when we know the cost of one article and want to find the cost of several of them.

2. Eggs are selling at 36¢ a dozen. How much will four dozen eggs cost?

Tell why we multiply to answer these questions:

3. Each page of Tom's stamp book holds 48 stamps. He has 8 full pages. How many stamps are in the book?

4. There are 9 rows of chairs in our room, and there are 12 chairs in each row. How many chairs are in our room?

5. Five children paid 80¢ **apiece** to buy a picture for their room. How much did the picture cost?

6. Our car can travel 18 miles on 1 gallon of gas. At that rate how far can it go on 8 gallons? At that rate how far can it go on 12 gallons?

7. One ticket to the show costs 44¢. How much will five tickets cost?

8. At 6 miles an hour, how far can you ride your bicycle in 4 hours?

9. There are 9 players on **every** baseball team. How many are there on 2 teams?

10. Bill delivers 84 papers every week. How many papers will he deliver in 4 weeks? How many will he deliver in 6 weeks?

71

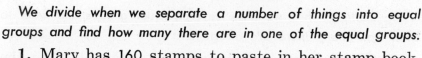

Why Do We Divide?

We divide when we separate a number of things into equal groups and find how many there are in one of the equal groups.

1. Mary has 160 stamps to paste in her stamp book. She plans to put the same number of stamps on **each** page, and there are 8 pages in her book. How many stamps should she put on each page?

We divide when we separate a number of things into equal groups and find how many groups there are.

2. Betty made 12 cupcakes. She wants to put 2 cakes on each plate. How many plates will she need?

We divide when we share equally a number of things and find how many each person gets.

3. Mrs. Hall gave Betty and Sue 100 pennies to divide equally between them. How many pennies will each girl get?

We divide when we cut something into equal pieces and find the size of each piece.

4. Jane has a ribbon that is 12 feet long. She wants to give half of it to Betty. How long will each piece of ribbon be?

When we know the total cost of several things that are alike, we divide to find the cost of one of them.

5. Jane paid $1.50 in all for 3 books. If the books were the same price, how much did one book cost?
Why do we divide to answer this question?

6. The price of a pair of skates is $4.50. Joe can save 50¢ a week. In how many weeks can he save enough to pay for the skates?

Without Pencils

Read each problem carefully. Decide which of the four processes—addition, subtraction, multiplication, or division—you will use to find the answer to the question that is asked. Then find the answer without using your pencil and paper.

How much?

1. Tom had 60¢. He earned 25¢ picking some cherries for Mrs. Brown. Then how much money did he have?

2. Jane bought 3 ten-cent notebooks. How much did the notebooks cost altogether?

3. Jack had $2.00. He bought a fishing pole for 50¢. How much money did he have left?

4. Bill has 70¢, and Tom has 85¢. Which boy has more money? How much more?

5. Eggs are 40¢ a dozen. How much should Mrs. Hall pay for a half dozen?

6. Betty wants to make 5 scrapbooks for the boys and girls at the hospital. She needs 12 sheets of paper for each scrapbook. How many sheets of paper should she get?

7. The girls helped Betty get pictures for the books. They now have 60 pictures. If Betty puts 3 pictures on each page, she has enough pictures for how many pages?

8. Alice wants to put 9 buttons on her new dress. She has already put 6 buttons on it. How many more buttons does she have to put on the dress?

9. How many 5-cent pencils can Jane buy with a quarter? How many pencils can Jack buy with a quarter and a dime?

73

Estimating Answers

After you read a problem and decide what process you should use to answer the question, it is a good idea to **estimate** what your answer should be. It will help you to know that your answer is **reasonable**.

1. A ticket to the movies costs 52 cents. How much should Mr. Hays pay for 4 tickets?

Estimate

$$\begin{array}{r} \$\ .50 \\ \times 4 \\ \hline \$2.00 \end{array}$$

Think: 52¢ is a little more than 50¢. If 1 ticket costs 50¢, 4 tickets will cost $2. Mr. Hays should pay a little more than $2 for the 4 tickets.

Now find the **exact** answer. Is it about the same as your estimate?

Exact answer

$$\begin{array}{r} \$\ .52 \\ \times 4 \\ \hline \$2.08 \end{array}$$

Estimate the answer to each problem. Then find the exact answer. Is your answer reasonable?

2. Mrs. White needs 3 loaves of bread that cost 16¢ a loaf. How much should she pay for the bread?

3. Mr. White delivers 48 quarts of milk each day. How many quarts does he deliver in a week?

4. At 18¢ a quart, how much does Mr. White get for the 48 quarts of milk he delivers each day?

5. It takes 12 sheets of paper to make a notebook for science. How many notebooks can be made from a package of paper that has 500 sheets in it?

6. Jim needs a sack of feed for his chickens. It will cost $2.95. He has a five-dollar bill. Does he have enough money also to buy a feed trough that costs $1.40?

7. Mr. Howard averaged 39 miles per hour. How far did he drive his car in 5 hours?

Extra Numbers in Problems

Some of these problems give facts that are not needed to answer the question. They are **unimportant**. Do not let them catch you! Decide which facts are **important** and pay no attention to the others.

Read each problem. Then make a list of all the facts in that problem. Cross out the unimportant facts. Remember, we use the important facts to solve the problem.

1. At the store Jack found a hammer marked $1.25 and a saw marked $2.19. He bought the saw and paid for it with a five-dollar bill. How much money did he have left after he paid for the saw?

    a. ~~The hammer costs $1.25.~~
       Think: *Jack did not buy the hammer.*
    b. The saw costs $2.19.
    c. Jack paid for the saw with a five-dollar bill.

2. Mary promised to make 8 meat and 10 cheese sandwiches for the picnic. Jane promised to make 6 of each kind. How many meat sandwiches did the girls make?

3. Mr. Bell ordered some bushes to plant in his yard. There were 3 lilacs, 2 butterfly bushes, 6 white rosebushes, 3 red rosebushes, and 4 yellow rosebushes. How many rosebushes did he order?

4. Bill wants some string for his kite. He saw some balls of string at the store that had 80 yards of string on them. They cost 69¢ a ball. How much should he pay for 2 balls of string?

5. In our room 33 of the 36 children bought tickets to the circus. Each ticket cost 15¢. How much did the children spend for circus tickets?

Can You Tell?

1. Jack, George, John, and Henry were talking about how much money they had spent for Savings Stamps.

If you know how much each spent, how can you find how much all the boys spent?

2. Perry knows how many minutes it takes to pull the weeds in one row of potatoes, and he knows how many rows he has.

Can he tell how long it will take him to pull the weeds in all the rows? How?

3. Ellen knows the number of yards of ribbon that she wants to buy and the cost of each yard.

How can she find how much all the ribbon will cost?

4. Ida knows how much money she can spend for party favors and the number of favors she needs.

Can she tell how much she can spend for each? How?

5. The conductor told Joe the number of miles the train traveled each hour. Joe knows how many hours he has been on the train.

How can he tell how far he has traveled?

6. Tom and Jim were counting their marbles. "I have 14 more than you," said Tom.

How could he know that?

7. Jim said, "I have $6.00, but I need $12.75 more to buy an E Bond." What is the price of an E Bond?

8. If Jack does not cash his $18.75 Bond for 10 years, he will get $25 for it. How much will he make on the Bond?

76

Helps in Solving Problems

These questions will help you to understand problems:

1. What are the four processes?

2. When we put groups together, we use one of two processes. What are the two processes?

3. When we put two or more equal groups together, do we multiply or add?

addition
subtraction
multiplication
division

4. When we take some away from a group, do we add or subtract?

5. When we separate a group into equal groups, what do we do to find how many are in each group?

6. When we know how many are in each of two groups, how do we find how many more are in one group than are in the other? How do we find how many fewer are in one group than are in the other?

7. When we know how many we want and how many we have, how do we find how many more we need?

8. When we know how many are in each of two groups, how do we find the difference?

9. When we know how many there are in all and how many there are of a certain kind, how do we find how many there are of the other kind?

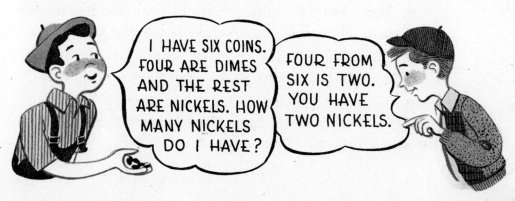

No Pencils

Read each problem carefully. Tell what process you use to answer the question. Why do you use that process? Give the answer to each problem without writing anything.

1. Jane promised to take 24 cupcakes to the picnic. She has already made 12 of them. How many more does she need to make?

2. John is 12 years old. He is three times as old as his little sister Nancy. How old is Nancy?

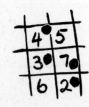

3. Bill has 72 marbles. He says that $\frac{1}{9}$ of them are agates. How many agates has he?

4. Little pumpkin pies cost 15¢ each. How much will Mrs. Winters have to pay for 6 of the pies?

5. Every Saturday from May until frost Grace takes flowers to sick people in town. One day she picked 8 asters for one bunch, 10 asters for another bunch, and 7 asters for a third bunch. How many asters did she pick that day?

6. Mrs. Allen bought 2 dozen eggs at 35¢ a dozen. How much did she pay for the eggs?

7. Jim has 75¢. How many 3-cent stamps can he buy?

8. Mary has 36 handkerchiefs to iron. She has ironed 24 of them. How many handkerchiefs has she yet to iron?

9. Thirty boys want to make teams for tug of war. Can they make 5 teams with 6 boys on each team?

10. Joe has a one-dollar bill. If he buys a model airplane for 80¢, will he have enough money left to pay 19¢ for a big red reflector for his bicycle?

78

Can You Finish the Problem?

The pupils in Grade 5 of the Highlawn School are testing each other to see how well they can tell what questions are asked in problems.

Each pupil tells part of a problem, and the "game" is for another pupil to tell the rest.

See if you can finish their problems.

Jane's: Last Saturday Mother bought a dress and a pair of shoes for me. They cost $7.68. Mother gave the clerk a $10-bill.

George's: I want to save my money so that I can buy a bicycle that costs $27.50. I have saved $18.79.

Henry's: Last summer Father and I set out 36 rows of tomato plants. In each row we had 48 plants.

Susan's: Last year Mother had to buy 4 pairs of shoes for me. Altogether, she paid $19.40 for the shoes.

Ruthie's: I had $15.75 saved, but I had to spend $3.50 for a pair of shoes and $2.48 for a sweater.

Jack's: At our camp last summer there were 26 boys. The expenses for each boy were $7.65.

Jim's: I bought an E Bond for $37.50. At the end of 10 years it will be worth $50.

Mary's: There are 52 weeks in a year. I saved 25¢ each week last year.

Joe's: I bought 7 ten-cent Savings Stamps for Jane and 5 for myself.

Solve each problem by answering the question that you asked.

I BOUGHT SOME THINGS AT THE STORE AND GAVE THE CLERK $10. HOW MUCH CHANGE DID I GET?

HOW MUCH DID YOU BUY?

What Else Should Be Told?

1. Laura purchased some goods at the department store. She gave the clerk a $10-bill. How much change should she have received?

2. Last summer Gordon West set out 8 rows of tomato plants. How many plants did Gordon set out altogether?

3. Robert Smith sold the corn he raised for $1.60 a bushel. How much did he receive for all the corn he sold?

4. Jack missed 3 words in his spelling test. How many words did he spell correctly?

5. Ruth Benton bought some ribbon for $1.25. How much did it cost a yard?

6. Ruth's father went on a business trip to Chicago by airplane. The average speed of the airplane was 200 miles an hour. How far away is Chicago?

7. Mr. Benton drove to Washington, D.C., in 7 hours. How far away is Washington?

8. John's uncle gave him a present of $5.00 on his birthday. How much money does John now have altogether?

9. Gordon bought 3 shirts. How much did he pay for them?

Our Science Collections

The pupils in the science class are making their fall collections. See if you can answer the questions to their problems **without your pencil**.

1. Jane pasted her seeds on a big piece of cardboard. She has seeds of 10 vegetables, 8 fall flowers, and 7 nuts. Of how many different plants has she the seeds?

2. Jim put seeds into little boxes which he pasted into a larger box. He paid 20¢ for boxes, 15¢ for cotton to put in them, and 30¢ for cellophane to cover them. How much did his supplies cost? How much money had he left from one dollar?

3. Ted wants 24 boxes for his seed collection, but he has only 18. How many more boxes does he need?

4. Carl has 27 different kinds of seeds. Bill has 34 kinds. How many more kinds of seeds has Bill than Carl?

5. Helen pressed leaves for her collection and pasted them into a notebook, which cost 25¢. She also bought paste for 10¢ and tape for 12¢. How much did her supplies cost?

Chapter 4
Our Number System

Big Numbers

"I wonder how far away the Big Dipper is," said Joe.

"Millions of miles, probably," answered Helen.

"That sounds like a very big number," said Jack. "I know for sure that it is a lot more than thousands."

Let us find out about millions, but first, let us see what we know about the other numbers.

Our Number System

We use number names and number figures to think about the numbers of things. We use **single** names and **single** figures to think about **single** groups. We use **compounded** names and **compounded** figures to think about **compounded** groups.

Eight
8

We think of numbers to nine as single groups. We have a single name and a single figure to stand for each group. We also think of ten as a single group, and we give it a single name, but there is no single figure for ten. We write 1 in ten's place and 0 in one's place like this: 10.

Fifteen
15

We think of each teen number as 1 ten and so many more. We give each teen number a compounded name and use two figures to write our idea. We write 1 in ten's place and the other figure in one's place.

We think of twenty, thirty, forty, and so on as so many tens. Fifty means 5 tens; so we think of fifty as 5 tens. To write the idea, we write 5 in ten's place and 0 in one's place: 50.

Fifty
50

Eighty-four means 8 tens and 4 ones, and that is the way we think about it. To write the idea, we write 8 in ten's place and 4 in one's place.

One hundred is 10 tens, and that is the way we think about it. To write our idea of one hundred, we write 1 in hundred's place. The 00 put the 1 in its proper place.

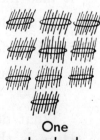
One
hundred
100

A Thousand

A hundred is 10 tens.	10 10 ——— 100	100 10 ——— 1000
A thousand is 10 hundreds.		10 10 ——— 100 10 ——— 1000
A thousand is 100 tens.		
A thousand is 10 times 10 times 10.		

Suppose we have a little cube like this:

We have one (1) cube.

This is 1.

Next, suppose we have ten of these cubes in a row. How many do we have?

Now let us look at 10 such rows. How many tens are there? What do we call 10 tens?

Here are 10.

10 tens are 1 hundred: 100.

Now let us pile up ten such rows. In the big cube there are 1 thousand little cubes. We write one thousand like this: 1000. The 1 is in thousand's place.

Here are 100.

One thousand means 10 hundreds, and it also means 100 tens.

What do you think 10 thousands mean?

What do you think 100 thousands mean?

Can you read these numbers:
2,000   10,000   50,000   100,000   600,000

What do you think 1000 thousands mean? Here is the way we write it: 1,000,000.

One thousand thousands are a million.

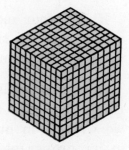
Here are 1000.

84

A Million

"So a million is a thousand thousands," said Helen. Springfield
"It would take a long time to count a million dollars."
"It might take a whole day," said Joe.
"I guess it would take a week," said Ruth.
What is your guess?
"See this second hand on my watch," said Miss Weldon.
"How long does it take to go around once?"
"Sixty seconds, or 1 minute," answered the class.
"You can count to 60 in 1 minute. Then how many dollars could you count in 1 hour?"
"Sixty times sixty, or 3600 dollars," answered Jack.
"We are in school 6 hours each day. How many dollars could you count in 1 school day"? asked Miss Weldon.

60 dollars in 1 minute	*3,600 dollars in 1 hour*
60	*6*
3600 dollars in 1 hour	*21,600 dollars in 1 day*

"If you took out a little time to rest, you could still count 20,000 dollars in 1 day. You go to school 5 days each week. How many dollars could you count in 1 school week?" asked Miss Weldon.

20,000 dollars in 1 day	*100,000 dollars in 1 week*
5	*4*
100,000 dollars in 1 week	*400,000 dollars in 1 month*

How many dollars could you count in 1 month? in 2 months? in $\frac{1}{2}$ month? in $2\frac{1}{2}$ months?

400,000 dollars in 1 month	*800,000 dollars in 2 months*
2	*200,000 dollars in $\frac{1}{2}$ month*
800,000 dollars in 2 months	*1,000,000 dollars in $2\frac{1}{2}$ months*

How long would it take you to count a million dollars?

100 mi.

1,000,000 DOLLAR BILLS

St. Louis

What Numbers Mean

Let us think about what numbers mean.

What is the value of the first **place** of any number? the second place? the third place? the fourth place? the fifth place? the sixth place? the seventh place?

Ten ones are ten.
Ten tens are one hundred.
Ten hundreds are one thousand.
Ten thousands are one ten-thousand.
Ten ten-thousands are one hundred-thousand.
Ten hundred-thousands are one million.

Millions *Hundred Thousands* *Ten Thousands* *Thousands* *Hundreds* *Tens* *Ones*

1 1 1 1 1 1 1

The **value** of each **place** is ten times as much as the value of the place to its right.

What does this number mean: 4,168,579?

The 9 means 9 ones, or 9
The 7 means 7 tens, or 70
The 5 means 5 hundreds, or .500
The 8 means 8 thousands, or 8,000
The 6 means 6 ten-thousands, or 60,000
The 1 means 1 hundred-thousand, or 100,000
The 4 means 4 millions, or 4,000,000
4,168,579

The figures tell how many of each value the number has.

---

1. Write each of these numbers to show what it means:
   64,057   809,261   7039   3,721,590   50,608   101,692
2. What is the purpose of zero in each number?
3. Tell what 5 means in each of these numbers:
   350   5025   15,002   5,052,500   65,274   2,527,496   585

86

Reading Large Numbers

When Jerry studies his geography lesson, he often has to read large numbers.

~~~~~~

The size of the United States is about 3,000,000 square miles. To be exact, it is 2,977,128 square miles. It has a population of about 150,000,000. In 1940 it had a population of 131,669,275.

~~~~~~

To make numbers easier to read, we separate or **point off** the figures, beginning at the right, into groups of three with commas. These groups are called **periods**. Each period has a name. The period at the left will not always have three figures.

Million	Thousand	One
2,	977,	128

Million	Thousand	One
131,	669,	275

To read a number, begin at the left. Read the numbers in each period, followed by the name of the period. We do not say the name of the first (one's) period.

2,977,128 is read: *Two million, nine hundred seventy-seven thousand, one hundred twenty-eight.*

150,000,000 is read: *One hundred fifty million.*

131,669,275 is read: *One hundred thirty-one million, six hundred sixty-nine thousand, two hundred seventy-five.*

620,000 is read: *Six hundred twenty thousand.*

15,102 is read: *Fifteen thousand, one hundred two.*

Reading Large Numbers

Read these statements about the geography of the United States:

1. The Mississippi River is 2470 miles long.

2. It is 3988 miles from the head of the Missouri River to the Gulf of Mexico.

3. Some of the largest national parks are: Yosemite—756,441 acres; Grand Canyon — 645,296 acres; Everglades—271,008 acres; Glacier—997,248 acres; Yellowstone — 2,213,207 acres; Great Smoky Mountains—461,004 acres.

4. Pikes Peak is 14,110 feet high; Mt. Rainier is 14,408 feet; Mt. Hood is 11,225 feet. Which of these peaks is the highest?

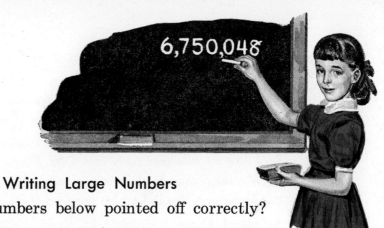

6,750,048

Writing Large Numbers

1. Are the numbers below pointed off correctly?

12,640,160   3,956,100   8,106,780

2. Copy these numbers, mark them off into periods, then read them:

34186	8808	650721	5001294	96058	18121913
75001	60000	5526409	438095	1100001	7890234

3. Which is easier to read?

75628	or	75,628	92875	or	92,875
126422	or	126,422	754100	or	754,100
3000000	or	3,000,000	1908164	or	1,908,164
125640728	or	125,640,728	9655862	or	9,655,862

When we write thousands and millions, we write them in periods and use commas to separate the periods.

4. Write these numbers with figures:

a. Seventy-eight thousand, four hundred.

b. Nine hundred forty-six.

c. Two million, twenty-four thousand, five hundred sixty.

d. One million, three hundred forty thousand, seven.

e. Six hundred ninety-one thousand.

f. Fifty thousand, six hundred forty-one.

g. One hundred one thousand, two hundred ten.

Other Ways of Reading Numbers

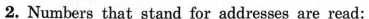

1945

I live at 1945 Oak Street.
My telephone number is 1945.
About 1945 people live here.

Do you see that 1945 may be read in three ways?

a. *I live at nineteen forty-five Oak Street.*
b. *My telephone number is one, nine, four, five.*
c. *About one thousand, nine hundred forty-five people live here.*

1. Read these numbers in three ways:

1492   1835   1015   1905   1700   1650   1950

2. Numbers that stand for addresses are read:

 a. I live at six hundred fifty-two Clark Street.
 b. I live at six fifty-two Clark Street.
 c. I live at six five two Clark Street.

3. Read these addresses in several ways:

347 Main Street   850 Ocean Drive   4412 Brooks Avenue

4. Telephone numbers are usually read by saying each figure as though it were a separate number.

2143R is read: two, one, four, three, R.
Zero in a telephone number is usually read as "oh."
2050 is read: two, oh, five, oh.
1600 may be read: one, six hundred.

5. Read these telephone numbers:

 241 8645R State 4500 6051 Red

6. Read these sentences:

 a. Alice was born June 5, 1908.
 b. Solomon's Temple was built about 2900 years ago.
 c. America was discovered by Columbus in 1492.
 d. Please call Greenleaf 4450.

90

What Do We Know about Numbers?

1. Read these numbers. Tell what each means.

    a. 6,458   18,300   20,417   1,816,439

    b.   802   159,604   105,009   300,700

    c. 40,020   3,001,500   2,150   8,900,000

2. What figure is in one's place in each number above? in ten's place? in hundred's place?

3. Read each number that has a figure in thousand's place; in hundred-thousand's place.

4. To mark off a number into periods, how many places do we group off with commas? With what place of the number do we start counting the figures for a period?

5. What is the name of the first period? the second period? the third period?

6. What is the purpose of zero in writing numbers?

7. In the numbers above, tell what each zero does.

8. Write these numbers:

    a. Eight thousand, three hundred forty-five.

    b. Two hundred forty-three thousand, seventy-nine.

    c. Six hundred four.

    d. Four million, one hundred thousand, nine hundred eighty.

    e. Seven hundred one thousand, four hundred.

    f. Fourteen thousand, five.

    g. Six million, four hundred thousand.

9. Tell what 4 means in each number you wrote.

10. Write the largest four-place number.

11. Write the smallest five-place number.

Roman Numerals

Both the Arabs and the Romans gave us a way to write numbers. In our everyday work we use the Arabic numbers. We write all our numbers with the 9 figures and zero.

| 1 | 2 | 3 | 4 | 5 | 6 | 7 | 8 | 9 | 0 |

The place of the figure in the number determines its value: 10 means ten; 100 means one hundred; 110 means one hundred ten; 1000 means one thousand.

The Romans wrote their numbers with seven letters.

I	V	X	L	C	D	M
1	5	10	50	100	500	1000

They had no zero and no place value.

We use the following plan to write Roman numbers:

Rule 1

When a letter is repeated, its value is repeated.

III is 3.   XXX is 30.   CC is 200.   MM is 2000.

Rule 2

When a letter is followed by a letter of less value, the number is the sum of the values of the letters.

VIII is 8.   LV is 55.   DC is 600.   MC is 1100.

Rule 3

When a letter has a letter of less value before it, the number is the difference between the values of the letters.

IV is 4. IX is 9. XL is 40. XC is 90. CD is 400.

We also use Rules 1, 2, and 3 together.

XXIX is 29. XLV is 45. XCIX is 99. CDXXIV is 424.

Read: XXXIX MCM CCVIII XCIX MCDXCIII

Write: 1900   1950   595   610   1766   1948

Round Numbers

Jack Hines had driven to Cincinnati with his father. "About how far is it from Chicago to Cincinnati?" asked Bill Reed.

"It is 300 miles in **round numbers**," answered Jack. The speedometer record which Jack had kept showed that it was 294 miles. When Jack said that it was 300 miles, he **rounded off** 294 to the nearest hundred. Often it is easier to give distances and amounts in round numbers than in exact numbers. Instead of saying that Kingsville has a population of 11,872, we may say that Kingsville has a population of about 12,000.

We round off a number when we give the nearest ten, hundred, or thousand instead of the exact number.

Exact	Round		Exact	Round		Exact	Round
98	100		616	600		3887	4000

1. Give the following amounts in round numbers:

To Nearest Ten	To Nearest Hundred	To Nearest Thousand
97 tons	608 people	1886 years
49 pounds	296 children	5895 bushels

2. The table below gives the distance by car between certain cities. Round off each distance to the nearest hundred miles:

Chicago to Atlantic City	819		Denver to Minneapolis	887
St. Louis to Detroit	515		Dallas to New Orleans	504
Washington to Birmingham	769		Chicago to Mexico City	2162
Memphis to Los Angeles	1846		San Francisco to Chicago	2212

Chapter 5
Two-Step Problems

Bob helps his father at the filling station. He made a chart to show the price of gasoline. How should Bob finish the chart below?

Regular		Ethyl	
1 Gal. $.22		1 Gal. $.25	
Tax .03		Tax .03	
Total $.25		Total $.28	
Gal.	Cost	Gal.	Cost
4	$1.00	4	$1.12
5	$1.25	5	
6		6	
7		7	
8		8	
9		9	
10		10	

Step 1

1 Gal. $.22
Tax   .03
Total $.25

Step 2

$ .25
    4
$1.00

94

Problems with Two Questions

1. Tom bought 4 marbles that cost 15¢ each. Jim and Joe wanted some like them, but there were no more at the store. So Tom sold all 4 marbles to them for 80¢.

    a. How much did Tom pay for the marbles?

    b. How much did he make by selling them?

First, answer question *a.* What process must we use to find the answer? What two facts will we need?

15¢ ×4 —— 60¢	Tom bought 4 marbles. Each marble cost 15¢. Tom paid 60¢ for the marbles.	80¢ −60¢ —— 20¢

Now look at question *b.* From it we know that Tom sold the marbles for more than they cost him. What process will we use to find how much more?

We need two facts. One is given in the problem: **Tom sold the marbles for 80¢**. The other fact is the answer to question *a*: **the amount Tom paid for them, 60¢**. Tom made 20¢ by selling them.

---

2. Mary bought 9 baby chickens at 5¢ each. When they were large enough to fry, she sold them for $5.40.

    a. How much did Mary pay for the chickens?

    b. How much did she make on these chickens?

3. Mrs. Allen bought 2 dozen eggs at 45¢ a dozen and a loaf of bread for 16¢.

    a. How much did the 2 dozen eggs cost?

    b. How much did she pay for both bread and eggs?

Two-Step Problems

In a two-step problem there are really two questions to be answered. One question is asked in the problem, but the other question is **hidden**. In order to solve a two-step problem, you must find, ask, and answer the hidden question.

Things to Do

1. Read the problem carefully so that you understand what it is about and so that you can tell the problem in your own words.

~~~~~~~~~~~~~~~~~~~~~~~~~~~~~~

Billy sold 53 papers, and James sold 61. How much did they both get for them if they sold the papers at 5¢ each?

~~~~~~~~~~~~~~~~~~~~~~~~~~~~~~

2. Read the problem again. This time you read between the lines to find and ask yourself the hidden question.

Billy sold 53 papers, and James sold 61.

How many papers did they both sell?

How much did they both get for them if they sold the papers at 5¢ each?

$$\begin{array}{r} 53 \text{ papers} \\ \underline{61 \text{ papers}} \\ 114 \text{ papers} \end{array}$$

3. Answer the hidden question as soon as you find it. You work just that much of the problem at this time.

4. Read the rest of the problem, putting the answer to the hidden question where it belongs.

How much did they both get for them if they sold the _114_ papers at 5¢ each?

5. Answer the question the problem asks.

114 papers × $.05 = $5.70

How to Solve Two-Step Problems

1. A fruit store man bought 48 dozen oranges at 35¢ a dozen. He sold them at 50¢ a dozen. How much did he make on the oranges?

Let us read between the lines to find the hidden question so that we can solve the problem.

$$\begin{array}{r} \$.50 \\ .35 \\ \hline \$.15 \end{array}$$

~~~~~~

A fruit store man bought 48 dozen oranges at 35¢ a dozen. He sold them at 50¢ a dozen. *How much did he make on each dozen* ?

How much did he make on 48 dozen oranges?

$$\begin{array}{r} \$\ .15 \\ 48 \\ \hline 1\ 20 \\ 6\ 0 \\ \hline \$7.20 \end{array}$$

~~~~~~

2. He bought 18 dozen lemons at 32¢ a dozen and sold them at 48¢ a dozen. How much did he make?

The amount that he made is called **profit**.

How do we find how much profit he made?

3. He bought 24 pecks of potatoes at 30¢ a peck and sold them at 42¢ a peck. How much profit did he make?

4. He bought 96 heads of lettuce at 7¢ a head and sold them at 12¢ a head. How much profit did he make on the lettuce?

5. He bought 48 bunches of celery at 9¢ a bunch and sold them at 15¢ a bunch. How much profit did he make?

6. He bought 36 baskets of peaches at $1.15 a basket and sold them at $1.50 a basket. How much was his profit?

7. He bought 16 baskets of plums at 45¢ a basket and sold them at 65¢ a basket. How much was his profit?

Two-Step Problems

In Column A, each problem is printed in the ordinary way with one of the questions hidden. In Column B, the question that is usually hidden is printed in the problem for you to read.

Read the problems in Column A, reading between the lines to find the hidden questions. See how many problems you can solve without looking at the problems in Column B. If you cannot find the hidden question in any problem in Column A, read the same problem in Column B, but solve the problem in Column A.

Column A

Bill sold 23 copies of a magazine, and James sold 16. How much did they both get for them at 15¢ each?

John paid 38¢ for a map book in geography and 45¢ for a workbook in history. He also spent as much for an arithmetic as he spent for both the workbook and the map book. How much did he spend for all the books?

If the cost of 2 oranges is 10 cents, what would be the cost of 12 oranges?

Column B

Bill sold 23 copies of a magazine, and James sold 16. How many did they both sell? How much did they both get for them at 15¢ each?

John paid 38¢ for a map book in geography and 45¢ for a workbook in history. How much did he spend for both? He also spent as much for an arithmetic as he did for both the workbook and the map book. How much did he spend for all the books?

If the cost of 2 oranges is 10¢, what is the cost of one orange? What would be the cost of 12 oranges?

Column A

Susan has saved $11.80. Today her father gave her $5.00. Susan wants to buy a winter coat that costs $23.75. How much more money must she save to buy the coat?

The children in our room sold popcorn to buy flags. They sold 72 sacks for 5¢ each. How many flags that cost 9¢ each can they buy with the money?

Joe had $12 in his bank. He spent all but $\frac{1}{4}$ of it for a raincoat. His father then gave him $5.00, which he put into his bank. How much money did Joe have in his bank then?

Paul Brown saved $43 last summer, but spent $14.65 of it for clothes in the fall. How much will he have to save this summer in order to have $60 by next fall?

Column B

Susan has saved $11.80. Today her father gave her $5.00. How much does she have now? Susan wants to buy a winter coat that costs $23.75. How much more money must she save to buy the coat?

The children in our room sold popcorn to buy flags. They sold 72 sacks for 5¢ each. How much did they get for the popcorn? How many flags that cost 9¢ each can they buy with the money?

Joe had $12 in his bank. He spent all but $\frac{1}{4}$ of it for a raincoat. How much did Joe have left in his bank? His father then gave him $5.00, which he put in his bank. How much money did Joe have in his bank then?

Paul Brown saved $43 last summer, but spent $14.65 of it for clothes in the fall. How much does he have left? How much will he have to save this summer in order to have $60 by next fall?

Two-Step Problems

1. Mary made 2 cherry pies for Mrs. Dan. The materials for both pies cost about 48¢. Mrs. Dan gave Mary 60¢ for each pie. How much did Mrs. Dan pay for both pies? How much did Mary make on the pies?

2. Mary made 2 cherry pies for Mrs. Dan. The materials for both pies cost about 48¢. Mrs. Dan gave Mary 60¢ for each pie. How much did Mary make on the pies?

What is the **difference** between the two problems?

Can you solve problem **2** before you find the answer to the first question in problem **1**?

Problem **2** is a **two-step** problem because we need to find a fact that is not given before we can answer the question in the problem. We must find this fact from facts that are given in the problem. We must ask and answer the "hidden" question that gives us this fact.

Read each problem carefully. Find and ask the hidden question. Answer the hidden question. Read the problem again, putting the answer to the hidden question where it belongs. Then answer the question the problem asks.

3. Mr. Black raised 90 bushels of potatoes. He sold 60 bushels. He wants to put the rest of the potatoes in 2-bushel sacks.

    a. _____?

    b. How many sacks does he need for the potatoes?

4. The cost of 3 pencils is 15¢.

    a. _____?

    b. How much should 12 of these pencils cost?

5. Joe had 26 books and got 4 new ones for his birthday. To make room for them on his bookshelf, he gave 8 books to the children's library. How many books did he have then?

6. Tom had 43 marbles. He gave 17 of them to Jerry and bought 8 new ones for himself. Then how many marbles did Tom have?

7. Betty had 28 bird pictures. She gave half of them to Jane. Then May gave Betty 5 other bird pictures. How many bird pictures did Betty have for her notebook?

8. Mrs. West bought 2 dozen eggs. She used 9 of them for an angel food cake. How many eggs did she have left?

9. Bill sold 24 papers each weekday and 32 papers each Sunday. How many papers did he sell each week?

10. Tom picked 16 apples. He shared them equally with 3 friends. Then he gave one of his apples to his dad. How many apples did Tom keep for himself?

11. Sam raised 18 bushels of potatoes. He sold 10 bushels at the store. Then Uncle Jim said he would buy half of the potatoes that were left. How many bushels of potatoes did Uncle Jim buy?

Oral Problems

1. Aunt Helen gave Sally and Beth 3 boxes of shells. Each box had 12 shells in it. If the girls divide the shells equally, how many will each girl have?

2. Mary is making a penwiper for each of the 9 girls in her club. She had 3 pieces of felt, and she cut 12 circles from each piece. How many circles can she tie together for each penwiper?

3. Dick sold 6 pumpkins at 25¢ each. How much did he get for them all?

4. Ann wants to make little bunches of asters, 3 asters to a bunch. She picked 13 asters. Then she picked 8 more. How many bunches can she make?

5. Joe delivered papers to 14 people each day. Two of his customers moved away, but soon he had 5 new ones. To how many people did he then deliver papers each day?

6. It takes 9 eggs to make Mrs. Allen's angel food cake. If she has 3 dozen eggs and makes 3 cakes, how many eggs will she have left?

7. For each of the 4 times that Bill ran errands for Mrs. Brown, she gave him a dime. With this money he bought a magazine for 25¢. How much did he have left?

8. Bob earned 15¢, 20¢, and 25¢ running errands for three people. With this money he bought a book that cost 60¢. How much had he left?

Practice in Adding

9. 635 + 410 + 297 + 118   **11.** 1418 + 906 + 462 + 2931

10. 700 + 52 + 1007 + 509   **12.** 1070 + 50 + 408 + 1980

The Camera Club

1. There are 16 members in the Camera Club. Each member pays 5¢ a week for dues. How much money is paid into the club for dues in one year, or 52 weeks?

2. It costs 35¢ to have a roll of film developed and 5¢ for each picture that is printed. Joe uses films that take 8 pictures. What should he pay to have a roll of film developed and 1 print made of each of the 8 exposures?

3. A film that takes 8 pictures in color costs $1.37. The same-sized film for black and white pictures costs 3 rolls for $1.20. What is the difference in price of a roll of the two kinds of film?

4. Jack suggested that they could save money by developing the films and printing the pictures themselves. A beginner's developing set cost $3.98. A better set cost $19.75. How much more did the better set cost than the beginner's set?

5. To have pictures enlarged, they pay $1.00 for 4 of one kind, or 36¢ each. How much less does each picture cost if they get 4 of a kind made rather than just one?

103

Two-Step Problems

1. Mr. Sellers bought 72 boxes of strawberries at 23¢ a box and sold them at 45¢ a box. How much did he make on the strawberries?

2. Mr. Sellers bought 60 dozen eggs at 33 cents a dozen and sold them at 45 cents a dozen. How much did he make?

3. Marie wants to buy a sweater and dress for herself and a gift for her mother. She has $10.00 to spend. The sweater costs $2.48, and the dress costs $3.75. How much will Marie have left to spend for the gift for her mother?

4. Jimmie had 14 sticks of chewing gum. He kept 2 sticks for himself and divided the rest among his 4 friends. How many sticks did he give to each friend?

5. Elmer Hall sells papers after school. The papers cost him 3¢ each, and he sells them for 5¢ each. Last week he sold 96 papers. How much did he make?

6. Mrs. Jenkins paid 60 cents for oranges that cost 5 cents each. She divided them among 6 girls. How many oranges did she give each girl?

104

Measures and Weights

1. In 1 foot there are ___*12*___ inches.

2. In 1 yard there are _____ feet.

3. In 1 yard there are _____ inches.

I LB.   16 OZ.

4. The one-pound weight balances the 16 one-ounce weights. There are _____ ounces in 1 pound.

5. There are _____ pounds in a ton.

6. The girls poured water from the quart bottles into the gallon measure. It took the water from _____ quart bottles to fill the gallon measure. There are _____ quarts in 1 gallon.

7. The grocer had a bushel of potatoes which he put into peck baskets. The bushel of potatoes filled _____ peck baskets. There are _____ pecks in a bushel.

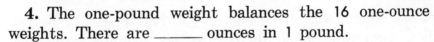

Length	Weight
12 inches = 1 foot	16 ounces = 1 pound
3 feet = 1 yard	2000 pounds = 1 ton

Capacity

Liquid	Dry
2 cups = 1 pint	2 pints = 1 quart
2 pints = 1 quart	8 quarts = 1 peck
4 quarts = 1 gallon	4 pecks = 1 bushel

105

Problems in Measures and Weights

Read **between the lines.** See if you can **find the hidden question** in each problem in Column A. If you cannot, then study the same problem in Column B. Do not use Column B unless you need to.

Column A

1. The fruit store man had 25 dozen oranges. How much can he get for them if he sells them at 5¢ apiece?

2. He bought 15 barrels of apples from a farmer. Each barrel held 3 bushels. How many pecks of apples did he buy?

3. Mr. Benson bought 24 yards of fencing material for his chicken yard. The material cost 15¢ a foot. How much did the material cost?

4. A farmer sold 12 bushels of hickory nuts at 15¢ a quart. How much did he get for them?

5. How much will two watermelons weighing 24 pounds and 18 pounds cost at 3¢ a pound?

Column B

1. The fruit store man had 25 dozen oranges. *How many oranges did he have?* How much can he get for them if he sells them at 5¢ apiece?

2. He bought 15 barrels of apples from a farmer. Each barrel held 3 bushels. *How many bushels did he buy?* How many pecks did he buy?

The Hidden Question

How many feet of fencing material did he buy?

The Hidden Question

How many quarts did he sell?

The Hidden Question

How much did both watermelons weigh?

106

Problems in Measures and Weights

1. The three Stollard boys gathered and husked 7 bushels of walnuts. They measured them out into peck sacks and sold them from house to house for 35 cents a peck. How much were they paid for the walnuts?

2. At Boy Scout Camp the boys were served ice cream at dinner. The camp cook had to buy 8 gallons of ice cream to have enough to go around. How much did the ice cream cost at 75 cents a quart?

3. A large grocery company bought 1200 one-peck sacks of potatoes. The potatoes cost the company $1.85 a bushel. How much did the company have to pay for all the potatoes?

4. How many rosettes can be made from 20 yards of ribbon if 9 inches are needed to make one?

5. A man wanted to buy 65 yards of wire fencing material. He was told that the cost of the material was 16¢ a foot. How much would he have to pay for the fencing material?

6. How much do 84 quarts of milk cost if the milk is sold at 7 cents a pint?

7. At 5 cents a pint, how much can a farmer get for 18 gallons of milk?

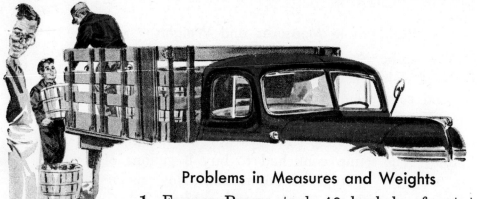

Problems in Measures and Weights

1. Farmer Brown took 60 bushels of potatoes to town on his truck. He sold the potatoes at the City Market at 75¢ a peck. How much did he receive for his potatoes?

2. He picked 16 bushels of choice cherries. He put them into quart boxes and sold them at 15¢ a quart. How much did he receive for his choice cherries?

3. He picked 38 bushels of peaches. By putting them into peck baskets and marketing them himself, he was able to sell them at 75¢ a basket. How much did he get for his peaches?

4. He picked 12 barrels of apples, each holding 3 bushels. He put the apples into sacks, each holding a peck. How many peck sacks of apples did he have?

5. Caleb and his brother gathered 3 bushels of chestnuts. They sold the chestnuts for 10 cents a pint. How much did they receive for them?

6. "Apples are selling at two prices," said Jack. "We can buy a bushel of apples for $1.50, or we can buy them by the peck at 45¢."

What is the difference in the two prices?

Grade A Milk........23¢ qt.
Buttermilk...........21¢ qt.
Chocolate Milk.......26¢ qt.

Coffee Cream........56¢ pt.
Butter...............78¢ lb.
Cottage Cheese.......26¢ pt.

The Milkman

1. Mrs. West bought 4 quarts of grade A milk. If she pays for it with a dollar bill, how much change should she get back?

2. Mrs. Jackson bought 1 quart of chocolate milk, 1 pint of coffee cream, and $\frac{1}{2}$ pound of butter. How much was her bill?

3. Mrs. Benton bought 1 pint of cottage cheese, 1 pound of butter, and 2 quarts of grade A milk. How much did she owe?

4. On one of his milk routes a milkman delivered 552 pints of milk. How many gallons of milk was that? How many quarts?

5. How many quart bottles can be filled with 72 gallons of milk? How many pint bottles can be filled with the same amount?

Chapter 6
Everyday Problems

The Average

1. The Ballard family drove 185 miles to visit their friends the Lakes. They made the trip in 5 hours. What was the **average** distance traveled each hour?

The Ballards did not drive at the same speed all the time. Going through towns they slowed down to 15 miles an hour. In the country they often traveled as fast as 50 miles an hour. But **suppose** they had traveled at the **same speed all the way**. Then they would have traveled the **same distance each hour**. That is what **average** means.

To find this average, we divide the total distance by the number of hours.

The Ballards would have traveled 37 miles per hour if they had traveled the same distance each hour.

$$\begin{array}{r} 37 \\ 5\overline{)185} \\ 15 \\ \hline 35 \\ 35 \\ \hline \end{array}$$

2. The Bell family took a four-day automobile trip during their vacation. They traveled 152 miles on Monday; 76 miles on Tuesday; 47 miles on Wednesday; and 205 miles on Thursday. What was the average distance they traveled each day?

3. On the first day they traveled from home to Camp Joy, a distance of 152 miles, in 4 hours. On the average, how many miles did they travel each hour?

4. Their expenses for the 4 days were as follows: $11.96 for the first day; $9.82 for the second day; $10.35 for the third day; and $7.59 for the fourth day. How much was the average expense for each day?

5. Jane and her father went for a trip one week end. They started on Friday evening and traveled 75 miles. On Saturday they traveled 215 miles, and on Sunday, 184 miles. Find the average distance traveled each day.

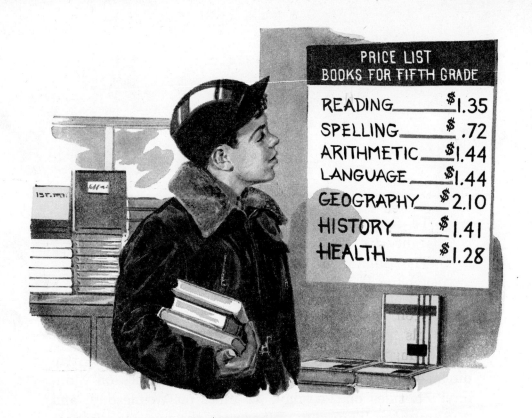

PRICE LIST
BOOKS FOR FIFTH GRADE

READING	$1.35
SPELLING	$ .72
ARITHMETIC	$1.44
LANGUAGE	$1.44
GEOGRAPHY	$2.10
HISTORY	$1.41
HEALTH	$1.28

The School Bookstore

In the school bookstore the price list of books for the fifth grade was tacked on the wall. When school started in September, the pupils were given a time to go to the bookstore to buy the books they needed.

1. How much do all the books on the list for the fifth grade cost?

2. How much is the average cost (to nearest cent)?

3. June Stanton's brother, who was in Grade 5 the year before, gave her the reading and language books. June bought the rest and paid for them with a 10-dollar bill. How much change should June receive?

4. Billy Jones bought all the books but the reading and arithmetic books. How much did each book that he bought cost on the average?

5. Jim Bender said, "I have to buy a geography and a language book. Dad gave me four dollars."
Does Jim have enough money to buy his books? How much will he have left?

6. Helen Hall bought all the books on the list except the speller. She bought a secondhand speller for 50¢. How much did her books cost?

7. In a small school there are 6 pupils in the fifth grade. How much will the books for the class cost?

8. Tom Brown bought a geography and a history. Joe Mills bought an arithmetic, a health book, a reader, and a language book. Who spent more for books? How much more?

9. Let us compare the prices of some of the books.
    a. An arithmetic costs *twice* as much as a speller.
    b. A geography costs about ____ times as much as a speller.
    c. A speller costs about ____ as much as a reader.
    d. Which books cost about the same amount?

10. Which boy, Harry or Walter, paid more for books?

Harry's books   Walter's books

Averages

1. Helen had these scores on her test record at the end of the last month of school: Arithmetic, 92; Reading, 92; History, 89; Language, 85; and Geography, 82. What was Helen's average score for the year?

First, find the total:

Arithmetic	92
Reading	92
History	89
Language	85
Geography	82
	440

Next, divide by the number:

$$\begin{array}{r} 88 \\ 5\overline{)440} \\ 40 \\ \hline 40 \\ 40 \end{array}$$

The total of Helen's scores is 440. Suppose that she had made the same score in each of her 5 subjects; that score would have been 88 in each subject. We say that her average was 88.

2. Here are the scores of William Watson in some of the tests he had in the fifth grade. Find his average score for each month. Find the average score in arithmetic for the year.

	Sept.	Oct.	Nov.	Dec.	Jan.	Feb.	March	April	May
Arithmetic	79	82	84	85	85	85	90	90	95
Reading	80	83	82	86	82	85	90	91	92
History	87	87	86	89	90	90	95	97	97
Language	84	84	83	87	85	87	87	89	92
Geography	90	89	90	93	93	93	93	93	94
Average									

How Well Can You Solve Problems?

1. During July Bill worked in Mr. Dan's grocery store. He worked 6 hours a day for 26 days. Mr. Dan paid him 25¢ an hour. How much did Bill earn at the grocery?

2. The pupils at Riley School made money by selling little felt caps made in their school colors. They bought 50 caps at 17¢ each and sold them all at 25¢ each. How much did they make on the caps?

3. Jim earned $9.90 in 6 days by mowing lawns. What were his average earnings each day?

4. Alice saves money to buy her school supplies. She has $2.85. How much more does she need in order to buy her reader for $1.58, her arithmetic for $1.28, and a notebook for $.25?

5. Jane made 4 dozen cookies on Saturday morning. In the afternoon she served 16 of them to the girls who came to visit her. How many cookies were left?

6. Mrs. Olds promised to take 60 cookies to the church supper. She has made 3 dozen of them. How many more cookies must she make?

7. Five boys and 6 girls are going on a picnic. Sue offered to make 3 sandwiches for each of them. How many sandwiches should she make?

8. Jim raised 45 pounds of onions. He sold 25 pounds at the grocery store. The rest he put into 5-pound sacks to keep for winter use. How many sacks did he need?

9. Jim sold 25 pounds of onions at 5¢ a pound. How much more does he need to get a model airplane that costs $1.59?

115

Review Problems

1. The Sports Shop advertised boys' baseball uniforms for $2.48 each. If 9 boys on the baseball team buy uniforms, how much will all the uniforms cost?

2. The Grant Junior High School bought 5 basketball sweaters to give to the members of the school team. The school paid $6.90 for the sweaters. How much did each sweater cost?

3. A clothing store had an after-Christmas sale. During the first day the store sold 7 overcoats for $17.50 each. How much did the store get for the overcoats?

4. Mr. Hunter bought an overcoat for $17.50, a suit of clothes for $23.48, and a pair of shoes for $3.98. How much did they cost altogether?

5. Mr. Hunter gave the clerk $50.00 in bills to pay for the things he bought. How much change did Mr. Hunter get back?

6. The store bought 8 spring suits of a certain kind, and paid $174.00 for them. How much did the store pay for each suit on the average?

116

Making and Saving Money

Tommy Bridges delivers the evening paper to a number of houses in Bland. He runs errands and does other jobs. Little by little he is saving his money. He is going to college some day and will use what he has saved to help pay his expenses.

1. He collects 24¢ for delivering a paper for a week. Of this he must turn in 18¢ to the publisher. During a certain week he delivered papers to 35 houses. How much did he make that week?

2. Tommy kept an account of the papers he delivered each week for a year. During the year he delivered, and collected for, an average of 32 papers a week. How much did he make delivering papers during the year?

3. In the spring he whitewashed some trees for the neighbors. The lime for it cost 50¢. He whitewashed 27 trees at 15¢ a tree. How much did he make doing that?

4. In the summer he mowed lawns and ran errands. He charged 50¢ for mowing a front lawn and 75¢ for mowing both front and back lawns. During July he mowed 6 front lawns and 8 front and back lawns. How much did he make mowing lawns in July?

5. Tommy has 47 of the 75 Savings Stamps needed to fill his stamp book. How many more Stamps does he need to fill his book? How much money must he save before he can fill his book and buy a Bond at $18.75?

Making and Saving Money

1. Tommy kept an account of the money he had received during the year. These are the amounts he made:

For delivering papers	$99.84
For whitewashing	3.55
For mowing lawns (June)	6.00
For mowing lawns (July)	9.00
For mowing lawns (August)	5.50
For running errands	5.20

How much did Tommy make during the year?

2. How much did Tommy make each month, on the average, for mowing lawns?

3. At the beginning of the year Tommy had $12.75. His uncle sent him $5.00 for his birthday. If he had kept all he had received during the year, how much would he have had at the end of the year?

4. During the year Tommy bought a suit, an overcoat, and shoes. He paid for his schoolbooks. He went a good many times to picture shows. He spent some money for other things. Tommy kept an account of all this, which he labeled, "What I Spent."

This is his account:

	What I Spent				
Jan.	$2.38	May	$6.57	Sept.	$24.50
Feb.	3.45	June	3.70	Oct.	1.75
March	4.20	July	8.95	Nov.	3.78
April	2.65	Aug.	19.75	Dec.	10.60

How much did he spend? How much did he have left?

Making and Saving Money

Helen Wallace is given an **allowance** of 25 cents each week by her parents. She also makes some money by helping out at home and by taking subscriptions for magazines.

During January last year, Helen made a record of the money she received and of the money she spent. She ruled a page of her notebook and kept her account like this:

What I Received		What I Spent	
Jan. 1. Money on hand	$2.78	Jan. 1. Picture show	$ .35
" 6. Selling magazines	.20	" 6. Candy	.20
" 8. Allowance	.25	" 9. Ice cream	.15
" 13. Selling magazines	.95	" 13. Picture show	.35
" 15. Allowance	.25	" 17. Ball game	.25
" 17. Cleaning kitchen	.40	" 20. Sweater	1.98
" 20. Errands	.30	" 25. Basketball game	.25
" 22. Allowance	.25	" 29. Candy and show	.50
" 25. Selling magazines	1.25	Total	$
" 29. Allowance	.25		
" 31. Sweeping and dusting	.50		
Total	$	Jan. 31. Money on hand	$____

How much did she have left at the end of the month?

119

Saving Money

Ruth Wilson is saving her money at the Riverside Bank. She has put in some money, and she has spent some. Now she is finding out how much money she should have left in her account.

Here are her figures. Did she figure correctly?

Make up one → Thur

October 1

How much I had in the bank
  the first of September $34.68
How much I put in the bank in September:
  What I had saved from my errands
    during the summer . . . . $ 9.35
  First   week, from allowance 50
  Second week,   "   " 50
  Third week,   "   " 50
  Fourth week,   "   " 50
                              Altogether $11.35

$34.68 ⎱ How much in bank if I had
  11.35 ⎰   not spent any
─────────
$46.03
 19.72 ◄   I spent: for shoes $ 4.75
─────────   for sweater   1.98
$26.31 ◄   for dress   2.50
This is how much   for suit   6.85
I should have in   for books   3.64
my account.   ─────────
                                      $19.72 ◄
             I drew this much
             from my account at the bank.

120

Saving Money

Every Monday is Bank Day at the Riverside School. The pupils bring the money they wish to save, and it is **deposited** in the Riverside Bank.

1. Ruth Wilson had $34.68 in her account the first of September. During the month she deposited $9.35 of her summer savings and $2.00 of her allowance money. How much did she then have in her account?

2. Ruth spent $19.72 for clothes and books. She drew this much out of her account. How much did she have left in her account?

3. Altogether the pupils at the Riverside School had $4,260.58 in the bank. When school began in September, they drew out $1,248.50 to help pay for their school-books and clothes. How much did they all have left in the Riverside Bank?

Grocery Bills

Mrs. Archer pays her grocery bill each Saturday morning. During the week when she buys things at the store, the grocer charges them and gives her a bill.

This is the way a bill looks:

Fifth Avenue Grocery

Phone 9876   842 5th Ave.

Lakeview, Ind._____ *Sept. 15,* 19___

Mrs. *W. R. Archer* _____

Account Forwarded	$4	62
1 loaf bread		15
1 doz. eggs		40
5 lb. sugar		43
1 lb. coffee		77
6 oranges		24
3 grapefruit		25
3 lb. beans		21
	2	45
	4	62
	$7	07

Your account to date. If error is found **return at once** for correction.

Is Mrs. Archer's bill correct?

Checking Grocery Bills

Here are some **bills** that Jack Woods made out for his customers. Check them to see if he added correctly.

Mrs. Archer

Account forwarded		$6.42
Bacon	$ .37	
Eggs	.35	
Apples	.48	1.20
		$7.62

Mrs. Brown

Account forwarded		$4.82
Coffee	$ .32	
Sugar	.35	
Eggs	.35	
Butter	.38	1.30
		$5.12

Mrs. Johnson

Account forwarded		$5.46
Sugar	$ .35	
Oranges	.28	
Bananas	.23	
Bread	.15	.96
		$6.42

Mrs. Hall

Account forwarded		$6.75
Roast	$1.63	
Potatoes	.56	
Spinach	.24	
Cabbage	.18	2.61
		$9.36

Mrs. Johnson

Account forwarded		$6.42
Ham	$2.57	
Potatoes	.56	
Butter	.38	
Grapefruit	.25	3.76
		$10.18

Mrs. Burton

Account forwarded		$2.47
Cheese	$ .28	
Butter	.38	
Apples	.48	
Beans	.25	1.39
		$4.96

Miss Hays

Account forwarded		$4.28
Bananas	$ .27	
Eggs	.72	
Bacon	.58	1.57
		$5.85

Mr. Black

Account forwarded		$8.10
Cheese	$ .36	
Butter	.38	
Orange juice	.27	1.01
		$9.11

Should customers check their bills? Why?
Should clerks check the bills they make out? Why?

Two-Step Problems

1. Henry Wells sold 28 magazines, and his sister Alice sold 18. How much were they both paid if they sold each magazine for 25¢?

2. Henry Wells and his sister paid 16¢ each for some magazines. They sold them for 25¢ each. How much did they make on 46 magazines?

3. Alice Wells has $14.65 in the school savings bank. How much more does she need to have enough to buy a coat that costs $16.75 and a dress that costs $7.98?

4. A grocer bought 120 dozen eggs at 27¢ a dozen and sold them at 32¢ a dozen. How much profit did he make?

5. During the month of July, William Henderson worked 6 hours a day for 26 days clerking in a grocery. He was paid at the rate of 25¢ an hour. How much was he paid for the month of July?

6. Jack Stump had $43.18 in the school savings bank. He drew out enough to buy a school suit for $16.75 and schoolbooks and supplies that cost $6.00. How much did he have left in the bank?

7. The pupils at the Consolidated High School bought 50 small flags on canes for 17¢ each. At the football game they sold all the flags on canes for 25¢ each. How much did they make?

An Auto Trip

This is Tom's record of the family's expenses on a week-end auto trip to visit friends.

EXPENSES OF AUTO TRIP				
	Friday	*Saturday*	*Sunday*	*Totals*
Food	$4.30	$5.98	$5.15	
Gasoline	$3.36	$5.60	$2.28	
Oil	$1.44		$ .72	
Repairs		$4.65	$1.35	
Totals				

Answer these questions from Tom's record:

1. What was the total spent for food?

2. What were the total expenses (gasoline, oil, repairs) on the car?

3. How much was spent each day?

4. What was the total cost of the trip?

5. This was how much per day on the average?

How Much Change?

Find the amount of each purchase and the amount of change Jack returned to each customer:

Mrs. White
Bacon......$ .53
Eggs....... .60
Butter...... .42
Sugar...... .30

Gave Jack: $5.00

How much change?

Mrs. Asher
Cheese.....$ .15
Bread...... .11
Beans...... .23
Peas...... .28

Gave Jack: $1.00

How much change?

Mrs. Brown
Cookies.....$ .27
Milk....... .18
Apples...... .24
Cheese...... .32

Gave Jack: $1.25

How much change?

Mrs. Ballard
Coffee......$ .32
Sugar...... .60
Cereal...... .22

Gave Jack: $1.50

How much change?

Mrs. Walters
Ham.......$3.60
Bacon...... .53
Chicken.... 1.14

Gave Jack: $10

How much change?

Mrs. Allen
Sausage.....$ .84
Cream...... .36
Eggs....... .60

Gave Jack: $2.00

How much change?

Mr. Jackson
Potatoes....$ .53
Butter...... .42
Eggs....... .60
Roast....... 1.07
Bacon...... .43

Gave Jack: $5.00

How much change?

Mrs. Easton
Peaches.....$ .55
Corn...... .28
Cake...... .39
Macaroni... .24
Cheese...... .18

Gave Jack: $2.00

How much change?

Mrs. Mason
Oranges....$ .28
Bread....... .16
Bacon...... .58
Butter...... .42
Sugar...... .60

Gave Jack: $5.00

How much change?

Mrs. West
Bacon......$ .60
Bread...... .16
Milk....... .16

Gave Jack: $1.00

How much change?

Mrs. Wells
Apples......$ .24
Eggs....... .60
Coffee...... .32

Gave Jack: $2.00

How much change?

Mrs. Holt
Milk.......$ .32
Bread...... .16
Sugar...... .30

Gave Jack: $5.00

How much change?

1. There are ___36___ ___inches___ in a yard.

2. There are _____ _____ in a gallon.

3. There are _____ pecks in a bushel.

4. There are _____ quarts in a bushel.

5. To change feet to yards, ___divide___ by **3**.

6. To change yards to inches, _____ by **36**.

7. To change hours to minutes, _____ by **60**.

8. To change weeks to days, _____ by **7**.

9. To change pints to gallons, _____ by **8**.

10. To change quarts to bushels, _____ by **32**.

From the list of words in the box choose the correct one for each of the blanks in the sentences below:

11. We measure the length of a sheet of paper in _____.

12. We measure the amount of milk in a bottle in _____.

13. We measure the distance between towns in _____.

14. We measure the weight of a package of tea in _____.

15. We measure the amount of coal Mr. Smith needs for his furnace in _____.

16. We measure the length of ribbon on a spool in _____.

17. We measure the quantity of apples on Farmer Brown's truck in _____.

18. We measure the quantity of strawberries Mrs. Jackson buys for shortcake in _____.

bushels
feet
gallons
inches
miles
ounces
pints
pounds
tons
yards

Chapter 7
Equal Parts

Parts of Things

Did you ever stop to think how often we use parts of things?

Bob wants to share his stick of candy with Tom and Jim. Why do you think he is working so hard at it? Could it be because he is trying to get the three pieces the same size? If he can get them equal, what part of the candy will each boy have?

How many apples has Jane? How many apples is she giving to Ann? Two of the five apples are two fifths of the apples. Jane is giving Ann two fifths of the apples.

Jack and Bill are comparing the lengths of their kite tails. Jack sees that the tail of his kite is one half as long as the tail of Bill's kite.

Have you used parts of things, or fractions, in the ways that these boys and girls have?

Equal Parts

When we divide an orange into 2 equal parts, each part is **one half** of the orange. This is the way we write one half with figures: $\frac{1}{2}$.

How many halves are in the whole orange? We may answer, "Two halves equal one." This is the way we write the answer: $\frac{2}{2} = 1$.

When we divide an apple into 3 equal parts, each part is **one third** of the apple. Two of the parts are two thirds of the whole apple. We write one third like this: $\frac{1}{3}$.

How many thirds are in the whole apple? We may answer, "Three thirds equal one." This is the way we write the answer: $\frac{3}{3} = 1$.

When we divide a pie into 4 equal parts, each part is **one fourth** of the whole pie. We write one fourth like this: $\frac{1}{4}$.

How much are 2 of the equal parts?
How much are 3 of the equal parts?
How much are 4 of the equal parts?
How many fourths are in the whole pie?
This is the way we write the answer: $\frac{4}{4} = 1$.

When we divide a stick of candy into 5 equal parts, each part is **one fifth** ($\frac{1}{5}$) of the whole stick.
How much are 2 of the equal parts?
How much are 3 of the equal parts?
How much are 4 of the equal parts?
How many fifths are in one? Write the answer.

129

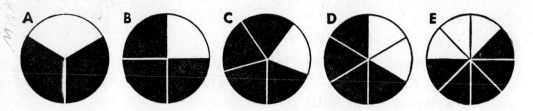

Equal Parts

Circle A is divided into three equal parts. Each part is *one third* of the circle. One third of the circle is white, and *two thirds* of it are black.

Circle B is divided into four equal parts. Each part is _____ of the circle. One fourth of it is white, and _____ of it are black.

Circle C is divided into five equal parts. Each part is _____ of the circle. One fifth of the circle is white, and _____ of it are black.

Circle D is divided into six equal parts. Each part is _____ of the circle. Two sixths are white, and _____ are black.

Circle E is divided into eight equal parts. Each part is _____ of the circle. Three eighths of it are white, and _____ are black.

What part of each square is white? What part of each square is black?

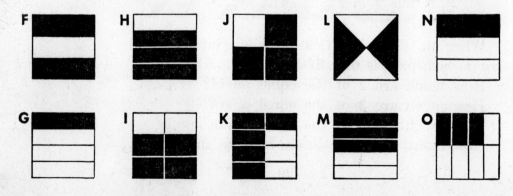

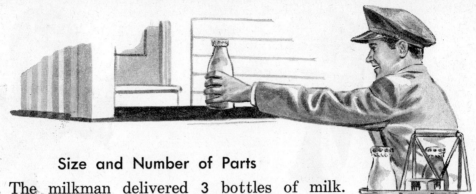

Size and Number of Parts

1. The milkman delivered 3 bottles of milk. How much milk did he deliver? Can we tell how much milk (exactly) he delivered? Must we know something about the size of the bottles? Why?

2. Jerry and his family ate 3 of the 4 equal parts of the pie. They ate **three fourths** of it. This is the way we write how much they ate: $\frac{3}{4}$. The figure 3 above the line tells the **number** of parts they ate, and the figure 4 below the line tells the **size** of each part.

3. Jane cut her cake into 8 equal parts. She gave Alice three of the parts, and she kept 5 of the parts for herself.

Each part is **one eighth**. She gave Alice three eighths, and she kept five eighths.

This is the way we write how much she gave Alice: $\frac{3}{8}$. The 3 tells the number of parts (pieces) she gave Alice, and the 8 tells the size of each part.

This is the way we write how much Jane kept for herself: $\frac{5}{8}$. The 5 tells the number of parts, and the 8 tells the size of each part.

The figure above the line tells the number of parts.
The figure below the line tells the size of the parts.

fracture, 1. To break. The carpenter fell from the ladder and fractured his arm. 2. A crack made by breaking.

fraction, 1. One or more of the equal parts of a whole. 2. A part broken off.

Fractions

A long time ago a fraction meant the *broken off* part of anything. The broken off part of a stick was, and still is, a fraction. The equal parts, the fractions, we are now studying were once called *brokens*. Pupils in schools long ago studied brokens. Really they studied parts or fractions.

We write a fraction, such as three fifths, like this: $\frac{3}{5}$. The figure below the line tells the size of the parts. It is called the **denominator**. In $\frac{3}{5}$, the 5 means that the size of each part is one fifth of the whole.

The figure above the line tells the number of parts. It is called the **numerator**. In $\frac{3}{5}$, the 3 means that there are 3 equal parts.

The numerator and the denominator are the **terms** of the fraction.

What does the figure 4 tell us? $\dfrac{4}{5}$ *numerator*

What does the figure 5 tell us? *denominator*

132

Halves, Fourths, Eighths

Miss West drew a big circle on the board.
Ted divided the circle into 2 equal parts.
He wrote: $\frac{2}{2} = 1$.

Bess divided the 2 halves. She divided each half into 2 equal parts. She said, "Two halves are four fourths. One half equals two fourths."

She wrote: $\frac{2}{2} = \frac{4}{4}$ and $\frac{1}{2} = \frac{2}{4}$.

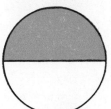

Tom divided the 4 fourths. He divided each fourth into 2 equal parts. He said, "Two halves are eight eighths. One half equals four eighths.

He wrote: $\frac{2}{2} = \frac{8}{8}$ and $\frac{1}{2} = \frac{4}{8}$.

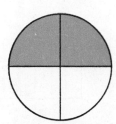

Bess said, "Four fourths are eight eighths; so one fourth equals two eighths.

She wrote: $\frac{4}{4} = \frac{8}{8}$ and $\frac{1}{4} = \frac{2}{8}$.

How many eighths are in 2 fourths? $\frac{2}{4} = \frac{?}{8}$

How many eighths are in 3 fourths? $\frac{3}{4} = \frac{?}{8}$

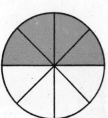

133

More about Halves

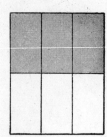

How many sixths are in the whole circle?
How many sixths are in the shaded half?

$1 = \frac{6}{6}$ $\frac{6}{6} = 1$ $\frac{3}{6} = \frac{1}{2}$ $\frac{1}{2} = \frac{3}{6}$

How many eighths are in one?
How many eighths are in one half?

$1 = \frac{8}{8}$ $\frac{8}{8} = 1$ $\frac{4}{8} = \frac{1}{2}$ $\frac{1}{2} = \frac{?}{8}$

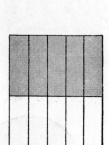

How many tenths are in one?
How many tenths are in one half?

$1 = \frac{10}{10}$ $\frac{10}{10} = 1$ $\frac{5}{10} = \frac{1}{2}$ $\frac{1}{2} = \frac{?}{10}$

How many twelfths are in one?
How many twelfths are in one half?

$1 = \frac{12}{12}$ $\frac{12}{12} = 1$ $\frac{6}{12} = \frac{1}{2}$ $\frac{1}{2} = \frac{?}{12}$

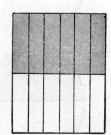

Ann said, "I do not need to draw circles to tell about halves. I can reason about halves and tell how many of any smaller-sized parts there are."

"How do you reason about sixteenths?" asked Ted.

"In **one** there are **16 sixteenths**. In **one half** there are just **half as many**, or **8 sixteenths**," answered Ann.

She wrote: $1 = \frac{16}{16}$ and $\frac{1}{2} = \frac{8}{16}$.

134

Thirds, Sixths, Ninths, Twelfths

When a circle, or anything, is divided into 3 equal parts, what do we call each part? How many thirds are in one?

$$1 = \frac{3}{3} \qquad \frac{3}{3} = 1$$

How many sixths are in one?
How many sixths are in one third?

$$1 = \frac{6}{6} \qquad \frac{6}{6} = 1 \qquad \frac{1}{3} = \frac{2}{6} \qquad \frac{2}{6} = \frac{1}{3}$$

How many ninths are in one?
How many ninths are in one third?
How many ninths are in two thirds?

$$\frac{9}{9} = 1 \qquad \frac{1}{3} = \frac{3}{9} \qquad \frac{2}{3} = \frac{6}{9}$$

How many twelfths are in one?
How many twelfths are in one third?
How many twelfths are in two thirds?

$$\frac{12}{12} = 1 \qquad \frac{1}{3} = \frac{?}{12} \qquad \frac{2}{3} = \frac{?}{12}$$

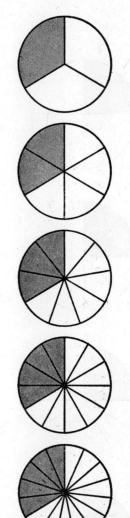

"I can reason about thirds as Ann did about halves," said Joe. "In one there are 15 fifteenths. In one third there are just one third as many, or 5 fifteenths."

He wrote: $1 = \frac{15}{15} \qquad \frac{1}{3} = \frac{5}{15}$.

"And then I know that in two thirds there are two times 5 fifteenths, or 10 fifteenths," continued Joe.

He wrote: $1 = \frac{15}{15} \qquad \frac{1}{3} = \frac{5}{15} \qquad \frac{2}{3} = \frac{10}{15}$.

How many eighteenths are in one? $\qquad 1 = \frac{?}{18}$

How many eighteenths are in one third? $\qquad \frac{1}{3} = \frac{?}{18}$

How many eighteenths are in two thirds? $\qquad \frac{2}{3} = \frac{?}{18}$

135

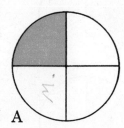

A

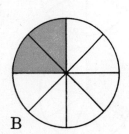

B

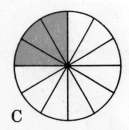

C

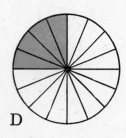

D

Studying Fourths

Circle A is divided into 4 equal parts.
Each part is one fourth ($\frac{1}{4}$) of the circle.
Two parts are $\frac{2}{4}$, or $\frac{1}{2}$, of the circle.
Three parts are $\frac{3}{4}$ of the circle.

Let us count the eighths, the twelfths,
and the sixteenths in each fourth of a circle.

Circle B shows $\frac{8}{8} = 1$.
How many eighths are in $\frac{1}{4}$?
How many eighths are in $\frac{2}{4}$? in $\frac{1}{2}$?
How many eighths are in $\frac{3}{4}$?

$\frac{1}{4} = \frac{?}{8}$ $\qquad$ $\frac{2}{4} = \frac{?}{8}$ $\qquad$ $\frac{3}{4} = \frac{?}{8}$ $\qquad$ $\frac{1}{2} = \frac{?}{8}$

Circle C shows $\frac{12}{12} = 1$.
How many twelfths are in $\frac{1}{4}$?
How many twelfths are in $\frac{2}{4}$? in $\frac{1}{2}$?
How many twelfths are in $\frac{3}{4}$?

$\frac{1}{4} = \frac{?}{12}$ $\qquad$ $\frac{2}{4} = \frac{?}{12}$ $\qquad$ $\frac{3}{4} = \frac{?}{12}$ $\qquad$ $\frac{1}{2} = \frac{?}{12}$

Circle D shows $\frac{16}{16} = 1$.
How many sixteenths are in $\frac{1}{4}$?
How many sixteenths are in $\frac{2}{4}$? in $\frac{1}{2}$?
How many sixteenths are in $\frac{3}{4}$?

$\frac{1}{4} = \frac{?}{16}$ $\qquad$ $\frac{2}{4} = \frac{?}{16}$ $\qquad$ $\frac{3}{4} = \frac{?}{16}$ $\qquad$ $\frac{1}{2} = \frac{?}{16}$

Fractions in Measures

1. What part of a gallon is one quart?

2. Two quarts are how many fourths of a gallon? One half gallon is how many fourths?

$$1 \text{ quart} = \tfrac{1}{4} \text{ gallon} \qquad 2 \text{ quarts} = \tfrac{1}{2} \text{ gallon}$$

3. How many pints are one quart? Is one pint half of one quart?

$$1 \text{ pint} = \tfrac{1}{2} \text{ quart}$$

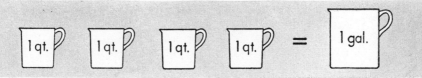

4. Each inch is what part of one foot?

5. How many inches (twelfths) are there in $\tfrac{1}{2}$ foot?

6. How many inches (twelfths) are there in $\tfrac{1}{3}$ foot?

7. $\tfrac{1}{2} = \tfrac{?}{12}$ $\qquad \tfrac{1}{3} = \tfrac{?}{12}$ $\qquad \tfrac{1}{4} = \tfrac{?}{12}$

8. Study the picture of the ruler, and tell which is the largest and which is the smallest fraction: $\tfrac{1}{2}$, $\tfrac{1}{3}$, or $\tfrac{1}{4}$.

9. How many dimes are in one dollar?

10. One dime is what part of one dollar?

11. How many dimes (tenths) are there in $\tfrac{1}{2}$ dollar?

12. How many dimes (tenths) are there in $\tfrac{1}{5}$ dollar?

13. Tell which is the larger and which is the smaller part of a dollar: $\tfrac{1}{2}$ or $\tfrac{1}{5}$.

Finding Parts of a Group

1. Aunt Helen sent Mary 12 beautiful pine cones from California. Mary shared the cones equally with three of her best friends. What fractional part of the cones did Mary give to each of her friends? What fractional part of the cones did she keep for herself?

How many cones did Mary keep? What is $\frac{1}{4}$ of 12?
How many cones did Mary give away? What is $\frac{3}{4}$ of 12?
$\frac{1}{4}$ of 12 = 3.
$\frac{3}{4}$ of 12 is 3 times as many as $\frac{1}{4}$.
So $\frac{3}{4}$ of 12 is 3 × 3, or 9.
Mary kept 3 cones, and she gave away 9 cones.

2. How many cones are $\frac{1}{3}$ of 12 cones? Then $\frac{2}{3}$ of 12 cones are how many times as many as $\frac{1}{3}$ of 12 cones? What is $\frac{1}{3}$ of 12? 4 $\frac{2}{3}$ of 12 = 2 × 4, or 8.

3. There are 16 ounces in a pound. How many ounces are $\frac{1}{8}$ of a pound? $\frac{3}{8}$ of a pound? $\frac{5}{8}$ of a pound?

4. How many inches are $\frac{2}{3}$ of a foot? $\frac{3}{4}$ of a foot?

138

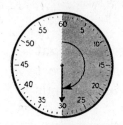   

Parts of an Hour

It takes 60 minutes, or 1 hour, for the minute hand to go around the face of the clock. There are 60 minutes in 1 hour.

How many minutes are in $\frac{1}{2}$ hour?

$\frac{1}{2}$ of 60 minutes = 30 minutes. $2\overline{)60}$ minutes, 30 minutes

There are 30 minutes in $\frac{1}{2}$ hour. $\frac{1}{2}$ hr. = 30 min.

How many minutes are in $\frac{4}{5}$ of an hour?

In $\frac{1}{5}$ of an hour there are $\frac{1}{5}$ of 60 minutes, or 12 minutes. Then in $\frac{4}{5}$ of an hour there are 4 × 12 minutes, or 48 minutes.

$$\frac{4}{5} \text{ hr.} = 48 \text{ min.}$$

Remember that there are 60 minutes in 1 hour. Answer these questions about parts of an hour:

1. $\frac{1}{3}$ of an hour = _____ minutes.

2. $\frac{1}{4}$ of an hour = _____ minutes.

3. $\frac{1}{5}$ of an hour = _____ minutes.

4. $\frac{1}{6}$ of an hour = _____ minutes.

5. $\frac{1}{10}$ of an hour = _____ minutes.

6. $\frac{1}{15}$ of an hour = _____ minutes.

7. $\frac{1}{20}$ of an hour = _____ minutes.

8. $\frac{1}{30}$ of an hour = _____ minutes.

9. $\frac{2}{3}$ of an hour = _____ minutes.

10. $\frac{3}{4}$ of an hour = _____ minutes.

11. $\frac{2}{5}$ of an hour = _____ minutes.

12. $\frac{3}{5}$ of an hour = _____ minutes.

13. $\frac{5}{6}$ of an hour = _____ minutes.

14. $\frac{3}{10}$ of an hour = _____ minutes.

15. $\frac{7}{10}$ of an hour = _____ minutes.

16. $\frac{8}{10}$ of an hour = _____ minutes.

Finding Parts

1. There are 576 pupils enrolled in the Eastmont School. About $\frac{3}{4}$ of the pupils attended the band concert that was given in the city park. About how many pupils attended the band concert?

$$
\begin{array}{r}
144 \\
4)\overline{576} \\
4 \\
\hline
17 \\
16 \\
\hline
16 \\
16 \\
\hline
\end{array}
\qquad
\begin{array}{r}
144 \\
3 \\
\hline
432 \\
\end{array}
$$

To find $\frac{1}{4}$ of 576, we divide 576 by 4. $\frac{1}{4}$ of 576 = 144.

To find $\frac{3}{4}$ of 576, we multiply 144 by 3. The answer is 432.

About 432 pupils attended the band concert.

2. The paper said that there were about 1200 people at the band concert and that $\frac{2}{3}$ of those there were school children. How many school children were there?

Find:

	(a)	(b)	(c)	(d)	(e)
3.	$\frac{2}{3}$ of 27	$\frac{5}{6}$ of 48	$\frac{3}{5}$ of 35	$\frac{3}{4}$ of 32	$\frac{2}{7}$ of 63
4.	$\frac{5}{8}$ of 64	$\frac{4}{9}$ of 72	$\frac{2}{5}$ of 40	$\frac{3}{8}$ of 56	$\frac{3}{7}$ of 49
5.	$\frac{5}{9}$ of 81	$\frac{2}{3}$ of 81	$\frac{3}{5}$ of 265	$\frac{5}{8}$ of 336	$\frac{3}{4}$ of 256

140

Finding Parts

1. During the summer months James Watson made $52.00 working in a store. James saved $\frac{3}{4}$ of what he made. How much did he save?

2. James and his friends built a log hut at their fathers' fishing camp. The hut cost $44.70 to build. James's share of the expense was $\frac{1}{6}$. How much was James's share?

3. James withdrew $7.45 from his savings to pay his share on the hut. How much did he have left in the savings?

One fact is missing: How much did he have in the savings? We can find this fact. It is the answer to problem **1**.

4. Tom had $27.60 in the school savings bank. He drew out $\frac{1}{3}$ of it to pay his share on the hut and to buy his camping equipment. How much did he have left for camping equipment after he paid $7.45 as his share on the hut?

Find:

	(a)	(b)	(c)	(d)
5.	$\frac{1}{6}$ of $8.40	$\frac{1}{2}$ of $31.70	$\frac{1}{5}$ of $17.65	$\frac{1}{3}$ of $16.80
6.	$\frac{3}{8}$ of $7.84	$\frac{3}{5}$ of $12.00	$\frac{3}{4}$ of $5.36	$\frac{2}{3}$ of $11.25

Chapter 8
Comparing Parts

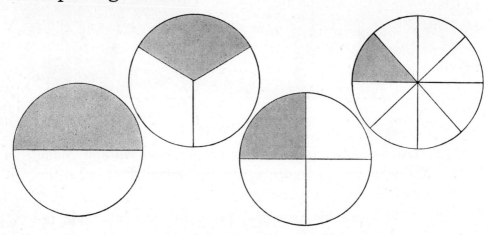

Number and Size of Parts

"How big is a fraction?" asked Walter.

"It depends on the size of each part," answered Nan.

"And it depends on the number of parts, too," said Jane.

1. Draw 3 circles on your paper. Be sure they are the same size. Divide one circle into halves, one into thirds, and one into fourths.

Look at the circles. Which is the largest, $\frac{1}{4}$, $\frac{1}{2}$, or $\frac{1}{3}$?

2. Draw another circle and divide it into eighths.

Which of the following is the largest fraction?

$$\frac{5}{8} \qquad \frac{3}{8} \qquad \frac{7}{8} \qquad \frac{4}{8} \qquad \frac{1}{8} \qquad \frac{6}{8} \qquad \frac{2}{8}$$

3. What does each fraction below mean? What figure tells the number of parts? What figure tells the size of the part?

$$\frac{2}{3} \qquad \frac{3}{4} \qquad \frac{5}{6} \qquad \frac{3}{5} \qquad \frac{1}{8} \qquad \frac{3}{8} \qquad \frac{7}{12} \qquad \frac{7}{8} \qquad \frac{5}{16} \qquad \frac{3}{5}$$

142

Size of Parts

"I have worked a third of my examples," said Jim.

"I have half of mine worked," said Jane.

The figure 3 in $\frac{1}{3}$ shows the size of the part Jim has done. In the denominator the 3 is not called three, but **third**, because it stands for, or tells, size. The 2 in $\frac{1}{2}$ does not tell two, but **half**. The denominator tells **size**.

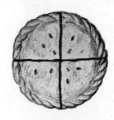

Mother is cutting a piece of fresh berry pie for Jim. Jim is thinking about the size of the piece of pie he would like to have. Do you think Jim is interested in fractions, at least, fractions of the pie?

Which is the biggest, the $\frac{1}{4}$ piece, the $\frac{1}{6}$ piece, or the $\frac{1}{8}$ piece?

Jane has broken her stick of candy into parts. There are 4 little pieces and 2 big pieces. She offers to share it with Jim.

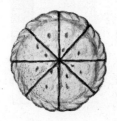

"Which will you take, four pieces or two pieces?" asked Jane.

"I'll take the four pieces," answered Jim. "NO! WAIT! Maybe there is a catch to it. Size counts, you know."

To compare fractions, we must pay attention to both the number of parts and the sizes of the parts.

143

Comparing Parts of the Same Size

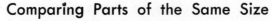

Two strips of paper that are the same length are divided into sixths.

How many sixths of strip A are shaded?

How many sixths of strip B are shaded?

Now let us compare $\frac{2}{6}$ and $\frac{5}{6}$.

Which is more, $\frac{2}{6}$ or $\frac{5}{6}$?

How much more is $\frac{5}{6}$ than $\frac{2}{6}$?

5 sixths is 3 sixths more than 2 sixths.

$\frac{5}{6}$ is $\frac{3}{6}$ more than $\frac{2}{6}$.

When the parts are the same size, the fraction with more parts is the larger fraction. When fractions have the same denominator, the fraction with the largest numerator is the largest fraction.

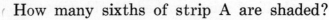

Which is the largest of anything, $\frac{1}{8}$, $\frac{3}{8}$, or $\frac{7}{8}$?

How much larger is $\frac{7}{8}$ than $\frac{3}{8}$?

7 eighths is 4 eighths larger than 3 eighths.

$\frac{7}{8}$ is $\frac{4}{8}$ larger than $\frac{3}{8}$.

When the parts are the same size, we compare the number of parts to find how much larger one fraction is than the other. When fractions have the same denominator, we compare the numerators to find how much larger one is than the other.

How much larger is $\frac{2}{3}$ than $\frac{1}{3}$?

How much larger is $\frac{3}{4}$ than $\frac{1}{4}$?

How much smaller is $\frac{2}{5}$ than $\frac{4}{5}$?

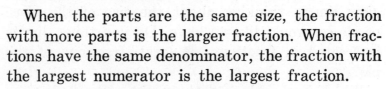

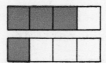

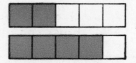

144

Comparing Sizes of Parts

1. Jane baked 2 cakes the same size. She cut one cake into 8 equal pieces. What is the size of each piece?

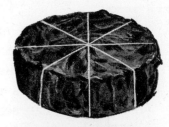

She cut the other cake into 6 equal pieces. What is the size of each piece of this cake?

Which piece of cake is larger, the $\frac{1}{8}$ or the $\frac{1}{6}$?

The parts are not the same size. The piece which is one eighth in size is smaller than the piece which is one sixth in size. One sixth is larger than one eighth, or one eighth is smaller than one sixth.

$\frac{1}{6}$ is larger than $\frac{1}{8}$. $\frac{1}{8}$ is smaller than $\frac{1}{6}$.

The fraction with the smaller denominator has the larger-sized parts, and the fraction with the larger denominator has the smaller-sized parts.

To compare fractions whose numerator is 1, we look at the denominators. The fraction with the largest denominator is the smallest fraction, and the fraction with the smallest denominator is the largest fraction.

2. Which is the larger, $\frac{1}{4}$ or $\frac{1}{5}$? $\frac{1}{2}$ or $\frac{1}{3}$? $\frac{1}{3}$ or $\frac{1}{4}$?

3. Read the largest fraction in each group below:

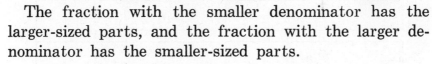

| $\frac{1}{2}$ | $\frac{1}{3}$ | $\frac{1}{4}$ | $\frac{1}{5}$ | $\frac{1}{3}$ | $\frac{1}{4}$ | $\frac{1}{2}$ | $\frac{1}{6}$ | $\frac{1}{3}$ | $\frac{1}{3}$ | $\frac{1}{6}$ | $\frac{1}{4}$ | $\frac{1}{12}$ |

4. Read the smallest fraction in each group above.

5. Would you rather have $\frac{1}{2}$ of a dollar or $\frac{1}{4}$ of a dollar?

6. Which would you rather have, $\frac{1}{2}$ pint or $\frac{1}{4}$ pint of ice cream?

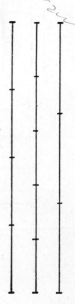

145

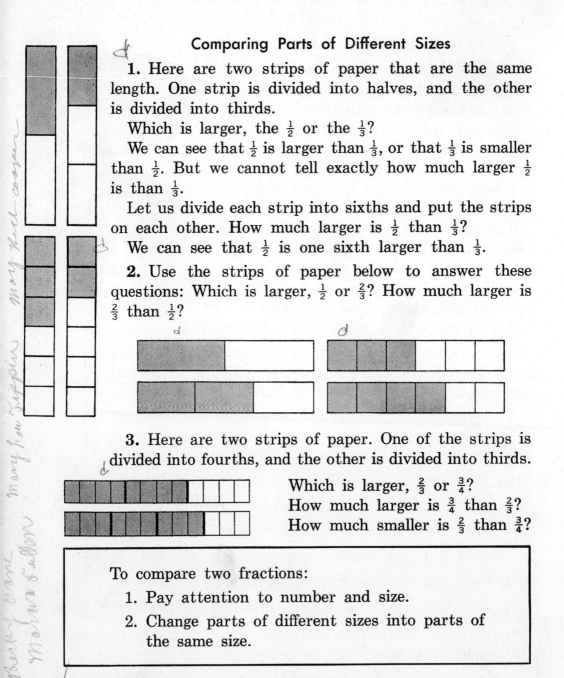

Comparing Parts of Different Sizes

1. Here are two strips of paper that are the same length. One strip is divided into halves, and the other is divided into thirds.

Which is larger, the $\frac{1}{2}$ or the $\frac{1}{3}$?

We can see that $\frac{1}{2}$ is larger than $\frac{1}{3}$, or that $\frac{1}{3}$ is smaller than $\frac{1}{2}$. But we cannot tell exactly how much larger $\frac{1}{2}$ is than $\frac{1}{3}$.

Let us divide each strip into sixths and put the strips on each other. How much larger is $\frac{1}{2}$ than $\frac{1}{3}$?

We can see that $\frac{1}{2}$ is one sixth larger than $\frac{1}{3}$.

2. Use the strips of paper below to answer these questions: Which is larger, $\frac{1}{2}$ or $\frac{2}{3}$? How much larger is $\frac{2}{3}$ than $\frac{1}{2}$?

3. Here are two strips of paper. One of the strips is divided into fourths, and the other is divided into thirds.

Which is larger, $\frac{2}{3}$ or $\frac{3}{4}$?
How much larger is $\frac{3}{4}$ than $\frac{2}{3}$?
How much smaller is $\frac{2}{3}$ than $\frac{3}{4}$?

To compare two fractions:

1. Pay attention to number and size.
2. Change parts of different sizes into parts of the same size.

Changing to Parts of the Same Size

"We can use the charts to compare parts," said Miss Wilson. "Suppose we want to compare one half and one third. We cannot compare halves and thirds exactly as halves and thirds. We have to change them to parts of the same size. We can see from the chart that one half equals three sixths and that one third equals two sixths. Which is larger, 3 sixths or 2 sixths? How much larger is 3 sixths than 2 sixths? How much larger is one half than one third?"

$$\frac{1}{2} = \frac{3}{6} \qquad \frac{1}{3} = \frac{2}{6} \qquad \frac{3}{6} \text{ is } \frac{1}{6} \text{ larger than } \frac{2}{6}.$$

$$\text{So } \frac{1}{2} \text{ is } \frac{1}{6} \text{ larger than } \frac{1}{3}.$$

1							
$\frac{1}{2}$				$\frac{1}{2}$			
$\frac{1}{4}$		$\frac{1}{4}$		$\frac{1}{4}$		$\frac{1}{4}$	
$\frac{1}{8}$	$\frac{1}{8}$	$\frac{1}{8}$	$\frac{1}{8}$	$\frac{1}{8}$	$\frac{1}{8}$	$\frac{1}{8}$	$\frac{1}{8}$

1											
$\frac{1}{3}$				$\frac{1}{3}$				$\frac{1}{3}$			
$\frac{1}{6}$		$\frac{1}{6}$		$\frac{1}{6}$		$\frac{1}{6}$		$\frac{1}{6}$		$\frac{1}{6}$	
$\frac{1}{12}$	$\frac{1}{12}$	$\frac{1}{12}$	$\frac{1}{12}$	$\frac{1}{12}$	$\frac{1}{12}$	$\frac{1}{12}$	$\frac{1}{12}$	$\frac{1}{12}$	$\frac{1}{12}$	$\frac{1}{12}$	$\frac{1}{12}$

1					
$\frac{1}{2}$			$\frac{1}{2}$		
$\frac{1}{3}$		$\frac{1}{3}$		$\frac{1}{3}$	
$\frac{1}{6}$	$\frac{1}{6}$	$\frac{1}{6}$	$\frac{1}{6}$	$\frac{1}{6}$	$\frac{1}{6}$

1											
$\frac{1}{2}$						$\frac{1}{2}$					
$\frac{1}{4}$			$\frac{1}{4}$			$\frac{1}{4}$			$\frac{1}{4}$		
$\frac{1}{12}$	$\frac{1}{12}$	$\frac{1}{12}$	$\frac{1}{12}$	$\frac{1}{12}$	$\frac{1}{12}$	$\frac{1}{12}$	$\frac{1}{12}$	$\frac{1}{12}$	$\frac{1}{12}$	$\frac{1}{12}$	$\frac{1}{12}$

1. Use the charts to help you answer these questions:

$$\frac{1}{2} = \frac{?}{4} \qquad \frac{1}{2} = \frac{?}{8} \qquad \frac{1}{2} = \frac{?}{12} \qquad \frac{1}{3} = \frac{?}{6} \qquad \frac{2}{3} = \frac{?}{6} \qquad \frac{1}{3} = \frac{?}{12}$$

$$\frac{1}{4} = \frac{?}{8} \qquad \frac{1}{4} = \frac{?}{12} \qquad \frac{3}{4} = \frac{?}{12} \qquad \frac{2}{3} = \frac{?}{12} \qquad \frac{1}{6} = \frac{?}{12} \qquad \frac{5}{6} = \frac{?}{12}$$

2. How much larger is $\frac{5}{6}$ than $\frac{2}{3}$?

3. How much larger is $\frac{7}{12}$ than $\frac{1}{2}$?

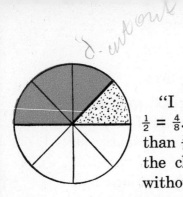

Changing to Parts of the Same Size

"I know that $\frac{1}{2}$ is more than $\frac{3}{8}$. I know that $\frac{1}{2} = \frac{4}{8}$. I compare $\frac{4}{8}$ and $\frac{3}{8}$ and find that $\frac{4}{8}$ is $\frac{1}{8}$ larger than $\frac{3}{8}$. So $\frac{1}{2}$ is $\frac{1}{8}$ larger than $\frac{3}{8}$. I can tell this from the chart or by drawing circles. How can I tell without the use of circles?" asked Carl.

"When we want to compare fractions that have different-sized parts, we must first change them to parts of the same size. When we compare $\frac{1}{2}$ and $\frac{1}{3}$, we change them to sixths: $\frac{1}{2} = \frac{3}{6}$, and $\frac{1}{3} = \frac{2}{6}$. Then we compare $\frac{3}{6}$ and $\frac{2}{6}$, and we know that $\frac{1}{2}$ is $\frac{1}{6}$ more than $\frac{1}{3}$," explained Miss Wilson.

Miss Wilson continued, "We do not have to use the circles or charts to change parts to the same size.

"To change $\frac{1}{3}$ to sixths, we must think that there are 6 sixths in 1. In $\frac{1}{3}$ there are $\frac{1}{3}$ of 6 sixths, or 2 sixths. To change $\frac{1}{2}$ to sixths, we must think that there are 6 sixths in 1. Then in $\frac{1}{2}$ there are $\frac{1}{2}$ of 6 sixths, or 3 sixths. Now all the parts are sixths. We can compare them."

$\frac{3}{4} = \frac{?}{16}$ The example asks, "How many sixteenths are in three fourths?" This is the way we think the answer: In 1 there are 16 sixteenths.

In $\frac{1}{4}$ there are $\frac{1}{4}$ of 16 sixteenths, or 4 sixteenths. In $\frac{3}{4}$ there are 3 × 4 sixteenths, or 12 sixteenths. So $\frac{3}{4} = \frac{12}{16}$.

Change $\frac{1}{3}$ and $\frac{3}{4}$ to twelfths, and then compare them.

Change $\frac{5}{6}$ and $\frac{3}{4}$ to twelfths, and then compare them.

148

Finding the Common Denominator

"Before we can compare two fractions, we must change them to parts of the same size. I understand that," said Susan. "But how can we tell which sized parts to change them to?"

"Denominators show size. If two fractions have different denominators, their parts are of different sizes. To compare two fractions with different denominators, we much first change them to parts of the same size. That is, we must change them so they will have the same denominator. We call it the **common denominator**.

"Suppose we want to compare $\frac{1}{2}$ and $\frac{1}{8}$. Look at the smaller part, the eighth. Can we divide a half into eighths? We know that we can change one half to eighths. Eighths are the sized parts that we use," explained Miss Wilson.

"Look at the larger denominator, 8. Can it be divided by the other denominator? Can we divide 8 by 2? Then 8 is the common denominator."

$$\frac{1}{2} = \frac{4}{8} \qquad \frac{4}{8} \text{ is } \frac{3}{8} \text{ more than } \frac{1}{8}.$$

Compare: $\frac{1}{2}$ and $\frac{1}{12}$ $\frac{1}{2}$ and $\frac{5}{12}$ $\frac{1}{3}$ and $\frac{5}{12}$ $\frac{1}{4}$ and $\frac{3}{8}$

          $\frac{1}{4}$ and $\frac{1}{12}$ $\frac{2}{3}$ and $\frac{5}{6}$ $\frac{3}{4}$ and $\frac{5}{16}$ $\frac{1}{2}$ and $\frac{3}{6}$

1. Jack ate $\frac{1}{4}$ of the watermelon, and his father ate $\frac{1}{2}$ of it. Who ate more and how much more?

2. Jane divided the brick of ice cream into 6 equal parts. She ate $\frac{1}{3}$ of it, and Tom ate $\frac{1}{2}$ of it. Who ate more and how much more?

Finding the Common Denominator

Suppose we want to compare $\frac{1}{2}$ and $\frac{1}{3}$ of something. The denominators are different; so we must find the common denominator. First, we see if either denominator is the common denominator. Can we divide 3 by 2? Next, we multiply 3 by 2. Can we divide 6 by 2? Can we divide 6 by 3? Then 6 is the common denominator.

$\frac{1}{2} = \frac{3}{6}$ $\frac{1}{3} = \frac{2}{6}$ $\frac{3}{6}$ is $\frac{1}{6}$ more than $\frac{2}{6}$. $\frac{1}{2}$ is $\frac{1}{6}$ more than $\frac{1}{3}$.

To compare two fractions with different denominators, change them to fractions having a common denominator.

To find the common denominator:

1. See if one denominator is the common denominator. Can we divide one denominator by the other?
2. If neither denominator is the common denominator, we multiply the larger denominator by 2, 3, 4, and so on until we get a product that can be divided evenly by the smaller denominator.

---

1. Which is larger, $\frac{3}{4}$ or $\frac{2}{3}$?

We know that 4 is not the common denominator. Why?
$2 \times 4 = 8$, but 8 is not the common denominator either.
$3 \times 4 = 12$. Why is 12 the common denominator?
Which is larger and how much larger?

	(a)	(b)	(c)
2.	$\frac{1}{4}$ or $\frac{3}{8}$ in.	$\frac{3}{8}$ or $\frac{5}{16}$ in.	$\frac{7}{8}$ or $\frac{15}{16}$ in.
3.	$\frac{3}{4}$ or $\frac{7}{8}$ in.	$\frac{1}{2}$ or $\frac{5}{8}$ in.	$\frac{1}{2}$ or $\frac{7}{16}$ in.

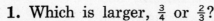
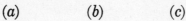
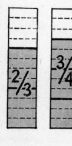

150

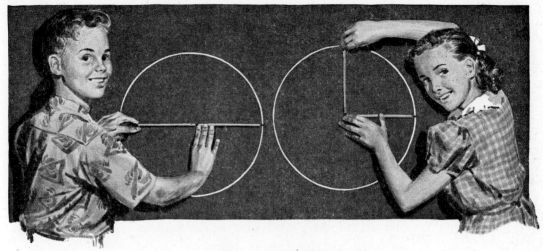

Larger or Smaller?

Jack is using his pencils to show one half. How is Jane using her pencils to show one fourth?

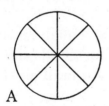

A

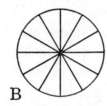

B

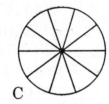

C

1. Use cards to frame:

In Circle A	In Circle B	In Circle C
a. $\frac{1}{2}$, $\frac{1}{4}$, $\frac{1}{8}$	*a.* $\frac{1}{3}$, $\frac{1}{6}$, $\frac{1}{12}$	*a.* $\frac{1}{2}$, $\frac{1}{5}$, $\frac{1}{10}$
b. $\frac{3}{4}$, $\frac{5}{8}$, $\frac{7}{8}$	*b.* $\frac{1}{2}$, $\frac{1}{4}$, $\frac{2}{3}$	*b.* $\frac{2}{5}$, $\frac{3}{5}$, $\frac{3}{10}$

Which is larger and how much larger?

In Circle A	In Circle B	In Circle C
2. $\frac{1}{2}$ or $\frac{3}{4}$	$\frac{2}{3}$ or $\frac{7}{12}$	$\frac{1}{2}$ or $\frac{6}{10}$
3. $\frac{1}{2}$ or $\frac{5}{8}$	$\frac{1}{3}$ or $\frac{1}{2}$	$\frac{2}{5}$ or $\frac{1}{2}$
4. $\frac{3}{4}$ or $\frac{7}{8}$	$\frac{3}{4}$ or $\frac{5}{6}$	$\frac{3}{5}$ or $\frac{7}{10}$

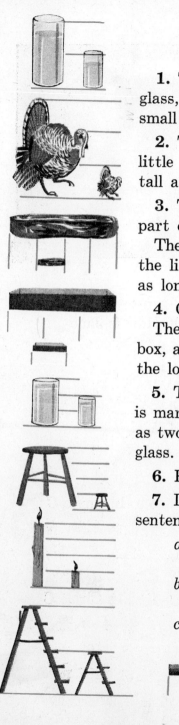

Using Fractions to Compare Sizes

1. The small glass is half as tall as the large glass, and the large glass is twice as tall as the small glass.

2. The big turkey is three times as tall as the little turkey. So the little turkey is _one third_ as tall as the big turkey.

3. The length of the little candy bar is what part of the length of the larger candy bar?

The larger candy bar is _____ times as long as the little bar, and the little bar is _____ _____ as long as the larger bar.

4. Compare the lengths of the two boxes.

The long box is ____ times as long as the short box, and the short box is _____ _____ as long as the long box.

5. The taller glass shows 3 equal divisions. It is marked into thirds. The shorter glass is as tall as two of the parts. So it is $\frac{2}{3}$ as tall as the taller glass.

6. How do the stools compare in height?

7. Look at the other pictures. Then read the sentences, saying the right word in each blank:

  a. The shorter candle is ____ _____ as tall as the longer candle.

  b. One step ladder is ____ _____ as tall as the other.

  c. The shorter pencil is ____ _____ as long as the longer pencil.

Using Fractions to Compare Groups

1. Let us compare the number of flowers in the two vases. There are 3 flowers in one vase and 6 flowers in the other vase. There are two 3's in 6. So there are two times as many flowers in one vase as there are in the other. Or there are half as many flowers in one vase as there are in the other.

2. There are 2 oranges on one plate and 6 oranges on the other plate. There are three times as many oranges on one plate as there are on the other. Or there are one third as many oranges on one plate as there are on the other plate.

3. Compare the number of things in each picture below. Find what part the smaller group is of the larger group. Then the larger group is how many times as large as the smaller group?

In picture A, there are **half** as many birds on the ground as there are in the birdbath. There are **twice** as many birds in the birdbath as there are on the ground.

Chapter 9
Dividing by Tens

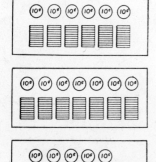

Dimes for Pennies

Mr. James, the banker, has new dime savers for the fifth-grade children. Bob is changing their pennies for dimes.

1. Bill has 60 pennies. He has them in piles of 10. How many tens does he have? How many dimes should Bob give him for them? How many tens are in 60?

2. Ann has 70 pennies. How many piles of 10 can she make? How many dimes should Bob give her? How many tens are in 70?

3. Jack has 52 pennies. How many piles of 10 does he have? How many pennies are left? How many dimes should he get? How many pennies will he have left?

154

Reviewing Tens

We add tens the way we add ones.

Add:

	(a)	(b)	(c)	(d)	(e)	(f)	(g)	(h)	(i)	(j)	(10)
1.	30	90	44	25	48	90	97	38	99	78	(18)
	40	60	65	81	75	88	40	62	11	96	

We subtract tens the way we subtract ones.

Subtract:

											(11)
2.	90	170	97	168	70	180	93	175	100	103	(20)
	50	80	57	88	55	95	46	97	67	76	(22)

We multiply tens the way we multiply ones.

Multiply:

											(33)
3.	20	80	43	71	52	55	68	56	584	126	(36)
	4	6	2	9	4	6	7	9	7	4	(37)

We divide tens the way we divide ones.

Divide:

	(a)	(b)	(c)	(d)	(e)	(f)	(g)	(53)
4.	3)60	9)450	3)69	6)426	4)816	9)765	8)984	(61) (62)

We multiply by tens the way we multiply by ones.

Multiply:

	(a)	(b)	(c)	(d)	(e)	(f)	(g)	(h)	(i)	
5.	50	76	432	400	370	807	58	436	387	(40)
	40	60	40	60	80	75	39	55	28	to (43)

How do we divide by tens?

We divide by tens the way we divide by ones. But we must be
careful to write each part of our answer in its proper place.

What Division Asks

1. What does the question $2\overline{)8}$ ask?

Back in the second or third grade we learned that $2\overline{)8}$ asks, *How many twos are in eight?*

To answer the question, we take a group of eight and arrange them in twos and count the twos.

We find there are four twos in eight. We answer, "Twos in eight, four. Four twos are eight."

This is the way we write our answer:

$$\begin{array}{r} 4 \\ 2\overline{)8} \\ \underline{8} \end{array}$$

2. What does the question $20\overline{)80}$ ask?

It asks, *How many twenties are in eighty?*

To answer the question, let us take a group of 8 tens, such as 8 bundles of toothpicks with 10 toothpicks in each bundle, and arrange them into groups of 2 tens, or twenties.

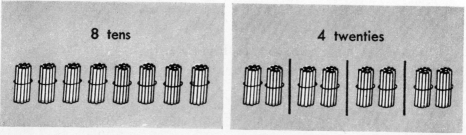

8 tens   4 twenties

We find that there are 4 twenties in eighty. We write our answer like this:

$$\begin{array}{r} 4 \\ 20\overline{)80} \\ \underline{80} \end{array}$$

We divide by tens the way we divide by ones.

How We Divide by Tens

1. Tom wants to put 80 post cards into 20 pockets of the card rack. How many cards will he put in each pocket if he puts the same number in each of them.

To answer the question, we divide 80 by 20.

First, we decide where to start writing our answer. We think, "Twenties in eight, no." So we know that our answer will not be tens. Now we think, "Twenties in eighty, yes." So we prepare to write our answer in one's place just above 0 in 80.

$$20\overline{)80}$$

We still have the answer to find. To do this, we think, "Twos in eight, four," and write 4 in one's place above 0 in 80.

$$20\overline{)80} \quad \begin{array}{r} 4 \\ \overline{80} \end{array}$$

Last, we multiply 20 by 4 and draw a line.

2. One hundred sixty Boy Scouts are going to march in the parade. The leaders plan to have them march in groups of 20. How many groups of Boy Scouts will be in the parade?

$$20\overline{)160} \quad \begin{array}{r} 8 \\ \overline{160} \end{array}$$

How to Divide by Tens

1. The principal of the Park School thought that the pupils would need 4200 sheets of paper for their writing practice. He knew that the paper came 60 sheets in a package. How many packages did he need to get?

$$60)\overline{4200}^{\downarrow}$$

First, decide where to start writing the answer. Then think, "Sixes in 42, 7." Write 7 in its proper place. Why do we write 7 in ten's place? Why is 70 and not 7 the answer?

$$\begin{array}{r} 70 \\ 60)\overline{4200} \\ \underline{420} \\ 0 \end{array}$$

Hundreds and thousands are divided just as tens are divided, but we must write each part of the answer in its proper place.

2. Explain how these numbers were divided:

$$\begin{array}{r} 700 \\ 60)\overline{42000} \\ \underline{420} \\ 00 \end{array} \qquad \begin{array}{r} 80 \\ 80)\overline{6400} \\ \underline{640} \\ 0 \end{array} \qquad \begin{array}{r} 800 \\ 80)\overline{64000} \\ \underline{640} \\ 00 \end{array} \qquad \begin{array}{r} 900 \\ 90)\overline{81000} \\ \underline{810} \\ 00 \end{array} \qquad \begin{array}{r} 90 \\ 50)\overline{4500} \\ \underline{450} \\ 0 \end{array}$$

3. Jack has 180 sea shells. If he puts 30 shells into a box, how many boxes will he need?

4. The fifth-grade pupils are giving a play. They have 300 tickets to sell. If each of the 30 pupils takes the same number of tickets, how many will each take?

Divide:

	(a)	(b)	(c)	(d)	(e)
5.	20)180	30)210	40)240	50)400	70)420
6.	80)720	80)320	60)480	20)140	50)450
7.	50)3500	40)3600	90)270	90)54000	80)32000

Dividing and Carrying

1. The boys are getting books from the public library. They are getting 20 books for each room at school, or 240 books in all. For how many rooms are they getting books?

```
      12
20) 240
    20
    40
    40
```

How do we know where to start writing the answer? How can we be sure the answer is right?

Check
```
   12
  ×20
  240
```

2. In the main reading room of the public library there are 1750 books. If they are placed 50 books on each shelf, how many shelves of books are there?

We decide where to start writing the answer: Fifties in 1, no. Fifties in 17, no. Fifties in 175, yes. The first figure in the answer is written over the 5 in 175, or in ten's place.

We think, "Fives in 17, 3." We write 3 in the answer, multiply, subtract, and bring down 0.

We think, "Fives in 25, 5." We write 5 and multiply.

There are 35 shelves of books.

```
       35
50) 1750
    150
    250
    250
```

Steps in Dividing

```
      ↓
  5)175
```

First Step

Decide where to start writing the answer.

```
    3
  5)175
```

```
      ↓
  50)1750
```

Second Step

Divide: Fives in seventeen, three. Write 3 in ten's place.

```
    3
  50)1750
```

```
    3
  5)175
    15
```

Third Step

Multiply: Notice that the product is **not more** than the partial dividend above it.

```
    3
  50)1750
     150
```

```
    3
  5)175
    15
     2
```

Fourth Step

Subtract: Notice that the remainder is **less** than the divisor.

```
    3
  50)1750
     150
      25
```

```
    3
  5)175
    15
    25
```

Fifth Step

Bring down the next figure.

```
    3
  50)1750
     150
      250
```

Now follow the same steps again. Begin with the second step.

```
    35
  5)175
    15
    25
```

Divide: Fives in twenty-five, five. Write 5 in one's place.

```
    35
  50)1750
     150
      250
```

Multiply: Notice that the product is not more than the partial dividend above it.

```
    35
  5)175
    15
    25
    25
```

Subtract: There is no remainder and there is nothing to **bring down**. The example is finished.

```
    35
  50)1750
     150
      250
      250
```

160

Practice

1. Notice how these examples are worked. Then copy each example and work it without looking at your book.

```
      43            69             619            86             65
20)860        20)1380        20)12380       80)6880        70)4550
   80           120             120            640            420
   --           ---             ---            ---            ---
   60           180              38            480            350
   60           180              20            480            350
   --           ---             ---            ---            ---
                                180
                                180
                                ---
```

Copy and divide:

	(a)	(b)	(c)	(d)	(e)
2.	20)11920	40)23120	60)28080	80)38240	30)19860
3.	50)32850	70)20020	90)25740	20)17460	40)33320
4.	60)49980	80)65840	30)25590	50)37650	70)59010
5.	90)74970	20)13760	40)18680	60)23760	80)31760
6.	30)11610	50)41850	70)27790	90)35730	20)16940
7.	40)15440	60)17220	80)22880	70)51310	90)67860

8. George and his father went to see the parade of sailors at Lakes Training Camp. There were 1680 sailors in the parade and 80 sailors in each company. How many companies of sailors were in the parade?

Problems

1. There are 360 pupils at Central School and an average of 30 pupils in each classroom. How many classrooms are in the school?

2. There are 30 pupils in the fifth-grade room. The principal has 960 tickets for them to sell. If he gives the same number of tickets to each pupil, how many will each pupil have to sell?

3. In the library of the Henley School there are 2400 books arranged on shelves. There are about 60 books on each shelf. How many shelves of books are there?

4. Miss Ward has 150 blotters for her class in handwriting. There are 30 pupils in her class. How many blotters can she give each pupil if she gives the same number to each?

5. Bess is reading her storybook at the rate of 20 pages an hour. In how many hours can she read the 240 pages in her book?

Zero in the Quotient

1. A large produce store bought 6240 dozen eggs. The eggs came in cases of 30 dozen each. How many cases of eggs were there?

First, decide where to start writing the answer.

Next, divide the hundreds, multiply, subtract, and bring down the next figure.

$$
\begin{array}{r}
20 \\
30\overline{)6240} \\
60 \\
\hline
24
\end{array}
$$

Now divide the tens: Thirties in 24, no. To hold the place in the answer above the 4 (ten's place), we write 0, and bring down the next figure.

Last, divide 240 (ones) by 30.

Our answer is 208 cases.

$$
\begin{array}{r}
208 \\
30\overline{)6240} \\
60 \\
\hline
240 \\
240 \\
\hline
\end{array}
$$

2. Notice how we divide in these examples:

$$
\begin{array}{r}
306 \\
70\overline{)21420} \\
210 \\
\hline
420 \\
420 \\
\hline
\end{array}
\qquad
\begin{array}{r}
507 \\
90\overline{)45630} \\
450 \\
\hline
630 \\
630 \\
\hline
\end{array}
\qquad
\begin{array}{r}
806 \\
60\overline{)48360} \\
480 \\
\hline
360 \\
360 \\
\hline
\end{array}
\qquad
\begin{array}{r}
706 \\
40\overline{)28240} \\
280 \\
\hline
240 \\
240 \\
\hline
\end{array}
$$

Copy and divide:

	(a)	(b)	(c)	(d)	(e)
3.	20)12180	40)12280	60)12480	80)16720	30)27240
4.	50)10350	70)14420	90)18720	20)14180	40)24320
5.	60)54180	80)56400	30)21150	70)42210	90)63180

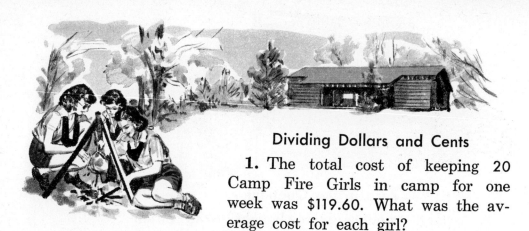

Dividing Dollars and Cents

1. The total cost of keeping 20 Camp Fire Girls in camp for one week was $119.60. What was the average cost for each girl?

```
        $5.98
20) $119.60
    100
    19 6
    18 0
     1 60
     1 60
```

We divide $119.60 by 20 in exactly the same way as we would divide 11960 by 20, **except** that we are careful to write each part of our answer in its proper place and to put the point in our answer above the point in the dividend.

2. Notice how we divide in these examples:

```
        $5.57              $5.63              $6.49              $8.64
50) $278.50          60) $337.80          70) $454.30          40) $345.60
    250                  300                  420                  320
    28 5                 37 8                 34 3                 25 6
    25 0                 36 0                 28 0                 24 0
     3 50                 1 80                 6 30                 1 60
     3 50                 1 80                 6 30                 1 60
```

Copy and divide:

	(a)	(b)	(c)	(d)
3.	20) $193.20	40) $112.80	60) $303.60	80) $598.40
4.	70) $444.50	50) $105.50	30) $189.90	20) $175.40
5.	60) $436.80	80) $657.60	70) $516.60	90) $815.40

Dividing Dollars and Cents

1. The 40 members of the Good Citizens Club ordered badges. The 40 badges cost $18.00. How much did each badge cost?

> We divide $18.00 by 40 the way we divide 1800 by 40. But we must be sure to write each part of our answer in its proper place and to put the point in its proper place. Where do we put the point? Is $.45 a reasonable answer?
>
> ```
>       $.45
> 40)$18.00
>    16 0
>     2 00
>     2 00
> ```

2. Notice how we divide in these examples:

```
      $.56            $.48            $.76            $.97
70)$39.20       90)$43.20       30)$22.80       60)$58.20
   35 0            36 0            21 0            54 0
    4 20            7 20            1 80            4 20
    4 20            7 20            1 80            4 20
```

Divide and check:

	(a)	(b)	(c)	(d)
3.	20)$19.60	40)$22.80	60)$22.20	80)$45.60
4.	50)$37.50	70)$46.90	90)$88.20	20)$9.60
5.	60)$27.60	80)$66.40	30)$29.40	50)$24.00

Dividing by 10

Study these examples:

```
       6              60              27             270            8075
   10) 60          10) 600        10) 270        10) 2700       10) 80750
       60              60              20             20             80
        0               0              70             70             75
                                       70             70             70
                                        0              0             50
                                                                     50
```

```
     $.60            $.06           $2.70          $2.75          $80.75
  10) $6.00       10) $.60       10) $27.00     10) $27.50     10) $807.50
      6 0             60              20             20             80
        0              0              70             75             75
                                      70             70             70
                                       0             50             50
                                                     50             50
```

"I know a short cut in dividing by tens," said Ward. "Drop the last zero in the number you want to divide, and you have the answer."

Sixty divided by 10 is 6. Sixty is 6 tens.

Six hundred divided by 10 is 60. Six hundred is 60 tens.

270 divided by 10 is 27.

3850 divided by 10 is 385.

4070 divided by 10 is 407.

This is *tricky*. You cut off the last zero and move the point one place to the left.

$108.90 divided by 10 is $10.89.

Divide each number by 10:

```
6Ø
6ØØ
27Ø
385Ø
407Ø
$27.5Ø
$108.9Ø
```

750   8600 $9.70 $68.50   89070   7060 $70.60

166

Review Practice

1. Add:

(a)	(b)	(c)	(d)	(e)	(f)
4876	2580	3692	5467	$37.68	$128.60
6073	1419	2538	1788	42.50	216.37
5192	7265	4477	3686	9.75	190.74
1648	5038	1008	2508	23.40	208.43

2. Subtract:

7083	6704	7890	8203	$78.60	$350.00
4625	2063	2897	5648	43.75	238.65

3. Multiply:

(a)	(b)	(c)	(d)	(e)	(f)	(g)
457	862	108	590	$7.65	$8.67	$5.86
15	28	74	87	73	96	86

Divide:

	(a)	(b)	(c)	(d)	(e)
4.	2)10076	3)1371	4)20704	5)4235	6)47118
5.	7)3976	8)26072	9)8865	20)14120	30)16140
6.	40)$332.80	50)$34.50	60)30360	70)20650	90)$77.40

Find:

	(a)	(b)	(c)	(d)
7.	$\frac{2}{3}$ of 228	$\frac{5}{8}$ of 520	$\frac{4}{9}$ of $7.65	$\frac{1}{7}$ of $5.25
8.	$\frac{3}{4}$ of 268	$\frac{1}{6}$ of 498	$\frac{3}{5}$ of $5.80	$\frac{7}{8}$ of $10.00
9.	$\frac{5}{9}$ of 405	$\frac{2}{9}$ of 297	$\frac{4}{7}$ of $2.10	$\frac{4}{5}$ of $15.95
10.	$\frac{3}{8}$ of 368	$\frac{6}{7}$ of 294	$\frac{5}{6}$ of $6.42	$\frac{7}{9}$ of $20.70

The Scout Camp

1. The Board of Directors of the Boy Scouts in Belton decided to buy and build a new camp for the Scouts in their city. They bought 20 acres of land along a stream in the hills. The total cost of the land was $2500. How much did the land cost per acre?

2. The Board had a lodge built, 2 headquarters huts, a kitchen, a fence around the land, and a swimming pool. The Board had to pay the following amounts:

For the lodge	$1173.80
For the huts	416.15
For the kitchen	672.35
For the fence	48.00
For the pool	375.00

How much did the Board pay for the improvements?

3. The Board bought $314.70 worth of new camp equipment. Find how much they spent for all—the land, the improvements, and the new equipment.

168

4. The Board of Directors had $1500 in the treasury. The Civic Club of the city gave them $1000 to use in buying and building the new camp. How much did the Board then have to spend?

5. If the Board needed $5500, how much money did they have to raise besides the $2500 they already had?

6. The Board received $463.87 in donations last year. If the Board were to receive the same amount each year for the next 5 years, how much would the Board receive?

$$\begin{array}{r} \$\ 463.87 \\ 5 \\ \hline \$2319.35 \end{array}$$

7. The Board found that it costs about 68¢ a day to keep a Boy Scout in camp. How much does it cost to keep one boy in camp for 14 days?

8. How much would it cost to keep 60 boys in camp for the 14 days?

9. Last summer the Boy Scouts built a memorial gateway at the entrance to the camp. They did the work themselves, but they had to pay $46.80 for materials. The 60 boys shared the expense equally. How much was each boy's share?

Chapter 10
Weights and Measures

Measures

It is very important for us to know about measures. Can you tell why? Try answering these questions:

What time is it? How long is it until Christmas? How tall are you? How much do you weigh? How long is your book? How wide is your room? How far is it to the next town? How far can you jump? If you have a quart of milk, to how many people can you serve a glass of milk?

How many nickels have the same value as a dollar?

Can you answer any of these questions without knowing something about measures?

Each measure is called a **unit**. Inch, yard, dozen, and quart are units of measure. There are both large and small units for measuring each sort of thing. The inch, foot, and yard are units of different sizes for measuring length. The unit we use depends on just what it is we want to measure.

170

Reviewing Weights and Measures

Complete the following sentences:

1. A peck is one of the _four_ equal parts of a bushel.

2. A quart is _____ _____ of a peck.

3. A quart is _____ _____ of a gallon.

4. There are _1760_ yards in a mile. There are _____ times as many feet in a mile, or _____ feet.

5. There are _____ pints in a quart, and there are _____ times as many in a gallon. In one gallon there are _____ pints.

6. There are _____ inches in a yard.

Find the answers:

7. How many quarts are in 5 bushels?

8. How many inches are in 4 yards?

9. How many feet are in 300 yards?

10. How many yards are in 288 feet?

11. How many yards are in $\frac{1}{4}$ of a mile?

12. How many feet are in $\frac{1}{3}$ of a mile?

13. How many pounds are in 17 tons?

14. How many pounds are in 560 ounces?

15. How many pecks are in 78 bushels?

16. How many gallons are in 552 quarts?

Time

1. What time does the watch show?

We write this time 2:20. We say it: **two twenty**.

2. If we write 2:20 A.M., what does it mean?

3. What time does the alarm clock show?

We write this time 8:50. We say it: **eight fifty**.

4. If we write 8:50 P.M., what does it mean?

The extra hand on this watch is the **second** hand. It moves around its circle in one minute. Each little mark on this circle measures one second. How many seconds are in a minute?

The alarm clock has an extra hand, too. This hand does not move by itself. What numbers are shown around its circle? What is it for?

5. The program began at 2:00 P.M. It was finished at 4:15 P.M. How long was the program?

ALARM SET

6. We started on the picnic at 9:30 A.M. and got back home at 4:20 P.M. How long were we gone?

Count the hours and minutes until noon. Then count those after noon. Add them.

7. It should take 5 hours to roast our turkey. We put it in the oven at 9:15 A.M. When should the turkey be done?

8. What part of a minute is 1 second? 30 seconds?

9. The train was 45 minutes late. It was due to arrive at 10:45 A.M. What time did it arrive?

10. The radio announcer said, "In ____ seconds it will be 7 o'clock.

Some Ways of Counting Time

A **decade** is ten. A **score** is twenty. A **century** is one hundred.

1. What does this mean: *It happened a decade ago?*

2. How old is a person who is three score and ten?

Our years are counted from the birth of Christ. We write **B.C.** after any year before that event, as 635 B.C. The letters mean "before Christ." Any year since the birth of Christ is called **A.D.**, meaning "in the year of our Lord" (anno Domini). When no letters follow a year, it means A.D.

The first century A.D. was the first hundred years after Christ's birth. The second century was from 101 A.D. to 200 A.D. The fifteenth century was from 1401 to 1500. We live in the **twentieth** century.

3. In 1933 the city of Chicago had a big fair which was called *A Century of Progress*. What do you think the fair was meant to show?

4. The first Thanksgiving was observed in Plymouth Colony by the Pilgrims on December 13, 1621. In 1789 President Washington set aside November 26 as a national Thanksgiving Day. In 1862 President Lincoln proclaimed the last Thursday in November as a national holiday. In what century was each of these dates?

700 B.C.

600 B.C.

400 B.C.

200 B.C.

CHRIST WAS BORN

200 A.D.

400 A.D.

600 A.D.

800 A.D.

1000 A.D.

1200 A.D.

1400 A.D.

1500 A.D.

1600 A.D.

1700 A.D.

1800 A.D.

1950 A.D.

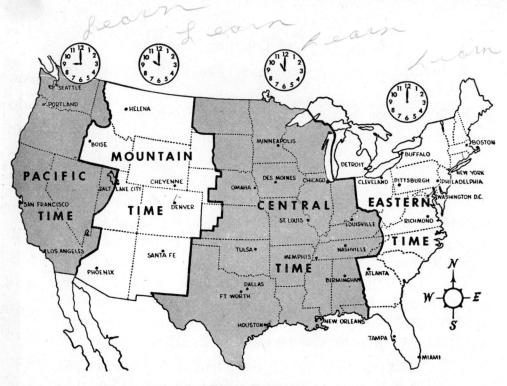

Time Zones

Jim and his father live in Los Angeles. They are going to listen to the broadcast of the Army-Navy football game.

"We had better turn on the radio. It's almost time for the game to start," said Mr. West.

"But it's not 10 o'clock yet," said Jim, "and the game doesn't start until 1:15."

"I know," said Mr. West, "but the game starts at 1:15 New York time and 10:15 our time."

When it is 12 o'clock noon in Los Angeles, it is 3 o'clock in the afternoon in New York, and when it is 12 o'clock noon in New York, it is 9 o'clock in the morning in Los Angeles.

Look at the map. It shows how the United States is divided into **time zones**.

1. How many time zones are there?

2. What are the time zones called?

3. The time in any one zone is exactly the same, but the time changes when we go from one zone to another. As we go east from one zone to another, we move our watches **forward** one hour. How do we move our watches when we go west from one zone to another?

4. James lives in Denver. He went with his father to Washington, D.C. He had to set his watch in Washington. What is the difference in time between these places?

5. Jack lives in Houston, Texas. The President will speak over the radio from Washington, D.C., at 9 P.M., Eastern Standard Time. At what time will Jack hear his speech, Central Standard Time?

6. When it is midnight in Chicago, what time is it in Seattle? When it is 9 P.M. in Seattle, what time is it in Chicago? When it is 12 noon in Seattle, what time is it in Chicago?

7. When the children are going to school (9 A.M.) in Los Angeles, what are the children in New York doing? What is the time in New York?

8. An airplane leaving New York at 3 A.M., Eastern Standard Time, requires 4 hours to fly to Chicago. When will it arrive in Chicago, Central Standard Time?

9. The Rose Bowl game was broadcast from California, starting at 3:30 P.M., Pacific Time. What time did the Chicago stations begin their broadcasts?

The Table of Time

The units most often used for measuring time are made into a table here. The abbreviations are also given. The table should help you to remember how units of time are related.

60 seconds (sec.)	= 1 minute (min.)
60 minutes	= 1 hour (hr.)
24 hours	= 1 day (da.)
7 days	= 1 week (wk.)
52 weeks, 365 days, or 12 months (mo.)	= 1 year (yr.)
366 days	= 1 leap year
10 years	= 1 decade
100 years	= 1 century

1. Mary can iron 4 shirts in an hour. About how long does it take her to iron one shirt?

2. Mr. Allen earns 85¢ an hour. He works 8 hours a day, 7 days a week. How much does he earn in a day? in a week? in a year?

3. Roy earns $175 a month. At this rate how much does he earn in a year?

4. It costs 10¢ to ride on the bus. Every day for one week Ann went to town and back on the bus. How much did she pay for bus fare for those trips?

5. George Washington was born in 1732. How many years ago was that? About how many centuries?

6. Say the right number for each blank:

a. 3 days = ___ hr.   b. 6 wk. = ___ days   c. $\frac{1}{4}$ hr. = ___ min.

d. $\frac{1}{2}$ yr. = ___ mo.   e. 5 min. = ___ sec.   f. $\frac{1}{3}$ hr. = ___ min.

g. 28 days = ___ wk.   h. 1 yr. 8 mo. = ___ mo.

Length

1. With your ruler, measure the length of this page. What unit of measure do you use?

2. What unit would you use to measure the width of your desk? the length of your room? Measure each one.

3. Draw a line on a piece of paper. Measure it. Did your line come exactly to an inch mark? If not, call its length the number of inches to which it comes **nearest**. The end of the line may be a little before or a little beyond an inch mark.

4. How many inches long is the line above? Look for the inch mark nearest the end of the line.

5. Look at the half-inch mark. Is the length of the line nearer $4\frac{1}{2}$ inches or 5 inches? Is it more accurate to say that the line is about $4\frac{1}{2}$ inches long than it is to say that the line is about 5 inches long?

6. Will your measurement be even more accurate if you measure with fourths of an inch? What will the measurement be to fourths of an inch? to eighths of an inch?

7. Measure the width of the room to the nearest yard. Now measure it in feet. Which measurement is more accurate?

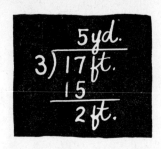

$$3\overline{)17 \text{ ft.}} \quad \begin{array}{r} 5\text{yd.} \\ \hline \end{array}$$
$$\underline{15}$$
$$2 \text{ ft.}$$

Changing Measures of Length

1. How many inches are 3 feet?

2. How many feet are 36 inches?

3. How many feet are 5 yards?

4. How many yards are 12 feet?

5. Do we multiply or divide to change a measurement to a larger unit? to a smaller unit?

6. When we measure a length, will we have a larger number of units if we use a small unit or a large unit of measure?

We multiply to change large units of measure to smaller units. We divide to change small units of measure to larger units.

7. Jack said, "My father is taller than your father. He is 72 inches tall, and your father is just 6 feet tall." Was Jack right?

To change 72 inches to feet, we divide 72 by 12.

To change 6 feet to inches, we multiply 6 by 12.

8. Jim is 4 feet 3 inches tall. What is his height in inches?

$$\begin{array}{r} 12 \\ \times 4 \\ \hline 48 \\ +3 \\ \hline 51 \end{array}$$

There are 12 inches in 1 foot; so in 4 feet there are 4 × 12 or 48 inches. But Jim is 3 inches more than 4 feet; so we add 3 inches to 48 inches. Jim is 51 inches tall.

---

9. Change 17 feet to yards. Will there be any feet left over? 17 feet = ____ yards and ____ feet.

10. Change 150 inches to feet. Will there be any inches left over? 150 inches = ____ feet and ____ inches.

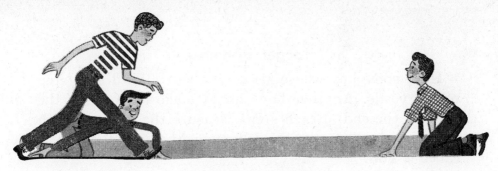

Estimating Length

With practice you will be surprised to learn how well you can **estimate** length.

1. Draw a line that you think is an inch long. Measure it. Was your estimate close to the right length?

2. Try 2 inches; 3 inches; 6 inches. Measure each one to see how close your estimate was to the measurement.

3. On the board draw a line that is a foot long. Measure it.

4. Estimate a yard of string in this way: With your left hand hold one end of the string at the end of your nose. With your right hand extend the string as far as you can stretch your arm. Hold this length and measure it with a yardstick. Is your reach long enough so that you can use it to estimate a yard?

5. You can estimate length on the floor by your step. We call this "stepping off" the length. With one heel against the wall take a long step. Hold it while someone measures this step. Is it nearly a yard long? Could you estimate a yard in this way?

Start with one heel against the wall. Stride across the room with long steps. Count your steps to estimate the width of the room. Measure the width with a yardstick. How was your estimate?

Longer Distances

Have some boy whose stride is about a yard long step off $5\frac{1}{2}$ yards. Another boy should make a mark on the floor at the end of each step. Measure the distance with a yardstick to see if it is about right. This distance is called a **rod**.

Count or measure the number of feet in this distance. Did you get $16\frac{1}{2}$ feet?

$$5\frac{1}{2} \text{ yd. or } 16\frac{1}{2} \text{ ft. = 1 rod (rd.)}$$

This will help you to get in mind the length of a rod:

Cut strips of paper 2 inches wide. Paste enough strips together to make one strip that measures $5\frac{1}{2}$ yards. Make heavy marks across it to show each yard. Make marks of some other color to show each foot. Then fasten the strip on the wall where you will see it often.

The **mile** is our longest unit of length. Locate some place that is about a mile from your home. When you need an idea of a mile, you can think of this distance.

There are 5280 feet in a mile (mi.). There are 320 rods in a mile.

1. The tank of Mr. Allen's car holds 16 gallons of gasoline. He can travel 18 miles on a gallon of gasoline. About what distance can he go on a tank of gasoline?

2. Suppose that Mr. Allen knows that the tank is about one fourth full. Can he safely make a 50-mile trip without buying more gasoline?

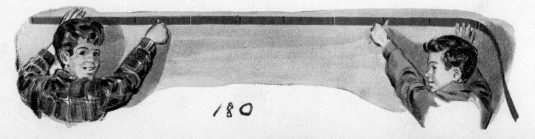

How Big Can Skippie's Pen Be?

Jack must make a pen for his new puppy. He has measured the place for the pen and found that it could be 30 ft. long and 20 ft. wide. How many feet of wire will he need to go around the pen?

Jack drew a picture of his pen. Its shape was a **rectangle**. He wrote the **dimensions** on his drawing. That is, he wrote the length on one side and the width on one end. He needs to find the distance around the pen. This is the **perimeter**.

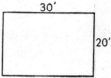

1. To find how many feet of wire to buy, Jack needs to know how many feet it will be around the pen. To find this distance, he must add the lengths of the four sides. How many feet will it be around the pen? What is the perimeter of the rectangle? How many feet of wire will Jack need?

2. Could Jack have added 30 ft. and 20 ft. and then multiplied by 2? Why?

3. Draw a rectangle that is 4 in. long and 3 in. wide. Find its perimeter.

4. What is the perimeter of a rectangle that is 15 rd. long and 12 rd. wide?

```
  30 ft.
  20 ft.
 ------
  50 ft.
  × 2
 ------
 100 ft.
```

5. The girls wanted to put new crepe paper around the window box. To find how much paper to cut, they measured the dimensions of the box. It was a rectangle 4 ft. long and 1 ft. wide. What was the perimeter of the box? How many feet of paper did they need?

Finding Perimeters

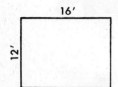

1. What is the perimeter of this rectangle?

The rectangle is 16 ft. long and 12 ft. wide. We may say that it is 16 ft. by 12 ft. We may write the dimensions: 16' by 12', or 16' × 12'. That little mark after a number means **feet**.

2. Find the perimeter of rectangles whose dimensions are:

15 ft. by 9 ft.   27' by 19'   18' × 15'   14' × 16'

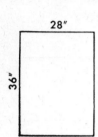

3. Two little marks after a number mean **inches**: 36 inches may be written 36″.

Find the perimeter of the rectangles with these dimensions:

36″ × 28″   30″ × 24″   22″ × 17″   16″ × 18″

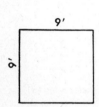

4. This is a **square**. All sides of a square are the same length. This square is 9' by 9'. What is its perimeter?

We can find the perimeter of this square by multiplying 9 by 4. Why?

5. When we say that a square is 5 inches on a side, we mean that its dimensions are 5″ × 5″. What is the perimeter of this square?

6. What is the perimeter of a square that is 19″ on a side? one that is 36″ on a side?

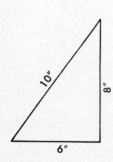

7. A **triangle** has three sides. To find the perimeter of a triangle, we add the lengths of the three sides.

Find the perimeter of this triangle.

8. The picture of a rectangle, a square, or a triangle is called a **figure**.

182

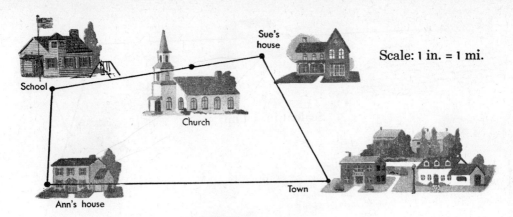

Scale: 1 in. = 1 mi.

Making a Map

Ann and Sue made a map to send to their pen pals. They let 1 inch on the map stand for 1 mile.

1. Measure the line from Ann's house to the school. This line is 1 inch long; so Ann lives 1 mile from school.

2. Measure the line from Sue's house to school. How far does Sue live from school?

3. How far does Sue live from the church? How far does Ann live from the church?

4. Measure the line from Sue's house to town. This line is $1\frac{1}{2}$ inches long; so the distance must be $1\frac{1}{2}$ miles.

5. How far does Ann live from town?

6. When Ann goes to visit Sue, she goes around by the school. How far must she go?

This little map is the same shape as the real place, but it is much smaller in size. A **certain length** on the map shows a **given distance**. This makes our map a **scale drawing**. The distances are measured by the **scale**. The scale here is: **1 in. = 1 mi.** We must know the scale in order to find what distances the lines mean. Such a map is **drawn to scale**.

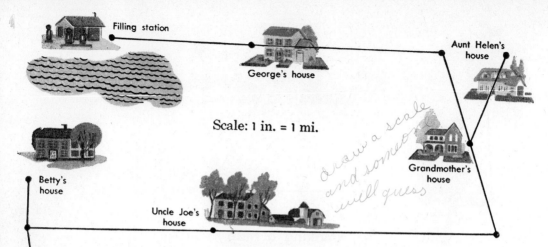

Scale: 1 in. = 1 mi.

Draw a scale and someone will guess

Bill Visits Uncle Joe

Bill went to visit his Uncle Joe, who lives on a farm in Iowa. Bill made a scale drawing to send to Tom. With it, Tom could get a better idea of the places Bill wrote about.

1. What scale did Bill use for his drawing?

2. How far does Uncle Joe live from town? from Bill's cousin George? from Bill's grandmother?

3. What is the distance from Grandmother's to Aunt Helen's? from Grandmother's to George's?

4. One morning George walked to the filling station. How far did he walk?

5. On Sunday Grandmother invited all the relatives to dinner. How far did each family have to go to reach her home?

6. How much farther did Betty's family have to go than any of the other families?

7. Uncle Joe needs gasoline. Will it be a shorter trip for him to go to the filling station for it or to go to town for it? How much shorter?

184

12 inches (in.) = 1 foot (ft.)	$16\frac{1}{2}$ feet = 1 rod
3 feet = 1 yard (yd.)	5280 feet = 1 mile (mi.)
$5\frac{1}{2}$ yards = 1 rod (rd.)	320 rods = 1 mile

Measuring Length and Distance

You will use the answers to some of these questions to find the answers to others. Check to be sure each one is right.

1. Nancy is to make the prize ribbons for the flower show. Each ribbon is to be 6″ long. How many can she make from a yard of ribbon?

2. Nancy needs 18 of the ribbons. How many yards of ribbon should she buy?

3. At 45¢ a yard, what should Nancy pay for the ribbon to make the prizes?

4. If Nancy pays for the ribbon with a five-dollar bill, how should the clerk count her change?

5. There are 9 children to share equally the cost of the prize ribbons. How much is each child's share?

6. Try to change these measures without looking at the table:

    a. 4 ft. = _____ in.
    b. 6 yd. = _____ ft.
    c. 12 yd. = _____ in.
    d. 27 ft. = _____ yd.
    e. 2 mi. = _____ rd.
    f. 2 mi. = _____ ft.
    g. 42 da. = _____ wk.
    h. 3 yr. = _____ mo.

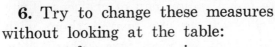

Measuring Liquids

1. Make a list of liquids that are commonly measured with each unit of liquid measure.

2. Do you know anything that is measured in half pints? What measure is the same as a half pint?

3. Mrs. Ellis bought 4 half pints of cream at 35¢ each. How much did she pay for the cream?

4. Cream also sells for 65¢ a pint. How much would Mrs. Ellis have saved by asking for pints instead of half pints?

5. How many pints of milk would 8 quarts make?

6. What part of a quart is a pint? What part of a gallon is a quart?

7. How many quart bottles can Mr. Abbot pour from 16 gallons of milk?

8. Each of the 32 children is to be served a glass of sweet cider at the party. How many gallons of cider will be needed? At 70¢ a gallon, how much will the cider for the party cost?

9. Mrs. White got a gallon can of cherries. They had not been sweetened; so she heated them with sugar and canned them in pint jars. About how many pint jars did she use?

10. At $1.69 a gallon, what will 3 gallons of canned cherries cost?

Table of Liquid Measure

2 cups or 2 half pints = 1 pint (pt.)

2 pints   = 1 quart (qt.)

4 quarts   = 1 gallon (gal.)

Weights

Bill Bender was helping his father feed and water the chickens.

"Bill, will you take that bucket and fill it with water for the chickens," said Mr. Bender. "No, not the big bucket. It will be too heavy for you to carry."

"How much does the big bucket hold?" asked Bill.

"Four gallons," answered his father.

"How much do 4 gallons of water weigh?" asked Bill.

Mr. Bender answered, "A pint's a pound the world around. Then how much do 4 gallons weigh?"

At school the next day, Bill told his class about it. He weighed an empty pint bottle. Then he filled it with water and weighed it. The pint bottle of water weighed about a pound more than the empty bottle.

"Sure enough," said Bill. "A pint of water weighs just about a pound."

1. How much does a quart of water weigh?

2. How much does a gallon of water weigh?

3. How much do 2 gallons of water weigh?

4. On the hot water tank at home, Bill read: **Capacity 30 gal.** How many pounds does the water in the 30-gallon tank weigh?

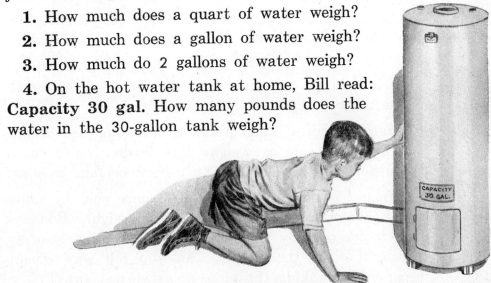

Measuring Weight

1. What unit would you use to measure your weight?

Table of Weight
16 ounces (oz.) = 1 pound (lb.)
2000 pounds   = 1 ton (T.)

2. How many ounces are in $\frac{1}{4}$ of a pound? $\frac{1}{2}$ of a pound? $\frac{1}{8}$ of a pound?

3. How many pounds are in $\frac{1}{4}$ of a ton? $\frac{1}{2}$ of a ton?

4. A quarter-pound box of tea costs 35¢. How much will a pound of tea cost?

A pound of tea will probably cost a little less than four times as much as a quarter of a pound. Things are often sold a little cheaper in larger quantities.

5. At $8.75 a ton, what will 15 tons of coal cost?

6. At $12.50 a ton, what will half a ton of coal cost?

7. A bushel of apples weighs about 50 pounds. Mr. Gable sold apples at 8¢ a pound. How much would he get for a bushel of them?

8. He paid $3.25 a bushel for the apples. How much did he make on each bushel?

Potatoes, fruits, and grains are among the things that are often sold by weight. The bushel is used as a **container**, but the weight must be a certain amount.

In many places things that were once sold by units of other measures are now sold by weight. Bananas used to be sold by the dozen. Potatoes were sold by the peck or by the bushel. Can you tell why weight measures are taking the place of other measures?

Tons and Tons

1. The picture shows a long coal train of 65 cars. In each car there is an average of 47 tons. How many tons of coal is the train hauling?

2. The cost of this coal at the coal mine was $3.75 a ton. How much was the cost of the trainload of coal?

3. The trainload is being hauled to a city where it will be delivered in trucks to homes. Because of the cost of hauling and trucking, the coal will cost each homeowner $8.40 a ton. Mr. Ballin has bought a supply of 9 tons for his home furnace. How much will the coal cost?

4. The 9 tons Mr. Ballin bought were ordinary tons, or "short" tons. A homeowner in England bought a supply of 8 tons for his furnace. But, as is the British custom, he bought his coal in "long" tons. Who bought more coal, Mr. Ballin or the Englishman?

2240 pounds = 1 long ton

5. Last winter Mr. Ballin used 12 tons of coal. By having his furnace repaired, he can manage to get along with 9 tons this winter. How much will Mr. Ballin save at $8.40 a ton?

Dry Measures

Many things that were once measured by dry measure are now measured by weight. Since some of the units are still used for convenience, we should at least know something about them.

Table of Dry Measure
2 pints (pt.) = 1 quart (qt.)
8 quarts = 1 peck (pk.)
4 pecks = 1 bushel (bu.)

1. Sam and Tom paid $4.00 for a bushel of cherries. They put the cherries into quart boxes, which they sold at 20¢ a quart. How much did they make?

2. Art raised potatoes last summer. His crop made 63 bushels. He sold the potatoes at $2.00 a bushel. How much did he get for them?

3. Mr. Axel at the Main Street Grocery bought some of Art's potatoes. He paid $2.00 a bushel for them. He sold them at 8¢ a pound. How much did he get for each bushel? (A bushel of potatoes weighs 60 pounds.) How much did he make on each bushel?

4. How many quarts would there be in 3 pecks of beans?

5. How many pounds would a half bushel of apricots weigh? (A bushel of apricots weighs 48 pounds.)

6. Jane and Sue picked blueberries to sell. They picked a half bushel and put them into pint boxes. How many pint boxes could they fill?

7. The girls sold the berries at 28¢ a box. How much money did they get for their berries?

190

Do You Know the Measures?

1. Tell what each unit below is used to measure:

inch	quart	dozen	foot	bushel
minute	yard	month	pound	peck
gallon	ounce	cup	ton	mile
century	rod	year	second	hour
pint	day	week	carat	degree

carat

2. Copy these statements, putting in the right numbers:

1 lb. = ___ oz.	1 gal. = ___ qt.	$\frac{1}{4}$ lb. = ___ oz.
1 hr. = ___ min.	1 T. = ___ lb.	8 qt. = ___ gal.
1 yd. = ___ ft.	1 yr. = ___ mo.	12 ft. = ___ yd.
1 doz. = ___ things	1 pt. = ___ cups	4 doz. = ___ things
1 wk. = ___ days	1 day = ___ hr.	$\frac{1}{2}$ T. = ___ lb.
1 ft. = ___ in.	1 qt. = ___ pt.	3 yr. = ___ mo.
1 min. = ___ sec.	1 yr. = ___ days	2 gal. = ___ cups

3. Change each measurement to the smaller unit:

1 hr. 15 min.	1 min. 20 sec.	3 gal. 1 pt.
2 yr. 3 mo.	4 yd. 1 ft.	6 lb. 8 oz.
5 gal. 2 qt.	1 T. 540 lb.	5 ft. 4 in.

4. To change to larger units, should we multiply or divide?

5. At what temperature does water freeze?

6. Explain a temperature of 8° below zero?

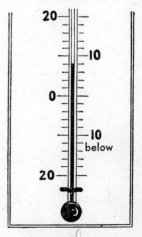

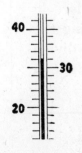

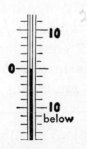

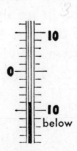

Chapter 11
Dividing by Tens and Ones

When to Divide

1. Sue bought 84 cookies to serve at her club meeting. How many cookies are there for each of the 21 members?

$$\begin{array}{r} 4 \\ 21\overline{)84} \\ \underline{84} \end{array}$$

To answer the question, we divide 84 by 21. There are about as many 21's in 84 as there are 2's in 8. We are dividing 84 ones by 21; so we write the 4 in one's place.

Each member may have 4 cookies.

2. The club members have 126 grab-bag prizes to wrap for the community fair. How many prizes should each of the 21 members wrap?

$$\begin{array}{r} 6 \\ 21\overline{)126} \\ \underline{126} \end{array}$$

Keep an eye on the figure in ten's place in the divisor. Decide where to start writing the answer. Divide by 2 (tens) just as you divide by 2. Think, "Twos in twelve, six." Write 6 in one's place, and multiply.

192

READING CHART	
6ᵗʰ Grade	■ ■ ■ ■ ■ ■
5ᵗʰ Grade	■ ■ ■ ■ ■ ■ ■

3. Last month the 54 pupils in the sixth grade read 324 books. How many books on the average did each pupil read?

4. Last month the 43 pupils in the fifth grade read 344 books. How many books on the average did each pupil read?

5. There are 168 pages in one of the books Sue got at the library. Sue can read 42 pages an hour. How many hours will it take her to read this book?

6. Jane has 105 inches of ribbon to make 21 bookmarks. How long can each bookmark be?

Copy and divide:

	(a)	(b)	(c)	(d)	(e)	(f)
7.	32)96	21)84	43)86	51)153	62)186	71)355
8.	83)249	94)188	12)48	13)39	11)99	24)48
9.	33)66	42)126	52)208	61)549	72)288	84)168
10.	93)279	34)68	51)459	91)819	24)72	32)160
11.	45)315	74)370	64)448	56)280	84)504	93)651
12.	25)100	36)144	44)264	53)477	65)390	73)657
13.	85)765	96)864	85)595	37)111	55)330	95)475

Dividing by Tens and Ones

$$42\overline{)1512}^{\downarrow}$$

In dividing by tens and ones, we divide the way we divide by tens. We keep an eye on the figure in ten's place in the divisor.

$$\begin{array}{r} 3 \\ 42\overline{)1512} \end{array}$$

For her birthday Lucy received a set of books. She is a good reader. She can read about 42 pages an hour. There are 1512 pages to read. How many hours will it take Lucy to read all the books in the set?

$$\begin{array}{r} 3 \\ 42\overline{)1512} \\ 126 \end{array}$$

We keep an eye on the figure in ten's place in the divisor and divide by 4 (tens) the way we divide by 4.

$$\begin{array}{r} 3 \\ 42\overline{)1512} \\ 126 \\ \hline 25 \end{array}$$

First, notice where we write the first figure in our answer. Think, "Forty-twos in 1, no. Forty-twos in 15, no. Forty-twos in 151, yes." We start to write our answer in ten's place above the 1 in 1512.

$$\begin{array}{r} 3 \\ 42\overline{)1512} \\ 126 \\ \hline 252 \end{array}$$

Divide: Fours in fifteen, three. We write 3 in our answer in its proper place.

Multiply: Multiply 42 by 3. Notice that the product, 126, is not greater than the partial dividend, 151, above it.

$$\begin{array}{r} 36 \\ 42\overline{)1512} \\ 126 \\ \hline 252 \end{array}$$

Subtract: Subtract 126 from 151. Notice that the remainder, 25, is less than the divisor, 42.

Bring down: Bring down the next figure, 2.

Now divide 252 by 42: Fours in twenty-five, six.

$$\begin{array}{r} 36 \\ 42\overline{)1512} \\ 126 \\ \hline 252 \\ 252 \end{array}$$

Multiply 42 by 6. Notice that the product is the same as the partial dividend above it. There is no remainder and there is nothing to bring down; so the dividing is finished.

194

Helping Others

1. The pupils in the fifth grade collected 550 magazines to send to the children in the hospital. They tied the magazines in bundles of 25 each. How many bundles did they have to send?

2. The 22 girls in the class collected and painted 484 spools. If each girl painted the same number, how many spools did each girl paint?

3. The girls gave 276 spools to the boys to make toys. The 12 boys divided the spools equally. How many spools did each boy get?

4. The girls used the 208 spools that were left to make spool dolls. They used 8 spools for each doll. How many dolls did they make?

Practice

1. Notice how these examples are worked:

```
        23            45              27             36              38
21) 483      32) 1440      41) 1107      62) 2232      73) 2774
    42           128            82            186            219
    ──           ───            ──            ───            ───
    63           160           287            372            584
    63           160           287            372            584
```

Copy and divide:

	(a)	*(b)*	*(c)*	*(d)*	*(e)*
2.	23) 1196	44) 2728	61) 5551	73) 1606	85) 3825
3.	32) 1440	45) 1935	62) 2852	74) 5328	91) 7917
4.	34) 2074	51) 2907	63) 4662	75) 5550	92) 3956
5.	32) 2976	52) 3484	64) 1536	81) 5265	31) 1457
6.	45) 1125	62) 3596	74) 4514	91) 8918	32) 2368
7.	51) 2346	63) 5292	75) 6150	92) 4876	32) 2688
8.	52) 3900	64) 2240	81) 6156	93) 6882	41) 3567
9.	53) 1749	65) 3445	32) 1792	51) 1479	63) 5985

10. Jerry read a story about Eskimos. In the story a dog team made a trip of 441 miles from noon April 2 to noon April 23. How many miles a day did the dog team average?

Zero in the Quotient

1. Jack lives on the farm. He has 36 hens. He keeps a record of the number of eggs they lay. During October they laid a total of 720 eggs. How many eggs on the average did each hen lay during October?

Study these examples:

$$
\begin{array}{r} 20 \\ 36)\overline{720} \\ 72 \\ \hline 0 \end{array}
\qquad
\begin{array}{r} 30 \\ 41)\overline{1230} \\ 123 \\ \hline 0 \end{array}
\qquad
\begin{array}{r} 50 \\ 56)\overline{2800} \\ 280 \\ \hline 0 \end{array}
\qquad
\begin{array}{r} 40 \\ 49)\overline{1960} \\ 196 \\ \hline 0 \end{array}
$$

2. Joe and his father are going on a 600-mile trip. If they average 30 miles an hour, how long will it take them to make the trip?

3. Tom went with his father on a 750-mile trip. The trip took 25 hours. Find the average number of miles traveled in an hour.

4. Jim is helping to set out 1000 cabbage plants. His father said, "I will plant the first row of 20 plants while you mark off the other rows."
How many rows of cabbage will they have?
How many rows should Jim mark off?

5. The 32 boys and girls in the class sold 1920 Christmas seals. What was the average number of Christmas seals sold by each pupil?

6. Henry said, "Father and I took a truckload of wheat to town. The wheat alone weighed 3180 pounds. A bushel of wheat weighs 60 pounds. How many bushels were in the load?"

197

Practicing Division

1. Study the work of each example carefully. Then copy the examples, and divide without the book. Check.

(a)	(b)	(c)	(d)	(e)
12	21	12	11	21
12)144	23)483	32)384	25)275	41)861
12	46	32	25	82
24	23	64	25	41
24	23	64	25	41

2. In these examples the correct quotient figures are given. Copy the examples and finish the dividing. Check each quotient.

13	11	13	41	22
13)169	24)264	12)156	12)492	31)682

Divide and check:

3. 12)168 21)441 23)299 34)374 22)286

4. 11)176 14)294 12)252 23)276 15)165

5. Watch the subtraction in these division examples. Study the examples. Then copy, work, and check them.

12	12	41	23	21
34)408	44)528	22)902	31)713	24)504
34	44	88	62	48
68	88	22	93	24
68	88	22	93	24

Divide and check:

6. 23)506 32)736 22)528 33)726 42)924

7. 42)882 23)759 81)891 12)372 31)651

8. 72)864 60)960 83)913 56)952 62)806

198

More Examples to Study and Work

1. We must often carry when we multiply. Study these examples. Then work and check them.

(a)	(b)	(c)	(d)	(e)
21	26	25	24	25
25)525	32)832	22)550	34)816	32)800
50	64	44	68	64
25	192	110	136	160
25	192	110	136	160

Divide and check:

2. 24)552 35)805 36)864 26)598 37)814

3. 45)945 56)728 43)946 37)777 63)945

4. 74)888 32)768 19)209 25)575 24)576

5. Many dividends have three or more figures. It will help us to find how many figures to use for the first partial dividend if we think of the numbers as bundles of thousands, hundreds, or tens.

Will we use 1 thousand, 10 hundreds, or 103 tens for the first partial dividend? Why?

How will we find the first quotient figure?

Why do we write this figure in ten's place in the quotient?

```
     24
43)1032
   86
   172
   172
```

Tell how the rest of the example is worked.

Divide and check:

6. 21)1092 74)1036 32)1088 64)1472 52)1248

7. 27)594 21)1134 44)1012 23)966 35)875

8. 22)550 42)1596 52)3900 45)990 83)1992

9. 41)3116 94)1504 38)456 26)1118 49)1127

199

Dividing Dollars and Cents

1. The 42 pupils in the fifth grade at the Wilson School planned an all-day picnic at Lincoln Park. They found that the total cost of everything they would need, including bus fares and the fruit and ice cream they wanted to get, would be $15.96. They decided to share the expense equally. How much was each pupil's share?

```
          $.38
      42)$15.96
          12 6
           3 36
           3 36
```

We divide $15.96 by 42 the way we would divide 1596 by 42. But we must be careful to write each part of our answer **in its proper place** and to put the point **in its proper place**.

2. During a certain week there were 72 girls at Camp Buddy. The total cost of running the camp that week was $313.92. How much was that for each girl?

Divide:

	(a)	*(b)*	*(c)*	*(d)*
3.	23)$11.96	44)$27.28	61)$55.51	73)$16.06
4.	23)$119.83	44)$273.68	61)$558.15	73)$166.44

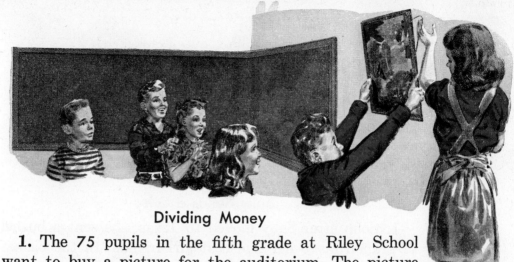

Dividing Money

1. The 75 pupils in the fifth grade at Riley School want to buy a picture for the auditorium. The picture costs $24.00. If they share the cost equally, how much should each pupil pay?

2. The 75 fifth-grade pupils are planning a trip to the museum. It will cost $18.75 to hire a bus to take them. If each pupil pays an equal share, how much should each one pay?

3. Each pupil must also pay 12¢ to go down into the coal mine at the museum. Each one has arranged to carry his lunch and to take 8¢ for milk. What should the trip cost each pupil?

4. How much should a pupil have left from a dollar bill after he pays for his trip?

Divide and check:

	(a)	(b)	(c)	(d)	(e)
5.	41)$21.73	83)$11.62	67)$17.42	15)$1.65	59)$14.16
6.	32)$20.48	50)$18.00	74)$25.16	35)$18.20	23)$11.96
7.	21)$11.76	13)$7.28	33)$6.93	24)$10.32	77)$20.79
8.	59)$8.85	66)$35.64	27)$3.24	76)$34.20	40)$22.40

Sally Sends a Gift

1. Soon after Sally moved to Texas, she sent a bushel of grapefruit to her five best girl friends. In the basket there were 50 grapefruit. The girls shared them equally. How many grapefruit did each girl get?

2. Sally paid $5.00 for the grapefruit. This included the cost of sending them. How much did Sally's gift to each of her 5 friends amount to?

3. At $5.00 a bushel, what would be the cost of each of the 50 grapefruit?

Work and check these division examples:

	(a)	(b)	(c)	(d)	(e)	(f)
4.	4)844	6)606	3)960	8)168	5)305	9)180
5.	6)84	5)110	9)468	7)518	4)904	8)952
6.	8)4368	4)2928	6)4518	3)1071	9)8532	7)6272
7.	4)824	7)2135	5)2015	6)5448	3)1527	9)6354
8.	7)$3.50	9)$9.27	5)$6.00	2)$17.04	8)$16.96	6)$5.94
9.	30)90	50)400	42)84	31)93	62)248	93)279
10.	34)204	47)188	54)432	83)747	79)553	68)340

Estimating Answers

Decide which of the three answers seems about right. Do not work the problem.

1. Nine boys bought a boat for $17.10. They divided the expense equally. How much was each boy's share? $2.00 $1.50 $2.50

2. Jim gathered 108 eggs one day. How many dozen eggs did he get?   10 doz.   8 doz.   9 doz.

3. One Sunday the West family went for a car ride. When they started, the speedometer showed 6492. When they got home, it showed 6587. How many miles did they ride?   100 mi.   5 mi.   15 mi.

4. Another Sunday the Wests took an 85-mile ride. They were gone about 3 hours. What was their average distance each hour?   20 mi.   30 mi.   40 mi.

5. Jack had a board 7 ft. long. He sawed off a piece $2\frac{5}{8}$ ft. long to mend his wagon. How long was the piece that was left?   3 ft.   4 ft. $4\frac{1}{2}$ ft.   8 ft.

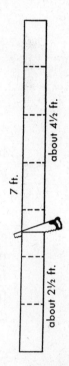

6. Ann bought a dress for $5.95 and a purse for $1.98. How much did her new things cost in all? $8.00 $6.00 $7.00.

7. Betty bought 3 yards of material for a new dress. She paid 89¢ a yard for it. How much did she pay for the material? $3.00 $2.25 $2.70.

8. Dan bought a model airplane for $1.35 and 2 bicycle tires for $3.30. How much did he spend in all? $8.00 $4.00 $4.50.

Now start over. Work each problem. Was your estimate about the same as your answer?

The Boy Scouts Go Camping

1. Twelve Boy Scouts planned a week-end trip to their hut. For their breakfasts they bought 3 pounds of bacon at 69¢ a pound and 3 loaves of bread at 16¢ a loaf. How much did these things cost?

2. At a farm near the hut the boys bought 3 dozen eggs at 35¢ a dozen, 1 gallon of milk for 40¢, and 1 pound of butter for 50¢. How much did they pay the farmer's wife for her produce? The boys paid the farmer's wife with a five-dollar bill. How much change did they get? Count the change.

3. Early Saturday morning the boys started on a hike. They were gone for 3 hours and walked about 9 miles. What was the average distance they walked each hour?

4. The total expenses for the week end amounted to $27.60. How much did each one pay if the twelve boys shared equally in the expenses?

Practicing Division

Keep an eye on the figure **in ten's place** in the divisor. Divide by tens and ones the way you would divide by ones.

Divide:

	(a)	(b)	(c)	(d)
1.	64)2816	81)7047	93)7905	41)3075
2.	53)2279	65)2795	82)5904	94)3948
3.	42)1932	54)2862	71)4331	83)6059
4.	31)2263	53)3445	64)3584	81)7938
5.	93)8928	41)2747	53)2915	65)2210
6.	82)5166	94)4888	65)1690	54)2376
7.	71)5964	83)6889	95)1425	43)3956

Practicing Multiplication

Study:

```
  5280              2042              6308
    12                26                41
 10 560            12 252            6 308
 52 80             40 84           252 32
 63,360            53,092          258,628
```

Multiply:

	(a)	(b)	(c)	(d)	(e)	(f)
8.	1335 9	2733 8	6219 2	3796 65	5723 78	7838 19
9.	$19.50 14	$23.72 25	$9.89 48	$8.52 30	$10.10 50	$5.05 16

x8

x9

x7

x6

x3

x5

x4

x2

Ring
the bell

205

Problems

1. Sarah paid $12.25 for a coat, $2.50 for a hat, and $4.50 for a pair of shoes. How much did Sarah spend?

2. How much more did Sarah have to pay for the coat than for the pair of shoes?

3. Sarah had $24.17 in her purse before she paid for her clothes. She paid $19.25 for the clothes she bought. How much did she have left after she paid for them?

4. Sarah owed the saleslady who waited on her $19.25. Sarah gave the saleslady a 20-dollar bill. How much change did Sarah get back?

5. William bought 4 shirts. He paid $7.60 for them. How much did he pay for each shirt?

6. William's father bought 3 shirts. Each shirt cost $1.38. How much did the shirts cost?

7. During the summer vacation William made $43.61 by running errands and by helping at the grocery. He saved most of it, but kept $\frac{1}{7}$ of it for spending money. How much did he keep for spending money?

Practice

Add:

	(a)	(b)	(c)	(d)	(e)	(f)
1.	5146	2856	9375	4087	7698	2657
	2738	5372	8031	5906	6742	1890
2.	$505.70	$376.35	$557.12	$643.31	$127.63	$989.40
	458.39	493.95	653.56	425.78	367.48	227.12
	263.45	326.30	280.55	655.93	408.23	337.21
3.	$527.50	$257.00	$735.60	$350.00	$486.35	$266.58
	358.46	625.40	207.75	468.28	275.53	407.10
	297.53	384.00	342.68	301.60	432.34	420.00
	654.40	259.63	128.50	280.42	729.63	500.00

Subtract:

	(a)	(b)	(c)	(d)	(e)	(f)
4.	7398	5681	6035	27,842	8002	9000
	4756	2385	4723	13,930	4375	3456
5.	$738.62	$785.70	$570.25	$564.75	$800.00	$1000.00
	427.53	453.35	246.80	257.80	356.79	785.75

Multiply:

	(a)	(b)	(c)	(d)	(e)	(f)
6.	748	562	784	2837	286	435
	4	5	7	9	28	73
7.	1467	3527	4276	3428	4634	3496
	9	8	2	56	47	18
8.	$27.50	$12.48	$7.65	$5.75	2600	4060
	37	25	38	50	78	19

Divide:

9. 5)9735 4)8924 8)19984 20)3540 40)11040 80)5200

10. 42)1134 61)5002 54)1404 22)1364 10)7850 30)2940

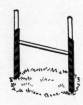

Test

Read these sentences, saying the right word for each blank space:

1. Susan bought 12 eggs at the store. She used 3 of them to make a cake. She used ____ ____ of the eggs.

2. To find $\frac{1}{4}$ of any number, _divide_ the number by _four_.

3. To find $\frac{1}{4}$ of anything, we divide it into ____ ____ parts.

4. To find $\frac{1}{6}$ of any number, we ____ the number by ____.

5. To find $\frac{5}{6}$ of any number, we ____ the number by ____, and then ____ by ____.

6. Find $\frac{7}{8}$ of 48.

7. Find $\frac{3}{4}$ of 1636.

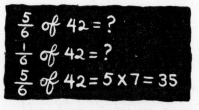

$$\frac{5}{6} \text{ of } 42 = ?$$
$$\frac{1}{6} \text{ of } 42 = ?$$
$$\frac{5}{6} \text{ of } 42 = 5 \times 7 = 35$$

8. Find $\frac{3}{4}$ of $17.36.

9. Find $\frac{7}{12}$ of 3240.

10. Find $\frac{4}{5}$ of $122.80.

11. Tens and hundreds are added, subtracted, multiplied, and divided the way ____ are added, subtracted, multiplied, and divided. But we must be careful to write our ten's answer in ____ place and our hundred's answer in ____ place.

12. When we have no number to write in a place, we write ____ in that place in order to put the numbers we do have in their proper places.

13. We multiply by tens the way we multiply by ____, but we must write our ten's answer in ____ place.

Kicking goals

14. We divide by tens the way we divide by ____, but we must write the answer we get in its proper place.

208

Test

See how many of the following sentences you can complete correctly. Tell the word that should go in each blank space.

1. In order to change feet to inches, we must *multiply* the number of feet by ___12___ .

2. In order to change inches to yards, we must _____ the number of inches by _____.

3. In order to change gallons to pints, we must _____ the number of gallons by _____.

4. In order to change quarts to gallons, we must _____ the number of quarts by _____.

5. In order to change pounds to ounces, we must _____ the number of pounds by _____.

6. In order to change ounces to pounds, we must _____ the number of ounces by _____.

Find the answers:

7. Add $28.65, $37.50, $19.62, $25.00, and $19.95.

8. From $250.00 subtract $138.48.

9. Multiply $40.76 by 95; $63.92 by 87.

10. Divide $353.28 by 8; $154.07 by 71; $205.26 by 33.

11. Find $\frac{1}{5}$ of $38.65; $\frac{2}{9}$ of $81.18; $\frac{3}{8}$ of $9.60.

12. Find $\frac{3}{5}$ of $18.35; $\frac{5}{6}$ of $72.84; $\frac{3}{10}$ of $40.

13. Find $\frac{2}{7}$ of 14,420; $\frac{1}{6}$ of 9636; $\frac{3}{4}$ of 100.

14. Find $\frac{5}{9}$ of $56.70; $\frac{5}{8}$ of $76.80; $\frac{1}{12}$ of $49.20.

15. Divide by 10: 8040; $10,010; 990; $73.40.

16. How many days are there in 8640 minutes?

Shooting goals

Chapter 12
Adding and Subtracting Fractions

Adding Parts

1. Mother cut her strawberry shortcake into **8** equal pieces. Father ate **2** pieces, and Jerry ate **3** pieces. How many pieces did they both eat?

2. Mother cut her strawberry shortcake into **8** equal pieces. Father ate **2** eighths, and Jerry ate **3** eighths. How much did they both eat?

3. Mother cut her strawberry shortcake into **8** equal pieces. Father ate $\frac{2}{8}$, and Jerry ate $\frac{3}{8}$. How much did they both eat?

Problems **1**, **2**, and **3** are really the same problem. This is the way we write what each one tells:

2 pieces	2 eighths		
3 pieces	3 eighths	$\frac{2}{8} + \frac{3}{8} = \frac{5}{8}$	$\frac{2}{8}$
5 pieces	5 eighths		$\frac{3}{8}$
			$\frac{5}{8}$

210

We add parts the way we add wholes.			
5 pencils	5 eighths		$\frac{5}{8}$
2 pencils	2 eighths	$\frac{5}{8} + \frac{2}{8} = \frac{7}{8}$	$\frac{2}{8}$
7 pencils	7 eighths		$\frac{7}{8}$

4. Mary is making a pudding. It takes $\frac{1}{3}$ of a cup of brown sugar and $\frac{1}{3}$ of a cup of white sugar. How much sugar is needed for the pudding?

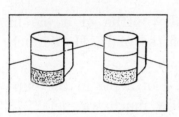 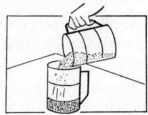 

5. Tell how we add the fractions in each box:

A			B			C		
2 fifths	$\frac{2}{5}$		1 fourth	$\frac{1}{4}$		3 sixths	$\frac{3}{6}$	
1 fifth	$\frac{1}{5}$		2 fourths	$\frac{2}{4}$		2 sixths	$\frac{2}{6}$	
fifths			fourths			sixths		

6. Add these fractions aloud:

(a)	(b)	(c)	(d)	(e)	(f)	(g)	(h)	(i)	(j)
$\frac{1}{6}$	$\frac{1}{8}$	$\frac{3}{10}$	$\frac{1}{5}$	$\frac{2}{5}$	$\frac{4}{8}$	$\frac{2}{6}$	$\frac{4}{8}$	$\frac{2}{8}$	$\frac{2}{7}$
$\frac{4}{6}$	$\frac{4}{8}$	$\frac{6}{10}$	$\frac{3}{5}$	$\frac{2}{5}$	$\frac{1}{8}$	$\frac{3}{6}$	$\frac{3}{8}$	$\frac{3}{8}$	$\frac{3}{7}$

7. Copy and add these fractions. Write the answers.

$\frac{5}{8}$	$\frac{2}{9}$	$\frac{1}{5}$	$\frac{3}{10}$	$\frac{5}{12}$	$\frac{1}{9}$	$\frac{2}{4}$	$\frac{1}{7}$	$\frac{5}{16}$	$\frac{1}{3}$
$\frac{2}{8}$	$\frac{5}{9}$	$\frac{2}{5}$	$\frac{4}{10}$	$\frac{2}{12}$	$\frac{4}{9}$	$\frac{1}{4}$	$\frac{3}{7}$	$\frac{4}{16}$	$\frac{1}{3}$

211

Subtracting Parts

1. Alice and Jerry found 4 pieces of pie in the cupboard. They ate 2 pieces of it. How many pieces were left?

2. Alice and Jerry found 4 fifths of a pie in the cupboard. They ate 2 fifths of it. How much was left?

3. Alice and Jerry found $\frac{4}{5}$ of a pie in the cupboard. They ate $\frac{2}{5}$ of it. How much was left?

Problems **1**, **2**, and **3** are really the same problem. This is the way we write what each one tells:

4 pieces	4 fifths		$\frac{4}{5}$
−2 pieces	−2 fifths	$\frac{4}{5} - \frac{2}{5} = \frac{2}{5}$	$-\frac{2}{5}$
2 pieces	2 fifths		$\frac{2}{5}$

> We subtract parts the way we subtract wholes.

Copy and subtract:

	(a)	(b)	(c)	(d)	(e)	(f)	(g)	(h)	(i)	(j)
4.	$\frac{2}{4}$ $\frac{1}{4}$	$\frac{2}{8}$ $\frac{1}{8}$	$\frac{4}{8}$ $\frac{1}{8}$	$\frac{2}{3}$ $\frac{1}{3}$	$\frac{3}{6}$ $\frac{2}{6}$	$\frac{5}{6}$ $\frac{4}{6}$	$\frac{7}{9}$ $\frac{2}{9}$	$\frac{6}{8}$ $\frac{3}{8}$	$\frac{5}{7}$ $\frac{2}{7}$	$\frac{9}{16}$ $\frac{4}{16}$
5.	$\frac{6}{7}$ $\frac{3}{7}$	$\frac{7}{8}$ $\frac{2}{8}$	$\frac{3}{4}$ $\frac{2}{4}$	$\frac{6}{8}$ $\frac{1}{8}$	$\frac{7}{8}$ $\frac{4}{8}$	$\frac{4}{5}$ $\frac{3}{5}$	$\frac{9}{12}$ $\frac{4}{12}$	$\frac{8}{16}$ $\frac{5}{16}$	$\frac{6}{9}$ $\frac{4}{9}$	$\frac{9}{10}$ $\frac{2}{10}$

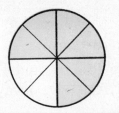 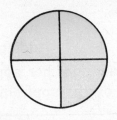 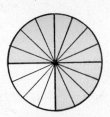

Changing to Lowest Terms

How many eighths of the circle are shaded?
How many fourths of the circle are shaded?

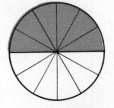

$$\frac{6}{8} = \frac{3}{4}$$

If we did not know that $\frac{6}{8} = \frac{3}{4}$ and we wanted to find out, we could divide the numerator and denominator by the same number, 2.

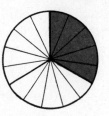

$$\frac{6 \div 2}{8 \div 2} = \frac{3}{4}$$

Changing $\frac{6}{8}$ to $\frac{3}{4}$ is called **changing to lowest terms**.

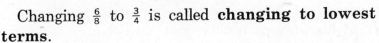

Ann's Work	Andrew's Work
$\frac{12}{16} = \frac{12 \div 4}{16 \div 4} = \frac{3}{4}$	$\frac{12}{16} = \frac{12 \div 2}{16 \div 2} = \frac{6}{8} = \frac{6 \div 2}{8 \div 2} = \frac{3}{4}$

Ann divided the numerator and the denominator by 4.
Andrew divided the numerator and the denominator by 2 and got $\frac{6}{8}$. This is correct as far as it goes. Then Andrew saw that he could divide 6 and 8 by 2. He did and got the same answer as Ann. Both Ann and Andrew got the same answer. Which work is simpler?

Change to lowest terms:

	(a)	(b)	(c)	(d)	(e)	(f)	(g)	(h)	(i)
1.	$\frac{8}{16}$	$\frac{10}{15}$	$\frac{8}{12}$	$\frac{6}{12}$	$\frac{6}{18}$	$\frac{5}{15}$	$\frac{12}{32}$	$\frac{24}{36}$	$\frac{4}{8}$
2.	$\frac{9}{18}$	$\frac{15}{20}$	$\frac{20}{24}$	$\frac{3}{36}$	$\frac{2}{8}$	$\frac{8}{32}$	$\frac{4}{6}$	$\frac{4}{12}$	$\frac{3}{9}$
3.	$\frac{16}{24}$	$\frac{9}{36}$	$\frac{12}{16}$	$\frac{4}{16}$	$\frac{15}{18}$	$\frac{4}{24}$	$\frac{6}{9}$	$\frac{8}{24}$	$\frac{2}{10}$

Adding Fractions

1. Ann gave $\frac{1}{4}$ of her apple to Jane and $\frac{1}{4}$ of it to Sue. What part of the apple did Ann give away?

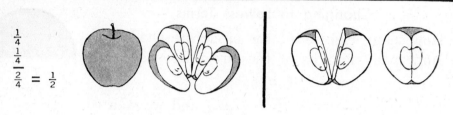

$$\begin{array}{l}\frac{1}{4}\\[2pt]\frac{1}{4}\\\hline\frac{2}{4}\end{array} = \frac{1}{2}$$

The sum of the parts is $\frac{2}{4}$. But $\frac{2}{4}$ can be changed to $\frac{1}{2}$. Ann gave away $\frac{1}{2}$ of her apple.

2. Dick gave $\frac{1}{6}$ of his stamps to Jim and $\frac{1}{6}$ to Ray. What part of his stamps did he give away?

3. Mary poured $\frac{1}{3}$ of a cup of grape juice into $\frac{1}{3}$ cup of water. What part of a cup did Mary fill?

4. Study these examples:

$$\frac{5}{8} + \frac{1}{8} = \frac{6}{8} = \frac{3}{4} \qquad \frac{5}{9} + \frac{1}{9} = \frac{6}{9} = \frac{2}{3} \qquad \frac{1}{6} + \frac{1}{6} = \frac{2}{6} = \frac{1}{3}$$

5. Add these fractions aloud. Remember: The sum may be a fraction that should be changed to lowest terms.

(a)	(b)	(c)	(d)	(e)	(f)	(g)	(h)	(i)
$\frac{1}{8}$	$\frac{1}{4}$	$\frac{1}{8}$	$\frac{5}{16}$	$\frac{1}{9}$	$\frac{4}{9}$	$\frac{5}{12}$	$\frac{2}{7}$	$\frac{1}{5}$
$\frac{3}{8}$	$\frac{1}{4}$	$\frac{5}{8}$	$\frac{3}{16}$	$\frac{4}{9}$	$\frac{2}{9}$	$\frac{1}{12}$	$\frac{3}{7}$	$\frac{3}{5}$

6. Add these fractions. Write the answer in lowest terms.

$\frac{1}{10}$	$\frac{1}{6}$	$\frac{3}{10}$	$\frac{7}{12}$	$\frac{5}{12}$	$\frac{3}{8}$	$\frac{1}{12}$	$\frac{1}{16}$	$\frac{1}{14}$
$\frac{3}{10}$	$\frac{1}{6}$	$\frac{3}{10}$	$\frac{1}{12}$	$\frac{5}{12}$	$\frac{3}{8}$	$\frac{5}{12}$	$\frac{3}{16}$	$\frac{1}{14}$

Subtracting Fractions

1. Mark a sheet of paper into 8 equal parts. Shade 5 of the parts. How many eighths did you shade? Now take away 1 of the 5 eighths. How many eighths are left?

Does 4 eighths = 1 half? $\frac{4}{8} = \frac{1}{2}$

Then $\frac{5}{8} - \frac{1}{8} = \frac{4}{8}$ or $\frac{1}{2}$.

2. Look at the circle below. It is divided into 8 equal parts. How many parts are shaded? Cover 1 of the 7 eighths. How many eighths are left? Now cover 3 of the 7 eighths. How many are left?

Think

$\frac{7}{8} - \frac{1}{8} = \frac{6}{8} = \frac{6 \div 2}{8 \div 2} = \frac{3}{4}$

$\frac{7}{8} - \frac{3}{8} = \frac{4}{8} = \frac{4 \div 4}{8 \div 4} = \frac{1}{2}$

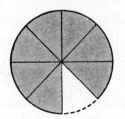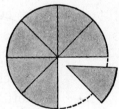

3. Fill a measuring cup $\frac{3}{4}$ full of water. Then pour $\frac{1}{4}$ of it into another measuring cup. How much water is left in the first cup?

$\frac{3}{4}$
$\frac{1}{4}$
―――
$\frac{2}{4}$ or $\frac{1}{2}$

Think

$\frac{2}{4} = \frac{2 \div 2}{4 \div 2} = \frac{1}{2}$

4. Bob lives $\frac{3}{8}$ of a mile from school, and Tom lives $\frac{1}{8}$ of a mile from school. How much farther from school does Bob live than Tom?

How much more is $\frac{3}{8}$ than $\frac{1}{8}$?

$\frac{3}{8}$
$\frac{1}{8}$
―――
$\frac{2}{8} = \frac{1}{4}$

215

Subtracting Fractions

1. Subtract these fractions aloud. Be sure that you change your answer to lowest terms.

(a)	(b)	(c)	(d)	(e)	(f)	(g)	(h)	(i)
$\frac{3}{4}$	$\frac{5}{8}$	$\frac{5}{6}$	$\frac{5}{6}$	$\frac{3}{8}$	$\frac{7}{8}$	$\frac{7}{9}$	$\frac{4}{6}$	$\frac{9}{10}$
$\frac{1}{4}$	$\frac{1}{8}$	$\frac{1}{6}$	$\frac{3}{6}$	$\frac{1}{8}$	$\frac{5}{8}$	$\frac{4}{9}$	$\frac{1}{6}$	$\frac{4}{10}$

2. Subtract and change to lowest terms:

$\frac{7}{12}$	$\frac{7}{16}$	$\frac{8}{10}$	$\frac{7}{8}$	$\frac{7}{10}$	$\frac{5}{16}$	$\frac{7}{9}$	$\frac{9}{16}$	$\frac{5}{14}$
$\frac{5}{12}$	$\frac{3}{16}$	$\frac{4}{10}$	$\frac{3}{8}$	$\frac{3}{10}$	$\frac{1}{16}$	$\frac{1}{9}$	$\frac{3}{16}$	$\frac{3}{14}$

3. Beth had $\frac{2}{3}$ of a cup of milk. She used $\frac{1}{3}$ of a cup to make biscuits. How much of the milk was left?

4. Mrs. Wells cut her pie into 8 equal pieces. Each piece was one eighth. There were 7 pieces left when Mary was ready to serve the pie for dinner. This was $\frac{7}{8}$ of the pie. Mary served 4 pieces, or $\frac{4}{8}$ of the pie. How many pieces were left? What part of the pie was left?

5. Jim drew a line $\frac{7}{8}$ of a foot long. Then he erased $\frac{3}{8}$ of a foot. How long was the line that was left?

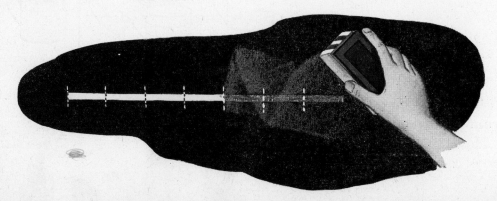

Improper Fractions

1. Look at the watermelon. It has been cut into halves. How many halves are there? Let us put the 2 halves together. Are the 2 halves equal to 1 whole watermelon?

$$2 \text{ halves} = 1 \text{ whole} \qquad \frac{2}{2} = 1$$

2. The 6 halves are equal to how many whole oranges?

$$\frac{6}{2} = 3$$

6 halves = 3 wholes

3. The picture below shows 3 half oranges. How many halves are equal to 1 whole orange? Then 3 halves are equal to 1 whole orange and a half.

$$\frac{3}{2} = 1\frac{1}{2}$$

3 halves = 1 whole and 1 half

4. Five halves are equal to 2 wholes and 1 half.

$$\frac{5}{2} = 2\frac{1}{2}$$

Fractions, as $\frac{1}{2}$ and $\frac{3}{4}$, are called **proper fractions**. They stand for, or show, parts of a whole.

Fractions, as $\frac{2}{2}$ and $\frac{8}{8}$, or $\frac{5}{2}$ and $\frac{6}{4}$, are called **improper fractions**. Fractions which stand for, or show, a whole thing or more than a whole thing are improper fractions.

Wholes and parts written together, as $2\frac{1}{2}$ and $6\frac{1}{4}$, are called **mixed numbers**.

Fraction Sums Equal to One

1. Edith had a candy bar that was divided into 5 equal parts. She ate $\frac{3}{5}$ of the candy bar at lunch and $\frac{2}{5}$ of it after school. How much of the candy did she eat?

$$\frac{\frac{3}{5}}{\frac{2}{5}} = 1$$

Edith ate $\frac{5}{5}$ of the candy bar. She ate the whole bar, or all of it.

2. Joe and Jim each bought $\frac{1}{2}$ pound of candy. How much candy did they both buy?

3. Ruth made a chain $\frac{2}{3}$ of a yard long. Jane made a chain $\frac{1}{3}$ of a yard long. They put their chains together. How long was the new chain?

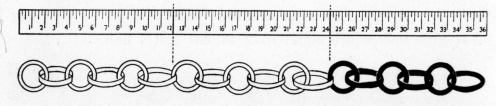

4. Sue practiced her music lesson for $\frac{4}{5}$ of an hour before lunch and for $\frac{1}{5}$ of an hour after lunch. How long did she practice altogether?

5. Add these fractions:

(a)	(b)	(c)	(d)	(e)	(f)	(g)	(h)	(i)	(j)
$\frac{1}{2}$	$\frac{1}{3}$	$\frac{1}{4}$	$\frac{1}{6}$	$\frac{1}{6}$	$\frac{3}{5}$	$\frac{5}{8}$	$\frac{5}{12}$	$\frac{5}{16}$	$\frac{1}{9}$
$\frac{1}{2}$	$\frac{2}{3}$	$\frac{3}{4}$	$\frac{5}{6}$	$\frac{1}{6}$	$\frac{2}{5}$	$\frac{3}{8}$	$\frac{7}{12}$	$\frac{3}{16}$	$\frac{7}{9}$

218

Fractions and Mixed Numbers

1. Alice used $\frac{2}{3}$ of a cup of brown sugar and $\frac{2}{3}$ of a cup of white sugar to make candy. How many cups of sugar did she use in all?

Look at the measuring cups. Do you see that Alice used 1 full cup and one third of another cup?

When we add $\frac{2}{3}$ and $\frac{2}{3}$, we get $\frac{4}{3}$. Then we change $\frac{4}{3}$ to the mixed number $1\frac{1}{3}$. We think, "1 whole is equal to $\frac{3}{3}$, and $\frac{4}{3}$ is one third more than $\frac{3}{3}$, or 1. $\frac{4}{3} = 1 + \frac{1}{3}$. So $\frac{4}{3}$ is equal to $1\frac{1}{3}$."

$$\frac{\frac{2}{3}}{\frac{2}{3}} $$
$$\frac{4}{3} = 1\frac{1}{3}$$

2. Henry had $\frac{4}{5}$ of a candy bar, and Elmer had $\frac{3}{5}$ of a candy bar just like it. Did they have more than 1 candy bar? How much more than 1 whole bar did they have?

3. Jack watched the big thermometer in front of the city hall. The temperature rose $\frac{2}{5}$ of a degree between 1 and 2 o'clock, and between 2 and 3 o'clock it rose $\frac{4}{5}$ of a degree. How many degrees warmer did it get in the two hours? Did it get as much as 1 degree warmer?

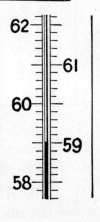

4. Add and change the answers to mixed numbers:

(a)	(b)	(c)	(d)	(e)	(f)	(g)	(h)	(i)	(j)
$\frac{4}{6}$	$\frac{4}{5}$	$\frac{5}{8}$	$\frac{2}{3}$	$\frac{6}{7}$	$\frac{5}{9}$	$\frac{4}{5}$	$\frac{3}{7}$	$\frac{7}{12}$	$\frac{5}{10}$
$\frac{3}{6}$	$\frac{2}{5}$	$\frac{6}{8}$	$\frac{2}{3}$	$\frac{5}{7}$	$\frac{5}{9}$	$\frac{4}{5}$	$\frac{6}{7}$	$\frac{6}{12}$	$\frac{6}{10}$

West   East

$\frac{3}{4}$ mi. $\frac{3}{4}$ mi.

Tom   Joe   Jim

Changing Sums to Mixed Numbers

1. Tom, Joe, and Jim live on the same highway. Tom lives $\frac{3}{4}$ of a mile west of Joe, and Jim lives $\frac{3}{4}$ of a mile east of Joe. How far apart do Tom and Jim live?

$$\begin{array}{r} \frac{3}{4} \\ \frac{3}{4} \\ \hline \frac{6}{4} = 1\frac{2}{4} = 1\frac{1}{2} \end{array}$$

$$\begin{array}{r} 1\frac{2}{4} \text{ or } 1\frac{1}{2} \\ 4\overline{)6} \\ \underline{4} \\ 2 \end{array}$$

1. Add the fractions: $\frac{3}{4} + \frac{3}{4} = \frac{6}{4}$.

2. Change the improper fraction to a mixed number.

Think

$\frac{4}{4} = 1$. So $\frac{6}{4} = \frac{4}{4} + \frac{2}{4} = 1 + \frac{2}{4} = 1\frac{2}{4}$.

3. Change the fraction to lowest terms.

Think

$\frac{2}{4} = \frac{2 \div 2}{4 \div 2} = \frac{1}{2}$

2. Grandmother used $\frac{7}{8}$ of a pound of butter to make cookies for a picnic and $\frac{7}{8}$ of a pound for other cookies. How much butter did she use for all the cookies?

3. Add these fractions aloud. Be sure that you change the improper fraction to a mixed number and change the fraction to lowest terms.

(a)	(b)	(c)	(d)	(e)	(f)	(g)	(h)	(i)
$\frac{4}{6}$	$\frac{5}{8}$	$\frac{7}{8}$	$\frac{3}{8}$	$\frac{7}{16}$	$\frac{11}{12}$	$\frac{2}{3}$	$\frac{5}{9}$	$\frac{9}{10}$
$\frac{5}{6}$	$\frac{5}{8}$	$\frac{5}{8}$	$\frac{7}{8}$	$\frac{11}{16}$	$\frac{9}{12}$	$\frac{2}{3}$	$\frac{7}{9}$	$\frac{9}{10}$

220

Taking a Part from a Whole

1. Jack had a whole apple. He cut it into 2 equal parts, or halves. He gave Jane $\frac{1}{2}$ of the apple, and he kept the rest for himself. What part of the apple did he keep for himself?

Think: 1 whole = 2 halves $1 = \frac{2}{2}$

$$\begin{array}{r} 2 \text{ halves} \\ -1 \text{ half} \\ \hline 1 \text{ half} \end{array}$$

$\frac{2}{2} - \frac{1}{2} = \frac{1}{2}$ $1 - \frac{1}{2} = \frac{1}{2}$

Jack kept $\frac{1}{2}$ of the apple.

2. Cut a paper plate into fourths. How many fourths are there? Now take away **1** of the fourths. How many fourths are left?

$$\begin{array}{r} 4 \text{ fourths} \\ -1 \text{ fourth} \\ \hline 3 \text{ fourths} \end{array}$$

$\frac{4}{4} - \frac{1}{4} = \frac{3}{4}$ $1 - \frac{1}{4} = \frac{3}{4}$

3. Jack, Jane, and Jerry divided the bulletin board into thirds. They used $\frac{2}{3}$ of it to display their arithmetic work and saved the rest of the space for other things. How much of the bulletin board was left for other things?

We think of the bulletin board as 1 whole, which is $\frac{3}{3}$, or all of it.

4. Subtract:

(a)	(b)	(c)	(d)	(e)	(f)	(g)	(h)	(i)	(j)
$\frac{6}{6}$	1	$\frac{4}{4}$	1	$\frac{5}{5}$	1	$\frac{3}{3}$	1	$\frac{8}{8}$	1
$\frac{5}{6}$	$\frac{5}{6}$	$\frac{3}{4}$	$\frac{3}{4}$	$\frac{1}{5}$	$\frac{1}{5}$	$\frac{1}{3}$	$\frac{1}{3}$	$\frac{5}{8}$	$\frac{5}{8}$

Adding Parts of Different Sizes

1. Janet wants to buy $\frac{1}{2}$ yard of ribbon for her dress and $\frac{1}{4}$ yard of the same ribbon for her hair. How much ribbon does she need to buy?

This is Janet's problem: $\frac{1}{2} + \frac{1}{4} = ?$

Janet thought: "The parts are not the same size; so I must change them to parts of the same size. I can divide halves into fourths. One half is two fourths. Two fourths and one fourth are three fourths."

Think

$\frac{1}{2} = \frac{2}{4}$

$\frac{1}{2} = \frac{2}{4}$
$\frac{1}{4} = \frac{1}{4}$

$\frac{3}{4}$

2. Use the circles to tell how we can answer this question: $\frac{1}{8} + \frac{1}{2} = ?$

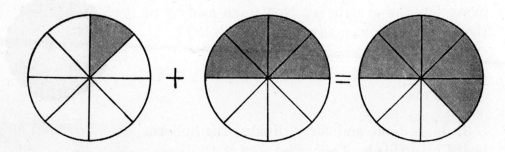

3. Add orally:

(a)	(b)	(c)	(d)	(e)	(f)
$\frac{1}{2} + \frac{1}{16}$	$\frac{3}{8} + \frac{1}{16}$	$\frac{3}{8} + \frac{1}{2}$	$\frac{1}{4} + \frac{1}{8}$	$\frac{1}{4} + \frac{3}{8}$	$\frac{1}{5} + \frac{7}{10}$

4. Copy and add:

$\frac{1}{4} + \frac{1}{16}$ $\frac{3}{8} + \frac{5}{16}$ $\frac{5}{8} + \frac{3}{16}$ $\frac{3}{4} + \frac{1}{8}$ $\frac{5}{8} + \frac{1}{4}$ $\frac{1}{2} + \frac{1}{8}$

5. Check these answers. Are there any mistakes?

$\frac{3}{4} + \frac{1}{16} = \frac{12}{16} + \frac{1}{16} = \frac{13}{16}$ $\qquad$ $\frac{3}{16} + \frac{1}{2} = \frac{3}{16} + \frac{8}{16} = \frac{11}{16}$

$\frac{1}{4} + \frac{5}{8} = \frac{2}{8} + \frac{5}{8} = \frac{7}{8}$ $\qquad$ $\frac{1}{3} + \frac{7}{12} = \frac{4}{12} + \frac{7}{12} = \frac{11}{12}$

Subtracting Unlike Parts

1. Mr. Potter had $\frac{3}{4}$ of a tank of gasoline when he took the family for a ride Sunday afternoon. When they got back home, the tank was just $\frac{1}{2}$ full. What part of a tank was used?

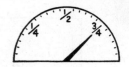

This is the problem: $\frac{3}{4} - \frac{1}{2} = ?$

Think: One half equals two fourths.

Now the problem is: $\frac{3}{4} - \frac{2}{4} = ?$

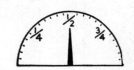

2. Subtract orally:

(a)	(b)	(c)
$\frac{9}{16} - \frac{1}{2} = ?$	$\frac{1}{2} - \frac{1}{4} = ?$	$\frac{7}{8} - \frac{1}{2} = ?$

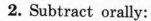

Copy and subtract:

	(a)	(b)	(c)	(d)	(e)	(f)
3.	$\frac{7}{16} - \frac{3}{8}$	$\frac{3}{8} - \frac{1}{4}$	$\frac{5}{16} - \frac{1}{4}$	$\frac{11}{16} - \frac{3}{8}$	$\frac{9}{16} - \frac{1}{2}$	$\frac{5}{9} - \frac{1}{3}$
4.	$\frac{3}{16} - \frac{1}{8}$	$\frac{7}{8} - \frac{3}{4}$	$\frac{7}{8} - \frac{1}{2}$	$\frac{5}{8} - \frac{1}{4}$	$\frac{1}{2} - \frac{1}{8}$	$\frac{11}{12} - \frac{5}{6}$
5.	$\frac{5}{8} - \frac{1}{2}$	$\frac{13}{16} - \frac{3}{4}$	$\frac{7}{8} - \frac{1}{4}$	$\frac{11}{16} - \frac{1}{2}$	$\frac{3}{5} - \frac{3}{10}$	$\frac{1}{2} - \frac{1}{6}$

6. When Alice came home from school, she saw $\frac{1}{2}$ of an apple pie on the table. She ate $\frac{1}{4}$ of the pie. How much was left?

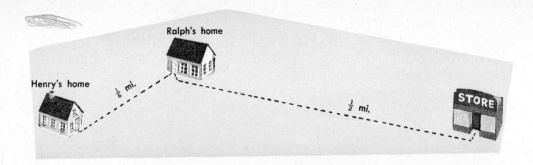

Henry's home

Ralph's home

$\frac{1}{6}$ mi.

$\frac{1}{2}$ mi.

STORE

Adding Unlike Fractions

1. Henry walked $\frac{1}{6}$ of a mile to Ralph's home and then $\frac{1}{2}$ mile farther to the store. How far did Henry walk in going from his home to the store?

$$\frac{1}{6} = \frac{1}{6}$$
$$\frac{1}{2} = \frac{3}{6}$$
$$\overline{}$$
$$\frac{4}{6} = \frac{2}{3}$$

First, we change the half to sixths so that the parts will be the same size, or so that the fractions will have a common denominator.

Next, we add the number of parts, or the numerators.

Then we change the answer to lowest terms.

$$\frac{1}{2} = \frac{2}{4}$$
$$\frac{3}{4} = \frac{3}{4}$$
$$\overline{}$$
$$\frac{5}{4} = 1\frac{1}{4}$$

2. Henry met Bill at the store. Bill walked from the store to Ralph's home with Henry and then $\frac{3}{4}$ mile farther to his own home. How far did Bill walk in going from the store to his home?

3. Study the examples:

A

$$\frac{1}{2} = \frac{4}{8}$$
$$\frac{3}{8} = \frac{3}{8}$$
$$\overline{}$$
$$\frac{7}{8}$$

B

$$\frac{1}{5} = \frac{2}{10}$$
$$\frac{3}{10} = \frac{3}{10}$$
$$\overline{}$$
$$\frac{5}{10} = \frac{1}{2}$$

C

$$\frac{1}{2} = \frac{4}{8}$$
$$\frac{7}{8} = \frac{7}{8}$$
$$\overline{}$$
$$\frac{11}{8} = 1\frac{3}{8}$$

D

$$\frac{1}{2} = \frac{3}{6}$$
$$\frac{5}{6} = \frac{5}{6}$$
$$\overline{}$$
$$\frac{8}{6} = 1\frac{2}{6} = 1\frac{1}{3}$$

Practice in Adding Fractions

1. Add these fractions:

(a)	(b)	(c)	(d)	(e)	(f)	(g)	(h)	(i)	(j)
$\frac{1}{9}$	$\frac{1}{3}$	$\frac{5}{12}$	$\frac{5}{16}$	$\frac{3}{5}$	$\frac{1}{6}$	$\frac{7}{10}$	$\frac{4}{7}$	$\frac{3}{8}$	$\frac{1}{5}$
$\frac{4}{9}$	$\frac{1}{3}$	$\frac{6}{12}$	$\frac{2}{16}$	$\frac{1}{5}$	$\frac{4}{6}$	$\frac{2}{10}$	$\frac{2}{7}$	$\frac{4}{8}$	$\frac{1}{5}$

2. Add these fractions. Be sure your answers are changed to lowest terms.

$\frac{1}{6}$	$\frac{1}{8}$	$\frac{3}{8}$	$\frac{5}{8}$	$\frac{5}{12}$	$\frac{3}{10}$	$\frac{9}{16}$	$\frac{4}{9}$	$\frac{1}{9}$	$\frac{1}{10}$
$\frac{1}{6}$	$\frac{3}{8}$	$\frac{3}{8}$	$\frac{1}{8}$	$\frac{3}{12}$	$\frac{5}{10}$	$\frac{5}{16}$	$\frac{2}{9}$	$\frac{2}{9}$	$\frac{3}{10}$

3. Add these fractions. The answers will be improper fractions. Change them to mixed numbers, and change the fractions, if they can be, to lowest terms.

$\frac{2}{3}$	$\frac{3}{4}$	$\frac{1}{4}$	$\frac{5}{6}$	$\frac{7}{8}$	$\frac{7}{12}$	$\frac{5}{9}$	$\frac{4}{5}$	$\frac{7}{16}$	$\frac{7}{10}$
$\frac{2}{3}$	$\frac{3}{4}$	$\frac{3}{4}$	$\frac{2}{6}$	$\frac{3}{8}$	$\frac{7}{12}$	$\frac{7}{9}$	$\frac{4}{5}$	$\frac{11}{16}$	$\frac{9}{10}$

4. Change to parts of the same size and add. Watch each answer. You may need to change it to lowest terms. It may be an improper fraction. You will change it to a mixed number, and maybe this fraction will need to be changed to lower terms.

$\frac{1}{3}$	$\frac{1}{5}$	$\frac{1}{2}$	$\frac{3}{10}$	$\frac{1}{10}$	$\frac{1}{2}$	$\frac{5}{6}$	$\frac{2}{3}$	$\frac{3}{4}$	$\frac{1}{4}$
$\frac{1}{6}$	$\frac{3}{10}$	$\frac{1}{6}$	$\frac{1}{2}$	$\frac{4}{5}$	$\frac{5}{8}$	$\frac{7}{12}$	$\frac{5}{9}$	$\frac{1}{2}$	$\frac{5}{12}$

5. Ann used $\frac{5}{6}$ yard of ribbon on her costume and $\frac{2}{3}$ yard of ribbon for her hair. How much ribbon did she use?

6. Tom bought $\frac{1}{2}$ pound of peanuts and $\frac{1}{4}$ pound of almonds. What part of a pound of nuts did he buy?

Subtracting Unlike Fractions

1. Tom lives $\frac{7}{8}$ of a mile from school, and Fred lives $\frac{3}{4}$ of a mile from school. How much farther does Tom walk to school than Fred?

$$\frac{7}{8} = \frac{7}{8}$$
$$\frac{3}{4} = \frac{6}{8}$$
$$\overline{\phantom{\frac{3}{4}}\ \frac{1}{8}}$$

The way to subtract $\frac{3}{4}$ from $\frac{7}{8}$ is to change the parts so that they will be the same size. If we think, "Three fourths equal six eighths," we will have no trouble.

7 eighths = 7 eighths
3 fourths = 6 eighths
    1 eighth

$$\frac{7}{8} - \frac{3}{4} = \frac{7}{8} - \frac{6}{8} = \frac{1}{8}$$

$$\frac{5}{6} = \frac{5}{6}$$
$$\frac{1}{2} = \frac{3}{6}$$
$$\overline{\phantom{\frac{1}{2}}\ \frac{2}{6}} = \frac{1}{3}$$

What must we do before we can subtract parts of different sizes? How do we change $\frac{1}{2}$ to $\frac{3}{6}$? How do we get 3 for the numerator of $\frac{3}{6}$? Why did we use 6 as the denominator?

$$\frac{3 \times 1}{3 \times 2} = \frac{3}{6}$$

To change $\frac{1}{2}$ to sixths, think, "How many 2's in 6?" Then you see that the 2 must be multiplied by 3. You also multiply the numerator, 1, by the 3.

2. Change to parts of the same size and subtract:

(a)	(b)	(c)	(d)	(e)	(f)	(g)	(h)	(i)	(j)	(k)
$\frac{1}{2}$	$\frac{5}{6}$	$\frac{7}{9}$	$\frac{5}{6}$	$\frac{7}{8}$	$\frac{4}{9}$	$\frac{11}{12}$	$\frac{11}{12}$	$\frac{7}{10}$	$\frac{5}{8}$	$\frac{7}{9}$
$\frac{1}{6}$	$\frac{1}{2}$	$\frac{2}{3}$	$\frac{1}{3}$	$\frac{1}{2}$	$\frac{1}{3}$	$\frac{2}{3}$	$\frac{3}{4}$	$\frac{2}{5}$	$\frac{3}{16}$	$\frac{2}{3}$

226

Parts of Different Sizes

After the big Thanksgiving dinner Mrs. West found $\frac{1}{2}$ of a pumpkin pie on one plate and $\frac{1}{3}$ of a pumpkin pie on another plate. She put both pieces on the same plate. How much of a pie did she have on the plate?

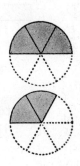

The way to add $\frac{1}{2}$ and $\frac{1}{3}$ is to change them to parts of the same size. We must think, "One half equals three sixths, and one third equals two sixths."

Now we can add:

1 half = 3 sixths	$\frac{1}{2} = \frac{3}{6}$	
1 third = 2 sixths	$\frac{1}{3} = \frac{2}{6}$	$\frac{1}{2} + \frac{1}{3} = \frac{3}{6} + \frac{2}{6} = \frac{5}{6}$
5 sixths	$\frac{5}{6}$	

Add:

	(a)	(b)	(c)	(d)	(e)	(f)	(g)	(h)	(i)	(j)
1.	$\frac{1}{2}$ $\frac{1}{8}$	$\frac{3}{4}$ $\frac{1}{8}$	$\frac{3}{16}$ $\frac{3}{4}$	$\frac{2}{3}$ $\frac{1}{6}$	$\frac{3}{8}$ $\frac{1}{2}$	$\frac{1}{4}$ $\frac{3}{8}$	$\frac{5}{16}$ $\frac{1}{4}$	$\frac{1}{16}$ $\frac{1}{4}$	$\frac{1}{4}$ $\frac{1}{2}$	$\frac{1}{8}$ $\frac{1}{4}$
2.	$\frac{1}{2}$ $\frac{1}{5}$	$\frac{1}{3}$ $\frac{1}{4}$	$\frac{1}{2}$ $\frac{3}{10}$	$\frac{1}{4}$ $\frac{1}{6}$	$\frac{1}{3}$ $\frac{1}{8}$	$\frac{2}{5}$ $\frac{1}{2}$	$\frac{2}{3}$ $\frac{1}{4}$	$\frac{3}{8}$ $\frac{1}{3}$	$\frac{2}{5}$ $\frac{1}{3}$	$\frac{1}{6}$ $\frac{1}{5}$

More about Adding

1. Joan had $\frac{1}{2}$ yard of tape on one spool and $\frac{2}{3}$ yard on another spool. How much tape did she have on both?

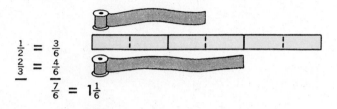

$$\begin{array}{l} \frac{1}{2} = \frac{3}{6} \\ \frac{2}{3} = \frac{4}{6} \\ \hline \frac{7}{6} = 1\frac{1}{6} \end{array}$$

$$\frac{1}{2} + \frac{2}{3} = \frac{3}{6} + \frac{4}{6} = \frac{7}{6} = 1\frac{1}{6}$$

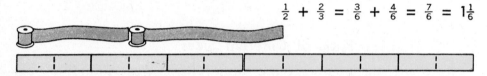

2. Walter ate $\frac{3}{4}$ of a cantaloupe, and John ate $\frac{2}{3}$ of a cantaloupe. How much did both of them eat?

3. A truck farmer set out $\frac{5}{6}$ of an acre of ground in tomatoes and $\frac{2}{3}$ of an acre in cabbage. How much ground did he plant in tomatoes and cabbage?

4. Study the examples below.

$$\begin{array}{l} \frac{1}{4} = \frac{3}{12} \\ \frac{1}{6} = \frac{2}{12} \\ \hline \frac{5}{12} \end{array} \qquad \begin{array}{l} \frac{1}{6} = \frac{5}{30} \\ \frac{9}{10} = \frac{27}{30} \\ \hline \frac{32}{30} = 1\frac{2}{30} = 1\frac{1}{15} \end{array} \qquad \begin{array}{l} \frac{3}{4} = \frac{15}{20} \\ \frac{3}{10} = \frac{6}{20} \\ \hline \frac{21}{20} = 1\frac{1}{20} \end{array}$$

Change to parts of the same size and add:

	(a)	(b)	(c)	(d)	(e)	(f)
5.	$\frac{2}{3} + \frac{1}{2}$	$\frac{4}{5} + \frac{2}{3}$	$\frac{3}{5} + \frac{5}{6}$	$\frac{3}{4} + \frac{3}{5}$	$\frac{3}{4} + \frac{5}{8}$	$\frac{1}{4} + \frac{3}{8}$
6.	$\frac{2}{3} + \frac{5}{8}$	$\frac{5}{6} + \frac{5}{8}$	$\frac{3}{4} + \frac{2}{3}$	$\frac{3}{4} + \frac{5}{6}$	$\frac{7}{12} + \frac{2}{3}$	$\frac{5}{8} + \frac{5}{6}$
7.	$\frac{11}{12} + \frac{5}{8}$	$\frac{5}{12} + \frac{3}{4}$	$\frac{1}{6} + \frac{9}{10}$	$\frac{3}{4} + \frac{7}{8}$	$\frac{3}{4} + \frac{9}{16}$	$\frac{2}{3} + \frac{3}{7}$
8.	$\frac{7}{8} + \frac{9}{16}$	$\frac{3}{4} + \frac{7}{10}$	$\frac{9}{10} + \frac{1}{2}$	$\frac{7}{12} + \frac{3}{4}$	$\frac{5}{6} + \frac{7}{12}$	$\frac{1}{9} + \frac{1}{6}$

Working with Fractions

Subtract:

	(a)	(b)	(c)	(d)	(e)	(f)	(g)	(h)	(i)	(j)
1.	$\frac{1}{2}$ $\frac{1}{5}$	$\frac{2}{3}$ $\frac{5}{8}$	$\frac{3}{5}$ $\frac{1}{2}$	$\frac{3}{8}$ $\frac{1}{6}$	$\frac{1}{4}$ $\frac{1}{10}$	$\frac{2}{5}$ $\frac{1}{3}$	$\frac{5}{6}$ $\frac{1}{4}$	$\frac{5}{6}$ $\frac{1}{2}$	$\frac{3}{10}$ $\frac{1}{4}$	$\frac{15}{16}$ $\frac{3}{4}$
2.	$\frac{3}{4}$ $\frac{5}{12}$	$\frac{1}{4}$ $\frac{1}{6}$	$\frac{3}{4}$ $\frac{2}{3}$	$\frac{5}{6}$ $\frac{5}{8}$	$\frac{9}{10}$ $\frac{1}{5}$	$\frac{3}{4}$ $\frac{3}{10}$	$\frac{1}{6}$ $\frac{1}{8}$	$\frac{9}{10}$ $\frac{3}{4}$	$\frac{11}{12}$ $\frac{1}{4}$	$\frac{3}{4}$ $\frac{1}{6}$

Add:

	(a)	(b)	(c)	(d)	(e)	(f)	(g)	(h)	(i)	(j)
3.	$\frac{3}{5}$ $\frac{3}{5}$	$\frac{1}{6}$ $\frac{1}{8}$	$\frac{2}{3}$ $\frac{1}{6}$	$\frac{5}{8}$ $\frac{5}{8}$	$\frac{1}{2}$ $\frac{1}{5}$	$\frac{5}{6}$ $\frac{1}{8}$	$\frac{3}{4}$ $\frac{7}{8}$	$\frac{2}{5}$ $\frac{3}{10}$	$\frac{7}{8}$ $\frac{5}{16}$	$\frac{3}{4}$ $\frac{1}{6}$
4.	$\frac{5}{6}$ $\frac{3}{4}$	$\frac{1}{4}$ $\frac{1}{8}$	$\frac{1}{3}$ $\frac{3}{5}$	$\frac{1}{6}$ $\frac{7}{12}$	$\frac{1}{4}$ $\frac{1}{3}$	$\frac{1}{3}$ $\frac{5}{8}$	$\frac{1}{4}$ $\frac{5}{6}$	$\frac{2}{3}$ $\frac{3}{8}$	$\frac{3}{4}$ $\frac{1}{10}$	$\frac{2}{9}$ $\frac{1}{6}$

5. Mrs. West used $\frac{3}{4}$ dozen eggs for cookies and $\frac{2}{3}$ dozen eggs for a cake. How many dozen eggs did she use?

6. Martha washes the breakfast and dinner dishes. It takes her about $\frac{1}{4}$ of an hour to wash the breakfast dishes and $\frac{1}{2}$ hour to do the dinner dishes. About how long does it take her to wash the dishes each day?

7. Alice is learning to cook. The recipe she is using reads: "Pour $\frac{1}{2}$ cup of milk into the sugar and stir. Then add $\frac{3}{4}$ cup of milk and stir again." How much milk does Alice need for the recipe?

$$\frac{2}{3} = \frac{4}{6}$$
$$-\frac{1}{2} = \frac{3}{6}$$
$$\frac{1}{6}$$

8. Alice poured $\frac{1}{3}$ cup of vinegar into $\frac{1}{2}$ cup of water. How much liquid was in the cup?

Fractions on Your Ruler

This is the picture of a part of a ruler. The part is 5 inches long. Each inch is divided into different-sized parts. The long lines divide each inch into halves; the middle-sized lines divide each inch into fourths; and the short lines divide each inch into eighths.

In each inch there are how many halves?

In each inch there are how many fourths?

In each inch there are how many eighths?

"I can add and subtract on my ruler," said Ann. "I drew a picture of my ruler and marked off the part inches as well as the whole inches. So I can tell the different-sized parts.

"To add $\frac{1}{2}$ and $\frac{3}{8}$, for example, I go out to the $\frac{1}{2}$-inch mark. Then I count $\frac{1}{8}$, $\frac{2}{8}$, $\frac{3}{8}$ farther, and there I am at $\frac{7}{8}$. So I know that $\frac{1}{2} + \frac{3}{8} = \frac{7}{8}$.

"To subtract $\frac{1}{2}$ from $\frac{7}{8}$, I start at the $\frac{7}{8}$-inch mark, and count back $\frac{4}{8}$, which is $\frac{1}{2}$, like this: $\frac{6}{8}$, $\frac{5}{8}$, $\frac{4}{8}$, $\frac{3}{8}$. And there I am at $\frac{3}{8}$. So $\frac{7}{8} - \frac{1}{2} = \frac{3}{8}$.

"To subtract on your ruler, you have to be careful where you start. To add, you go to the right. To subtract, you go to the left."

Use your ruler or the picture:

Find and point to:	Move on:	Where are you?	Write:
1. $\frac{1}{2}$-inch mark	$\frac{1}{4}$ inch	*three fourths*	$\frac{1}{2} + \frac{1}{4} = \frac{3}{4}$
2. 1 -inch mark	$\frac{3}{4}$ inch	_____	$1 + \frac{3}{4} = ?$
3. $1\frac{1}{2}$-inch mark	$\frac{3}{8}$ inch	_____	$1\frac{1}{2} + \frac{3}{8} = ?$
4. $1\frac{3}{4}$-inch mark	1 inch	_____	$1\frac{3}{4} + 1 = ?$
5. $1\frac{3}{4}$-inch mark	$\frac{1}{2}$ inch	_____	$1\frac{3}{4} + \frac{1}{2} = ?$

Find and point to:	Move back:	Where are you?	Write:
6. $\frac{1}{2}$-inch mark	$\frac{1}{4}$ inch	*one fourth*	$\frac{1}{2} - \frac{1}{4} = \frac{1}{4}$
7. 1 -inch mark	$\frac{3}{4}$ inch	_____	$1 - \frac{3}{4} = ?$
8. $\frac{3}{4}$-inch mark	$\frac{3}{8}$ inch	_____	$\frac{3}{4} - \frac{3}{8} = ?$
9. $1\frac{3}{4}$-inch mark	$\frac{1}{2}$ inch	_____	$1\frac{3}{4} - \frac{1}{2} = ?$
10. $2\frac{1}{2}$-inch mark	$\frac{3}{4}$ inch	_____	$2\frac{1}{2} - \frac{3}{4} = ?$
11. $2\frac{3}{4}$-inch mark	1 inch	_____	$2\frac{3}{4} - 1 = ?$
12. $2\frac{3}{4}$-inch mark	$1\frac{1}{2}$ inch	_____	$2\frac{3}{4} - 1\frac{1}{2} = ?$

$\frac{1}{2} + \frac{1}{4} = \frac{3}{4}$

$\frac{7}{8} - \frac{1}{4} = \frac{5}{8}$

Use your ruler to find:

13. $\frac{1}{4} + \frac{3}{4} = ?$ $\frac{3}{4} - \frac{1}{4} = ?$ $\frac{1}{4} + \frac{3}{8} = ?$ $\frac{7}{8} - \frac{1}{2} = ?$

Chapter 13
Mixed Numbers

Fractions and Whole Numbers

The fifth-grade girls are having a candy sale at school.

1. Mrs. Wells bought a 2-pound box of fudge and a $\frac{1}{2}$-pound box of sea foam. How many pounds of candy did she buy?

$$\begin{array}{r} 2 \\ \frac{1}{2} \\ \hline 2\frac{1}{2} \end{array}$$

How do we add a whole number and a fraction?

2. Jane worked at the candy counter $\frac{3}{4}$ of an hour in the morning and 1 hour in the afternoon. How long did she work at the candy counter?

$$\begin{array}{r} \frac{3}{4} \\ 1 \\ \hline 1\frac{3}{4} \end{array}$$

How do we add a fraction and a whole number?

3. Copy and add:

(a)	(b)	(c)	(d)	(e)	(f)	(g)	(h)	(i)
10	1	4	$3\frac{3}{8}$	5	16	8	5	$1\frac{1}{2}$
$\frac{2}{3}$	$6\frac{2}{3}$	$\frac{1}{3}$	5	$\frac{1}{8}$	$\frac{7}{8}$	$2\frac{3}{4}$	$\frac{3}{10}$	5

232

2⅓ mi.   ⅓ mi

Adding Mixed Numbers and Fractions

1. Jim rides his bicycle to school. It is $2\frac{1}{3}$ miles from his home to the courthouse and $\frac{1}{3}$ of a mile farther to school. How far is it from Jim's home to school?

$$2\frac{1}{3}$$
$$\frac{1}{3}$$
$$\overline{2\frac{2}{3}}$$

2. Mrs. Allen needs $2\frac{1}{4}$ cups of sugar for a cake and $\frac{1}{4}$ of a cup for the filling. How many cups of sugar does she need?

$$2\frac{1}{4}$$
$$\frac{1}{4}$$
$$\overline{2\frac{2}{4}} = 2\frac{1}{2}$$

Study these examples. Tell how they were added.

$\frac{2}{3}$	$8\frac{3}{4}$	$6\frac{1}{2}$
$9\frac{2}{3}$	$\frac{3}{4}$	$\frac{1}{2}$
$\overline{9\frac{4}{3}} = 10\frac{1}{3}$	$\overline{8\frac{6}{4}} = 9\frac{2}{4} = 9\frac{1}{2}$	$\overline{6\frac{2}{2}} = 7$

---

3. Jack caught a fish that weighed $\frac{3}{4}$ of a pound. Then he caught another fish that weighed $1\frac{1}{4}$ pounds. How many pounds of fish had he?

4. Tom went to the store for his mother. He bought a 5-pound sack of sugar and $3\frac{1}{2}$ pounds of rice. How many pounds did the two packages weigh?

5. Copy and add:

(a)	(b)	(c)	(d)	(e)	(f)	(g)	(h)	(i)
$\frac{1}{8}$	$\frac{4}{5}$	$5\frac{5}{9}$	$\frac{5}{8}$	$\frac{11}{12}$	$18\frac{1}{4}$	$4\frac{1}{5}$	$8\frac{1}{4}$	$7\frac{1}{3}$
$3\frac{7}{8}$	$4\frac{4}{5}$	$\frac{8}{9}$	$6\frac{3}{8}$	$6\frac{5}{12}$	$\frac{3}{4}$	$\frac{3}{5}$	$\frac{1}{4}$	$\frac{2}{3}$

Adding Mixed Numbers

1. Tom walks $1\frac{1}{5}$ miles from his home to the highway. There he takes the bus and rides $4\frac{3}{5}$ miles to school. How far does Tom live from school?

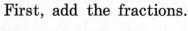

First, add the fractions.	$1\frac{1}{5}$
Next, add the whole numbers.	$4\frac{3}{5}$
	$5\frac{4}{5}$

2. Jack went to the cupboard for candy for himself and the friends who were visiting him. In one box he found $2\frac{3}{8}$ chocolate bars, and in another box he found $1\frac{3}{8}$ bars. How much candy did he find in all?

3. Mrs. Burns needs $1\frac{1}{3}$ cups of flour for a pie and $4\frac{1}{3}$ cups of flour for rolls. How many cups of flour does she need?

4. Jack collected tin cans and old paper to sell. He started to work at 9 o'clock and worked until 11:30. Then he worked $1\frac{1}{2}$ hours after lunch. How many hours was that?

5. One piece of curtain material was $3\frac{1}{3}$ yards long; another piece was $1\frac{1}{3}$ yards long. Jane sewed the two pieces together. How long was the material then?

6. Add these mixed numbers:

(a)	(b)	(c)	(d)	(e)	(f)	(g)	(h)	(i)
$5\frac{1}{5}$	$4\frac{1}{8}$	$8\frac{1}{3}$	$3\frac{3}{5}$	$5\frac{4}{7}$	$10\frac{2}{5}$	$12\frac{5}{12}$	$5\frac{3}{7}$	$17\frac{1}{9}$
$7\frac{2}{5}$	$6\frac{3}{8}$	$4\frac{1}{3}$	$8\frac{1}{5}$	$3\frac{2}{7}$	$6\frac{2}{5}$	$14\frac{5}{12}$	$25\frac{3}{7}$	$6\frac{2}{9}$

234

Watch the Sum

1. On two Saturdays Joe and Jim worked to build a house for their dog. They worked $6\frac{1}{2}$ hours one Saturday and $4\frac{1}{2}$ hours the next Saturday. How many hours did they work on the two Saturdays?

$$\begin{array}{r} 6\frac{1}{2} \\ 4\frac{1}{2} \\ \hline 10\frac{2}{2} = 11 \end{array}$$

2. Joe mowed the lawn for Mr. Brown. It took him $2\frac{1}{2}$ hours to cut the grass and $\frac{1}{2}$ hour to clip the grass along the sidewalk. How many hours did Jack work?

3. Joe needs $2\frac{1}{4}$ yards of canvas to make a skate sail for himself and $1\frac{1}{4}$ yards to make one for his sister. How many yards of canvas does he need for both sails?

$$\begin{array}{r} 2\frac{1}{4} \\ 1\frac{1}{4} \\ \hline 3\frac{2}{4} = 3\frac{1}{2} \end{array}$$

4. Betty lives $5\frac{1}{2}$ blocks from the post office. How far must she walk in going to the post office and back home?

5. Copy and add. Change the sum of the fractions to lowest terms.

(a)	(b)	(c)	(d)	(e)	(f)	(g)	(h)	(i)
$16\frac{1}{4}$	$3\frac{1}{4}$	$5\frac{1}{4}$	$6\frac{1}{2}$	$12\frac{2}{9}$	$15\frac{2}{9}$	$8\frac{1}{8}$	$14\frac{3}{10}$	$1\frac{1}{8}$
$20\frac{1}{4}$	$6\frac{3}{4}$	$3\frac{1}{4}$	$8\frac{1}{2}$	$30\frac{4}{9}$	$10\frac{1}{9}$	$7\frac{1}{8}$	$5\frac{7}{10}$	$3\frac{3}{8}$

Adding Mixed Numbers

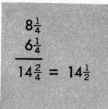

$$8\tfrac{1}{4}$$
$$6\tfrac{1}{4}$$
$$14\tfrac{2}{4} = 14\tfrac{1}{2}$$

1. Harry rode his bicycle $8\tfrac{1}{4}$ miles in the morning and $6\tfrac{1}{4}$ miles in the afternoon. How far did he ride his bicycle that day?

2. "I have gained $3\tfrac{1}{4}$ pounds," said Alice. "When school closed in June, I weighed $65\tfrac{3}{4}$ pounds. How much do I weigh now?"

3. Harry sold $3\tfrac{1}{3}$ pounds of old paper one week and $10\tfrac{2}{3}$ pounds the next week. How many pounds of old paper did he sell in the two weeks?

4. Betty used $1\tfrac{1}{4}$ cups of water and $2\tfrac{3}{4}$ cups of milk in a pudding. How much milk and water together did she use?

5. Betty baked some fruitcakes. She used $3\tfrac{3}{8}$ pounds of pecans and $2\tfrac{3}{8}$ pounds of walnuts. How many pounds of nuts did she use?

6. Explain these examples:

$4\tfrac{1}{5}$	$12\tfrac{1}{4}$	$6\tfrac{2}{3}$	$5\tfrac{3}{4}$
$5\tfrac{1}{5}$	$16\tfrac{3}{4}$	$5\tfrac{2}{3}$	$2\tfrac{3}{4}$
$9\tfrac{2}{5}$	$28\tfrac{4}{4} = 29$	$11\tfrac{4}{3} = 12\tfrac{1}{3}$	$7\tfrac{6}{4} = 8\tfrac{2}{4} = 8\tfrac{1}{2}$

Add. Remember to change your answers to lowest terms.

	(a)	(b)	(c)	(d)	(e)	(f)	(g)	(h)
7.	$12\tfrac{1}{8}$	$2\tfrac{1}{3}$	$13\tfrac{1}{2}$	$4\tfrac{4}{5}$	$4\tfrac{5}{8}$	$9\tfrac{5}{16}$	$12\tfrac{3}{16}$	$3\tfrac{5}{8}$
	$16\tfrac{3}{8}$	$14\tfrac{2}{3}$	$14\tfrac{1}{2}$	$3\tfrac{2}{5}$	$6\tfrac{5}{8}$	$11\tfrac{1}{16}$	$6\tfrac{6}{16}$	$1\tfrac{1}{8}$
8.	$16\tfrac{3}{4}$	$6\tfrac{9}{16}$	$18\tfrac{7}{8}$	$14\tfrac{1}{9}$	$15\tfrac{1}{6}$	$16\tfrac{5}{12}$	$12\tfrac{3}{10}$	$7\tfrac{1}{3}$
	$9\tfrac{3}{4}$	$7\tfrac{9}{16}$	$6\tfrac{7}{8}$	$10\tfrac{2}{9}$	$8\tfrac{5}{6}$	$9\tfrac{1}{12}$	$15\tfrac{2}{10}$	$8\tfrac{2}{3}$

Subtracting Mixed Numbers

Jane, Ellen, and Susan were making dresses for their dolls.

1. Jane had 1 yard of goods. She used $\frac{3}{8}$ yard.

2. Ellen had $1\frac{5}{8}$ yards of goods. She used $\frac{3}{8}$ yard.

3. Susan had $1\frac{3}{8}$ yards of goods. She used $\frac{5}{8}$ yard.

How much goods had each girl left?

$$1 = \frac{8}{8}$$
$$\underline{\frac{3}{8}}$$
$$\frac{5}{8}$$

$$1\frac{5}{8}$$
$$\underline{\frac{3}{8}}$$
$$1\frac{2}{8} = 1\frac{1}{4}$$

$$1\frac{3}{8} = \frac{11}{8}$$
$$\underline{\frac{5}{8} = \frac{5}{8}}$$
$$\frac{6}{8} = \frac{3}{4}$$

Jane had 1 yard, or $\frac{8}{8}$ yard. When she used $\frac{3}{8}$ yard, she had $\frac{5}{8}$ yard left.

Ellen used $\frac{3}{8}$ yard of her $1\frac{5}{8}$ yards; so she had $1\frac{2}{8}$ yards left. Since $\frac{2}{8} = \frac{1}{4}$, she had $1\frac{1}{4}$ yards left.

Susan had $1\frac{3}{8}$ yards. $1\frac{3}{8} = \frac{8}{8} + \frac{3}{8} = \frac{11}{8}$ yards. When she used $\frac{5}{8}$ yard, she had $\frac{6}{8}$ yard left. Since $\frac{6}{8} = \frac{3}{4}$, she had $\frac{3}{4}$ yard left.

Taking a Whole Number from a Mixed Number

$25\frac{1}{2}$
18
———
$7\frac{1}{2}$

1. Jim needed a strip of wood 18 inches long for his kite. He had a strip of wood that was $25\frac{1}{2}$ inches long. He sawed the board in two. He kept the board that was 18 inches long and threw the other piece away. How long was the piece that he threw away?

2. Jane's mother bought $4\frac{1}{4}$ yards of dress goods. She used 3 yards to make a dress for herself. How much cloth did she have left?

3. Jack and some other Boy Scouts went on a hike. They walked $8\frac{3}{4}$ miles to Clear Lake. They came back home by a new road. It was only 8 miles by this road. How much shorter was one road than the other?

4. Jim and Joe gathered $4\frac{1}{4}$ bushels of pecans. Jim took 2 bushels and left the rest for Joe. How many bushels were left for Joe?

5. Mrs. Henry baked $6\frac{1}{2}$ dozen cookies for the school bake sale. The children returned the 2 dozen cookies that they did not sell. How many cookies did they sell?

6. Copy and subtract:

(a)	(b)	(c)	(d)	(e)
$8\frac{1}{4}$	$6\frac{2}{3}$	$24\frac{1}{8}$	$10\frac{4}{5}$	$16\frac{7}{8}$
6	6	8	6	10

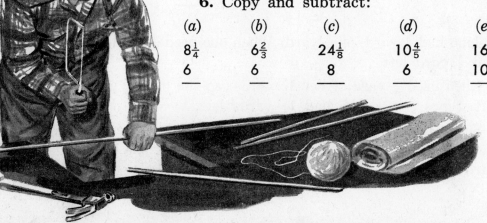

Subtracting Mixed Numbers

1. Bill and Tom have bicycles with cyclometers on them. Saturday Bill rode his bicycle $9\frac{5}{10}$ miles, and Tom rode his bicycle $7\frac{2}{10}$ miles. Bill rode his bicycle how much farther than Tom rode his?

$$9\frac{5}{10}$$
$$7\frac{2}{10}$$
$$2\frac{3}{10}$$

2. Jack Smith ran the 50-yard dash in $9\frac{8}{10}$ seconds, and Tom Brown ran it in $8\frac{2}{10}$ seconds. How much faster did Tom run than Jack?

$$9\frac{8}{10}$$
$$8\frac{2}{10}$$
$$1\frac{6}{10} = 1\frac{3}{5}$$

3. Mary found two dress patterns that she liked. One pattern called for $2\frac{5}{8}$ yards of cloth, and the other called for $2\frac{3}{8}$ yards. How much more cloth did the one pattern call for than the other?

$$2\frac{5}{8}$$
$$2\frac{3}{8}$$
$$\frac{2}{8} = \frac{1}{4}$$

4. Jane had $8\frac{3}{4}$ yards of cloth. She used $4\frac{1}{4}$ yards to make her costume for the play. How many yards of cloth did she have left? Did she have enough left to make another costume?

5. Henry's father is $71\frac{7}{8}$ inches tall, and Henry is $54\frac{3}{8}$ inches tall. Henry's father is how much taller?

6. Mary bought $6\frac{1}{2}$ yards of lace for her dress. She used $4\frac{1}{2}$ yards of the lace. How much lace did she have left?

$$6\frac{1}{2}$$
$$4\frac{1}{2}$$
$$2$$

7. One book weighs $3\frac{5}{16}$ pounds. Another weighs $1\frac{1}{16}$ pounds. What is the difference in weight between the two books?

8. Subtract these mixed numbers:

(a)	(b)	(c)	(d)	(e)	(f)	(g)	(h)	(i)
$15\frac{3}{4}$	$9\frac{3}{4}$	$10\frac{2}{3}$	$16\frac{7}{8}$	$12\frac{4}{5}$	$9\frac{5}{6}$	$12\frac{5}{7}$	$7\frac{7}{12}$	$9\frac{7}{9}$
$6\frac{3}{4}$	$6\frac{1}{4}$	$6\frac{1}{3}$	$8\frac{3}{8}$	$12\frac{1}{5}$	$2\frac{1}{6}$	$8\frac{3}{7}$	$7\frac{5}{12}$	$3\frac{4}{9}$

Mixed Numbers from Whole Numbers

1. Jack picked 8 bushels of apples, and Jane picked $3\frac{1}{2}$ bushels. How many more bushels of apples did Jack pick than Jane?

$$8 = 7\frac{2}{2}$$
$$3\frac{1}{2} = 3\frac{1}{2}$$
$$\overline{4\frac{1}{2}}$$

There are no parts to subtract $\frac{1}{2}$ from. We must use one of the wholes in 8. 1 whole = 2 halves, or $1 = \frac{2}{2}$; so $8 = 7\frac{2}{2}$. Now we can subtract $3\frac{1}{2}$ from $7\frac{2}{2}$.

2. Susan picked 1 bushel of apples, and little June picked $\frac{3}{4}$ of a bushel. Susan said, "I picked one fourth of a bushel more than June picked."

Was Susan right?

3. Copy and subtract:

(a)	(b)	(c)	(d)	(e)	(f)	(g)	(h)
5	16	7	8	10	14	5	16
$1\frac{1}{4}$	$11\frac{2}{3}$	$2\frac{5}{8}$	$5\frac{3}{10}$	$8\frac{3}{4}$	$6\frac{7}{8}$	$4\frac{1}{3}$	$5\frac{3}{5}$

Subtracting Mixed Numbers

1. Jack rode his bicycle $4\frac{1}{5}$ miles to deliver the morning papers and $2\frac{3}{5}$ miles to deliver the evening papers. How much farther did he ride in the morning than in the afternoon?

We cannot subtract $\frac{3}{5}$ from $\frac{1}{5}$. We use one of the 4 wholes. $1 = \frac{5}{5}$; so $4\frac{1}{5} = 3\frac{6}{5}$. Now subtract the fraction. Then subtract the whole number.

$$4\frac{1}{5} = 3\frac{6}{5}$$
$$2\frac{3}{5} = 2\frac{3}{5}$$
$$\overline{ 1\frac{3}{5}}$$

2. Paul is $57\frac{1}{4}$ inches tall, and Ray is $53\frac{3}{4}$ inches tall. How much taller is Paul than Ray?

$$57\frac{1}{4} = 56\frac{5}{4}$$
$$53\frac{3}{4} = 53\frac{3}{4}$$
$$\overline{ 3\frac{2}{4} = 3\frac{1}{2}}$$

3. A box of apples weighs $50\frac{3}{10}$ pounds. The empty box weighs $2\frac{5}{10}$ pounds. How much do the apples weigh?

4. Jane weighs $64\frac{1}{2}$ pounds with her coat on. The coat weighs $2\frac{7}{8}$ pounds. How much does Jane weigh with her coat off?

5. Jim drew a line $8\frac{3}{8}$ inches long. Then he erased $5\frac{7}{8}$ inches of it. How long was the line left on the board?

6. Tim jumped $4\frac{1}{2}$ feet, and Joel jumped $3\frac{3}{4}$ feet. How much farther did Tim jump than Joel?

7. Copy and subtract:

(a)	(b)	(c)	(d)	(e)	(f)	(g)	(h)	(i)
$10\frac{1}{8}$	$6\frac{1}{6}$	$18\frac{3}{10}$	$16\frac{1}{3}$	$8\frac{4}{9}$	$11\frac{1}{12}$	$12\frac{3}{16}$	$8\frac{1}{8}$	$7\frac{1}{10}$
$3\frac{3}{8}$	$2\frac{5}{6}$	$7\frac{5}{10}$	$8\frac{2}{3}$	$7\frac{5}{9}$	$5\frac{5}{12}$	$8\frac{7}{16}$	$4\frac{5}{8}$	$3\frac{7}{10}$

Adding Mixed Numbers and Fractions

1. Study these examples. Explain each example:

$$1\tfrac{1}{4} = 1\tfrac{1}{4}$$
$$\tfrac{1}{2} = \tfrac{2}{4}$$
$$\overline{}$$
$$1\tfrac{3}{4}$$

$$\tfrac{1}{2} = \tfrac{3}{6}$$
$$4\tfrac{1}{6} = 4\tfrac{1}{6}$$
$$\overline{}$$
$$4\tfrac{4}{6} = 4\tfrac{2}{3}$$

$$7\tfrac{3}{4} = 7\tfrac{3}{4}$$
$$\tfrac{1}{2} = \tfrac{2}{4}$$
$$\overline{}$$
$$7\tfrac{5}{4} = 8\tfrac{1}{4}$$

$$5\tfrac{1}{2} = 5\tfrac{3}{6}$$
$$\tfrac{5}{6} = \tfrac{5}{6}$$
$$\overline{}$$
$$5\tfrac{8}{6} = 6\tfrac{2}{6} = 6\tfrac{1}{3}$$

2. Jane made her dress for the school play. She used $1\tfrac{1}{4}$ yards of green cloth and $\tfrac{1}{2}$ yard of red cloth. How many yards of cloth did she use to make the dress?

3. David worked $4\tfrac{1}{2}$ hours pulling weeds from Mr. West's lawn, but he did not finish the job. He had to go back the next day. It took him $\tfrac{1}{4}$ of an hour to finish. How many hours did David work?

4. Mrs. West bought $\tfrac{1}{2}$-pound of bacon and a roast that weighed $5\tfrac{3}{4}$ pounds. How much meat did she buy?

5. How much ribbon is $2\tfrac{1}{8}$ yards and $\tfrac{7}{8}$ yard?

6. Mrs. West needs $2\tfrac{3}{4}$ yards of silk to line Jane's coat. She can buy two remnants at a low price. One piece has $\tfrac{3}{4}$ yard, and the other has $1\tfrac{1}{2}$ yards. Will these two pieces be enough?

7. Add: 2 hours, $\tfrac{1}{2}$ hour, and $\tfrac{1}{2}$ hour.

Add:

	(a)	(b)	(c)	(d)	(e)	(f)	(g)	(h)	(i)
8.	$3\tfrac{5}{8}$ $\tfrac{7}{16}$	$6\tfrac{11}{16}$ $\tfrac{1}{2}$	$\tfrac{1}{2}$ $8\tfrac{11}{12}$	$12\tfrac{1}{3}$ $\tfrac{8}{9}$	$6\tfrac{2}{3}$ $\tfrac{5}{9}$	$\tfrac{1}{2}$ $4\tfrac{9}{16}$	$6\tfrac{1}{5}$ $\tfrac{9}{10}$	$4\tfrac{1}{2}$ $\tfrac{3}{4}$	$1\tfrac{1}{6}$ $\tfrac{8}{18}$
9.	$4\tfrac{2}{3}$ $\tfrac{7}{12}$	$6\tfrac{1}{8}$ $\tfrac{15}{16}$	$5\tfrac{3}{4}$ $\tfrac{5}{12}$	$6\tfrac{3}{4}$ $\tfrac{3}{16}$	$8\tfrac{3}{8}$ $\tfrac{13}{16}$	$7\tfrac{3}{4}$ $\tfrac{9}{16}$	$6\tfrac{7}{8}$ $\tfrac{1}{4}$	$9\tfrac{1}{3}$ $2\tfrac{5}{12}$	$2\tfrac{3}{10}$ $\tfrac{4}{5}$

Adding Mixed Numbers and Fractions

1. Explain these examples:

$$8\tfrac{1}{2} = 8\tfrac{5}{10}$$
$$\tfrac{2}{5} = \tfrac{4}{10}$$
$$\overline{\phantom{8\tfrac{9}{10}}}$$
$$8\tfrac{9}{10}$$

$$9\tfrac{1}{2} = 9\tfrac{5}{10}$$
$$\tfrac{3}{5} = \tfrac{6}{10}$$
$$\overline{\phantom{9\tfrac{11}{10}}}$$
$$9\tfrac{11}{10} = 10\tfrac{1}{10}$$

$$\tfrac{1}{6} = \tfrac{8}{48}$$
$$8\tfrac{5}{16} = 8\tfrac{15}{48}$$
$$\overline{\phantom{8\tfrac{23}{48}}}$$
$$8\tfrac{23}{48}$$

$$7\tfrac{2}{15} = 7\tfrac{4}{30}$$
$$\tfrac{1}{6} = \tfrac{5}{30}$$
$$\overline{\phantom{7\tfrac{9}{30}}}$$
$$7\tfrac{9}{30} = 7\tfrac{3}{10}$$

$$\tfrac{5}{8} = \tfrac{15}{24}$$
$$7\tfrac{7}{12} = 7\tfrac{14}{24}$$
$$\overline{\phantom{7\tfrac{29}{24}}}$$
$$7\tfrac{29}{24} = 8\tfrac{5}{24}$$

$$\tfrac{7}{10} = \tfrac{21}{30}$$
$$2\tfrac{7}{15} = 2\tfrac{14}{30}$$
$$\overline{\phantom{2\tfrac{35}{30}}}$$
$$2\tfrac{35}{30} = 3\tfrac{5}{30} = 3\tfrac{1}{6}$$

2. Jack's jumping rope was $8\frac{1}{2}$ feet long before he tied on a piece 3 feet long. How long was the rope then?

3. Alice's mother bought 2 pieces of cloth at the remnant sale. She bought $\frac{1}{4}$ yard in one piece and $2\frac{1}{6}$ yards in another piece. How many yards of cloth did she buy?

4. Find the answers:

(a)	(b)	(c)	(d)	(e)
$\frac{1}{2} + 5\frac{1}{4} =$	$3\frac{1}{2} + \frac{1}{8} =$	$2\frac{1}{12} + \frac{1}{2} =$	$8\frac{5}{12} + \frac{2}{3} =$	$6\frac{1}{4} + \frac{3}{8} =$
$\frac{3}{8} + 8\frac{1}{2} =$	$\frac{1}{2} + 4\frac{5}{16} =$	$4\frac{1}{2} + \frac{3}{10} =$	$\frac{2}{5} + 8\frac{1}{10} =$	$\frac{1}{4} + 5\frac{5}{12} =$

Copy and add:

	(a)	(b)	(c)	(d)	(e)	(f)	(g)	(h)	(i)	(j)
5.	$7\frac{1}{2}$	$8\frac{1}{4}$	$6\frac{1}{2}$	$4\frac{3}{4}$	$16\frac{1}{3}$	$\frac{1}{3}$	$5\frac{1}{5}$	$8\frac{1}{8}$	$4\frac{1}{4}$	$6\frac{2}{3}$
	$\frac{3}{5}$	$\frac{2}{5}$	$\frac{1}{3}$	$\frac{1}{6}$	$\frac{1}{8}$	$6\frac{1}{2}$	$\frac{3}{10}$	$\frac{1}{6}$	$\frac{1}{3}$	$\frac{1}{4}$
6.	$5\frac{3}{4}$	$6\frac{7}{8}$	$5\frac{5}{8}$	$\frac{2}{3}$	$10\frac{3}{4}$	$8\frac{5}{6}$	$5\frac{1}{2}$	$5\frac{3}{4}$	$\frac{7}{8}$	$3\frac{3}{8}$
	$\frac{2}{3}$	$\frac{2}{3}$	$\frac{1}{3}$	$6\frac{7}{8}$	$\frac{5}{6}$	$\frac{1}{4}$	$\frac{5}{9}$	$\frac{1}{3}$	$5\frac{5}{6}$	$\frac{1}{6}$

243

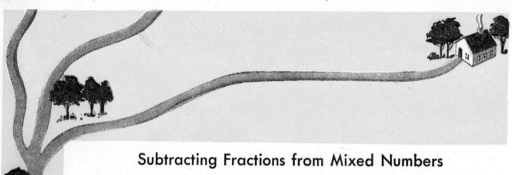

Subtracting Fractions from Mixed Numbers

1. "The Smith cottage is $7\frac{3}{4}$ miles from here. Drive out this road $\frac{1}{2}$ mile and take the crossroad to the right," said the boy at the fruit stand by the side of the road. How far is it from the crossroad to the cottage?

	Tell how these examples were worked:	
$7\frac{3}{4} = 7\frac{3}{4}$	$11\frac{1}{4} = 11\frac{3}{12}$	$8\frac{5}{6} = 8\frac{5}{6}$
$\frac{1}{2} = \frac{2}{4}$	$\frac{1}{12} = \frac{1}{12}$	$\frac{1}{3} = \frac{2}{6}$
$7\frac{1}{4}$	$11\frac{2}{12} = 11\frac{1}{6}$	$8\frac{3}{6} = 8\frac{1}{2}$

2. A whole piece of cheese weighed $5\frac{7}{8}$ pounds. The grocer cut off a piece that weighed $\frac{3}{4}$ of a pound. For how many pounds should the grocer charge a man who wants to buy what is left?

3. Mrs. Baker is using a cooky recipe which calls for $2\frac{3}{4}$ cups of sugar. She has $\frac{1}{2}$ cup of sugar. How much more sugar does she need for the cookies?

Subtract		Check
$4\frac{2}{3} = 4\frac{4}{6}$		$4\frac{3}{6}$
$\frac{1}{6} = \frac{1}{6}$		$\frac{1}{6}$
$4\frac{3}{6} = 4\frac{1}{2}$		$4\frac{4}{6} = 4\frac{2}{3}$

4. Copy, subtract, and check:

(a)	(b)	(c)	(d)	(e)
$1\frac{1}{2}$	$6\frac{3}{4}$	$5\frac{3}{4}$	$5\frac{2}{3}$	$3\frac{3}{4}$
$\frac{1}{4}$	$\frac{3}{8}$	$\frac{5}{12}$	$\frac{1}{6}$	$\frac{1}{8}$

Using a Whole in Subtracting

1. Alice needs $3\frac{1}{3}$ yards of ribbon. She has $\frac{2}{3}$ of a yard. How many more yards does she need?

To find "how many more?" we subtract.

We cannot take $\frac{2}{3}$ from $\frac{1}{3}$. We must use 1 of the 3 wholes that we have. We change the 1 to $\frac{3}{3}$. Then $3\frac{1}{3} = 2\frac{3}{3} + \frac{1}{3} = 2\frac{4}{3}$.

Now we subtract $\frac{2}{3}$ from $2\frac{4}{3}$.

Alice needs $2\frac{2}{3}$ yards of ribbon.

$$3\frac{1}{3} = 2\frac{4}{3}$$
$$\frac{2}{3} = \frac{2}{3}$$
$$\overline{\qquad 2\frac{2}{3}}$$

Look at the picture below. Do you see that $3\frac{1}{3} - \frac{2}{3} = 2\frac{2}{3}$?

 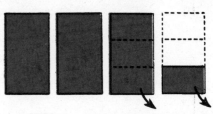

2. Jack spent $1\frac{1}{4}$ hours studying arithmetic and $\frac{3}{4}$ of an hour studying history. How much longer did he study arithmetic than he studied history?

3. Use the picture to answer this question: $4\frac{1}{4} - \frac{3}{4} = ?$

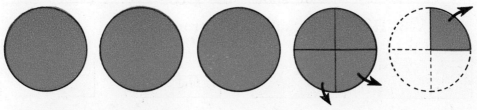

4. Copy and subtract:

(a)	(b)	(c)	(d)	(e)	(f)	(g)	(h)	(i)
$6\frac{1}{5}$	$7\frac{3}{8}$	$5\frac{5}{12}$	$8\frac{1}{3}$	$8\frac{1}{6}$	$9\frac{3}{16}$	$10\frac{1}{5}$	$7\frac{7}{10}$	$9\frac{1}{9}$
$\frac{4}{5}$	$\frac{7}{8}$	$\frac{7}{12}$	$\frac{2}{3}$	$\frac{5}{6}$	$\frac{5}{16}$	$\frac{3}{5}$	$\frac{9}{10}$	$\frac{4}{9}$

Using a Whole in Subtracting

Sam and Ted were taping the handles of their badminton rackets.

1. Sam had $1\frac{3}{4}$ yards of tape. He used $\frac{2}{3}$ of a yard. How much tape was left?

$$1\frac{3}{4} = 1\frac{9}{12}$$
$$\frac{2}{3} = \frac{8}{12}$$
$$\overline{\qquad\qquad 1\frac{1}{12}}$$

We first change the fourths and thirds to twelfths, or to parts of the same size. Next, we subtract the fractions. Then we subtract the whole numbers.

2. Ted had $1\frac{2}{3}$ yards of tape. He used $\frac{3}{4}$ of a yard. How much tape did he have left?

$$1\frac{2}{3} = 1\frac{8}{12} = \frac{20}{12}$$
$$\frac{3}{4} = \frac{9}{12} = \frac{9}{12}$$
$$\overline{\qquad\qquad\qquad\quad \frac{11}{12}}$$

We cannot subtract the twelfths. We cannot take $\frac{9}{12}$ from $\frac{8}{12}$. We use the 1 whole that we have. We change it to $\frac{12}{12}$. So $1\frac{2}{3} = 1\frac{8}{12} = \frac{12}{12} + \frac{8}{12} = \frac{20}{12}$. Now we take $\frac{9}{12}$ from $\frac{20}{12}$.

3. How do we subtract $\frac{1}{2}$ from $3\frac{1}{4}$?

  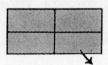 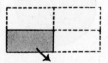

4. Copy and subtract:

(a)	(b)	(c)	(d)	(e)	(f)	(g)	(h)	(i)
$4\frac{1}{6}$	$3\frac{5}{6}$	$5\frac{1}{2}$	$6\frac{1}{3}$	$8\frac{1}{8}$	$7\frac{1}{3}$	$9\frac{2}{3}$	$11\frac{1}{2}$	$10\frac{2}{5}$
$\frac{1}{2}$	$\frac{7}{8}$	$\frac{5}{6}$	$\frac{3}{4}$	$\frac{3}{4}$	$\frac{1}{5}$	$\frac{5}{12}$	$\frac{9}{16}$	$\frac{1}{2}$

Adding Mixed Numbers

1. Mrs. West bought 2 chickens. One weighed $4\frac{1}{4}$ pounds, and the other weighed $5\frac{1}{2}$ pounds. How much did both chickens weigh?

$$4\frac{1}{4} = 4\frac{1}{4}$$
$$5\frac{1}{2} = 5\frac{2}{4}$$
$$\overline{9\frac{3}{4}}$$

2. One day Mrs. White gathered $7\frac{3}{4}$ dozen eggs. The next day she gathered $7\frac{5}{12}$ dozen eggs. How many eggs did she gather in all?

$$7\frac{3}{4} = 7\frac{9}{12}$$
$$7\frac{5}{12} = 7\frac{5}{12}$$
$$\overline{14\frac{14}{12} = 15\frac{2}{12} = 15\frac{1}{6}}$$

3. Tell how these mixed numbers were added:

$$4\frac{1}{4} = 4\frac{1}{4}$$
$$2\frac{1}{2} = 2\frac{2}{4}$$
$$\overline{6\frac{3}{4}}$$

$$5\frac{1}{6} = 5\frac{1}{6}$$
$$9\frac{1}{2} = 9\frac{3}{6}$$
$$\overline{14\frac{4}{6} = 14\frac{2}{3}}$$

$$7\frac{3}{4} = 7\frac{6}{8}$$
$$8\frac{7}{8} = 8\frac{7}{8}$$
$$\overline{15\frac{13}{8} = 16\frac{5}{8}}$$

4. Mary brought $2\frac{1}{2}$ pounds of candy to the school party, and Jane brought $1\frac{3}{4}$ pounds. How many pounds of candy did they both bring?

5. A lady bought two short pieces of silk at a sale. One was $\frac{5}{6}$ yard, and the other was $\frac{1}{2}$ yard. How much silk was in both pieces?

6. One day Jerry played baseball for $2\frac{1}{3}$ hours and went swimming in the pool for $\frac{3}{4}$ of an hour. How much time altogether did he spend on baseball and swimming?

Add:

	(a)	(b)	(c)	(d)	(e)	(f)	(g)	(h)	(i)
7.	$3\frac{1}{4}$	$3\frac{3}{4}$	$9\frac{9}{16}$	$8\frac{3}{4}$	$6\frac{3}{8}$	$14\frac{1}{8}$	$8\frac{3}{4}$	$7\frac{1}{4}$	$6\frac{1}{2}$
	$4\frac{1}{2}$	$5\frac{3}{8}$	$4\frac{1}{2}$	$6\frac{7}{8}$	$6\frac{1}{2}$	$6\frac{1}{4}$	$9\frac{1}{2}$	$8\frac{3}{8}$	$3\frac{7}{8}$
8.	$7\frac{3}{8}$	$2\frac{1}{4}$	$8\frac{1}{2}$	$6\frac{3}{4}$	$8\frac{3}{4}$	$15\frac{7}{8}$	$8\frac{1}{2}$	$8\frac{7}{8}$	$1\frac{1}{2}$
	$6\frac{3}{4}$	$12\frac{3}{8}$	$15\frac{5}{8}$	$10\frac{1}{8}$	$7\frac{3}{8}$	$12\frac{1}{2}$	$12\frac{1}{8}$	$9\frac{1}{4}$	$3\frac{2}{5}$

Adding Mixed Numbers with Carrying

To add mixed numbers, first we add the fractions. Then we add the whole numbers.

$$3\frac{1}{2} = 3\frac{3}{6}$$
$$4\frac{1}{3} = 4\frac{2}{6}$$
$$\overline{\phantom{4\frac{1}{3} = }7\frac{5}{6}}$$

First, we add the fractions. But before we can add them, we must change them to parts of the same size. $\frac{3}{6} + \frac{2}{6} = \frac{5}{6}$. We write $\frac{5}{6}$ under the fractions.

Then we add the whole numbers and write our answer in its proper place.

$$3\frac{1}{2} = 3\frac{3}{6}$$
$$4\frac{2}{3} = 4\frac{4}{6}$$
$$\overline{\phantom{4\frac{2}{3} = }7\frac{7}{6}} = 8\frac{1}{6}$$

First, we add the fractions: $\frac{3}{6} + \frac{4}{6} = \frac{7}{6} = 1\frac{1}{6}$. We write the $\frac{1}{6}$ and carry the 1 to the whole numbers.

Then we add the whole numbers: 1 (carried) and 3 are 4, and 4 are 8.

1. Mrs. West wants to buy a carpet for the stairs and a runner for the hall. Jim measured the stairs and the hall. Jim said, "We need $10\frac{2}{3}$ yards of carpet for the stairs and $8\frac{2}{3}$ yards for the hall. We need $19\frac{1}{3}$ yards in all." Was Jim right?

2. A rope, $12\frac{1}{2}$ feet long, is fastened to another rope, $16\frac{7}{8}$ feet long. How long are the two pieces of rope?

3. Mrs. Wallace baked $2\frac{1}{2}$ pounds of butter cookies and $3\frac{3}{4}$ pounds of oatmeal cookies. How many pounds of cookies did she bake?

4. Copy and add:

(a)	(b)	(c)	(d)	(e)	(f)	(g)	(h)	(i)	(j)
$2\frac{1}{2}$	$4\frac{2}{3}$	$3\frac{2}{5}$	$8\frac{3}{4}$	$7\frac{1}{2}$	$3\frac{7}{12}$	$9\frac{1}{2}$	$5\frac{2}{3}$	$7\frac{2}{3}$	$1\frac{1}{4}$
$4\frac{1}{4}$	$7\frac{1}{2}$	$2\frac{3}{5}$	$5\frac{3}{8}$	$6\frac{5}{8}$	$4\frac{2}{3}$	$10\frac{1}{2}$	$6\frac{3}{4}$	$8\frac{1}{2}$	$3\frac{1}{6}$

5. How do we add these mixed numbers?

$$2\tfrac{3}{4} = 2\tfrac{9}{12}$$
$$5\tfrac{1}{6} = 5\tfrac{2}{12}$$
$$\overline{\phantom{5\tfrac{1}{6}}}$$
$$7\tfrac{11}{12}$$

$$4\tfrac{5}{6} = 4\tfrac{10}{12}$$
$$5\tfrac{1}{4} = 5\tfrac{3}{12}$$
$$\overline{\phantom{5\tfrac{1}{4}}}$$
$$9\tfrac{13}{12} = 10\tfrac{1}{12}$$

$$4\tfrac{5}{6} = 4\tfrac{25}{30}$$
$$4\tfrac{3}{10} = 4\tfrac{9}{30}$$
$$\overline{\phantom{4\tfrac{3}{10}}}$$
$$8\tfrac{34}{30} = 9\tfrac{4}{30} = 9\tfrac{2}{15}$$

6. Jim lives $5\tfrac{3}{4}$ blocks from school. How far does he walk in going to school in the morning and back home in the afternoon?

7. Jim and Joe picked $13\tfrac{1}{2}$ bushels of apples in the morning. In the afternoon they stopped when they had picked $9\tfrac{1}{2}$ bushels. How many bushels of apples did they pick that day?

8. Bob bought $2\tfrac{3}{4}$ pounds of butter for his mother on Tuesday and $3\tfrac{1}{2}$ pounds on Saturday. How many pounds of butter did he buy on both days?

9. Jane went with her father on a trip in the car. They drove $158\tfrac{3}{10}$ miles on Saturday and $224\tfrac{5}{10}$ miles on Sunday. How many miles did they drive?

10. Mrs. West bought $7\tfrac{1}{3}$ yards of cloth to cover a chair and $11\tfrac{1}{4}$ yards to cover a sofa. How much cloth did she buy?

Subtracting Mixed Numbers

$6\frac{3}{4} = 6\frac{3}{4}$
$2\frac{1}{2} = 2\frac{2}{4}$
$\overline{\qquad 4\frac{1}{4}}$

1. The water at one end of the swimming pool is $6\frac{3}{4}$ feet deep. At the other end it is only $2\frac{1}{2}$ feet deep. How much deeper is the water at one end than at the other?

$68\frac{1}{2} = 68\frac{2}{4}$
$56\frac{1}{4} = 56\frac{1}{4}$
$\overline{\qquad 12\frac{1}{4}}$

2. Tom is $56\frac{1}{4}$ inches tall, and his father is $68\frac{1}{2}$ inches tall. What is the difference in their heights?

3. Tell how these examples were worked:

$11\frac{1}{4} = 11\frac{3}{12}$
$11\frac{1}{12} = 11\frac{1}{12}$
$\overline{\qquad \frac{2}{12} = \frac{1}{6}}$

$18\frac{3}{5} = 18\frac{6}{10}$
$5\frac{1}{10} = 5\frac{1}{10}$
$\overline{\quad 13\frac{5}{10} = 13\frac{1}{2}}$

$15\frac{5}{6} = 15\frac{5}{6}$
$8\frac{1}{3} = 8\frac{2}{6}$
$\overline{\quad 7\frac{3}{6} = 7\frac{1}{2}}$

4. In the running broad jump Tom jumped $10\frac{3}{4}$ feet. Joe jumped $9\frac{1}{2}$ feet. How much farther did Tom jump than Joe?

5. Jim ran the 50-yard dash in $8\frac{4}{5}$ seconds, and Bill ran it in $8\frac{2}{5}$ seconds. Which boy ran faster and how much faster?

6. Subtract. If any of your answers are not in lowest terms, change them to lowest terms.

(a)	(b)	(c)	(d)	(e)	(f)	(g)	(h)	(i)
$10\frac{3}{5}$	$14\frac{1}{2}$	$15\frac{1}{2}$	$8\frac{5}{6}$	$8\frac{7}{12}$	$9\frac{3}{4}$	$8\frac{5}{6}$	$17\frac{11}{12}$	$9\frac{5}{7}$
$6\frac{2}{5}$	$2\frac{3}{8}$	$6\frac{1}{10}$	$4\frac{1}{6}$	$6\frac{1}{2}$	$5\frac{1}{2}$	$3\frac{1}{2}$	$6\frac{1}{6}$	$1\frac{1}{3}$

Subtracting Mixed Numbers

To subtract mixed numbers, we subtract the parts first. Then we subtract the whole numbers. We carry back a whole and use it with the fraction when we need it.

After we change the fractions to parts of the same size, we notice that we cannot take $\frac{3}{6}$ from $\frac{2}{6}$. We use 1 of the 7 wholes with the $\frac{2}{6}$. $1 = \frac{6}{6}$; so $7\frac{2}{6} = 6\frac{8}{6}$. Now we take $\frac{3}{6}$ from $\frac{8}{6}$, and we take 2 from 6.
The answer is $4\frac{5}{6}$.

$$7\frac{1}{3} = 7\frac{2}{6} = 6\frac{8}{6}$$
$$2\frac{1}{2} = 2\frac{3}{6} = 2\frac{3}{6}$$
$$\overline{\qquad\qquad\qquad 4\frac{5}{6}}$$

1. Some of the pupils in the fifth grade wish to find how much each one gained in weight during the past year. Each pupil's weight now and his weight a year ago are shown in the chart below. Find how much each pupil gained in weight.

Name	Weight One Year Ago	Weight Now	Gain in Pounds
Betty W.	$99\frac{3}{4}$	114	
Anna G.	$65\frac{1}{16}$	$72\frac{1}{4}$	
William B.	$86\frac{3}{4}$	$90\frac{1}{2}$	
Raymond A.	$54\frac{3}{4}$	$61\frac{7}{16}$	

2. Copy and subtract:

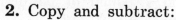

(a)	(b)	(c)	(d)	(e)	(f)
$12\frac{1}{2}$	$7\frac{1}{6}$	$8\frac{3}{4}$	$15\frac{1}{3}$	$10\frac{1}{4}$	12
$5\frac{2}{3}$	$4\frac{1}{3}$	$6\frac{7}{8}$	$8\frac{1}{2}$	$6\frac{1}{3}$	$6\frac{7}{8}$

Adding Three Mixed Numbers

Study these examples. Tell how they were added:

$5\frac{1}{2} = 5\frac{3}{6}$

$3\frac{2}{3} = 3\frac{4}{6}$

$4\frac{1}{6} = 4\frac{1}{6}$

$12\frac{8}{6} = 13\frac{2}{6} = 13\frac{1}{3}$

$6\frac{1}{2} = 6\frac{6}{12}$

$8\frac{1}{3} = 8\frac{4}{12}$

$4\frac{1}{4} = 4\frac{3}{12}$

$18\frac{13}{12} = 19\frac{1}{12}$

$7\frac{1}{2} = 7\frac{12}{24}$

$4\frac{1}{3} = 4\frac{8}{24}$

$3\frac{1}{8} = 3\frac{3}{24}$

$14\frac{23}{24}$

Copy and add:

	(a)	(b)	(c)	(d)	(e)	(f)	(g)	(h)	(i)
1.	$8\frac{1}{3}$	$4\frac{1}{8}$	$6\frac{1}{4}$	$5\frac{1}{3}$	$5\frac{1}{4}$	$1\frac{1}{4}$	$6\frac{1}{3}$	$8\frac{1}{2}$	$3\frac{1}{6}$
	$2\frac{5}{6}$	$2\frac{5}{8}$	$2\frac{1}{2}$	$2\frac{1}{6}$	$\frac{1}{3}$	$3\frac{5}{6}$	$5\frac{5}{12}$	$11\frac{1}{3}$	$4\frac{1}{8}$
	$7\frac{5}{6}$	$6\frac{7}{8}$	8	$5\frac{1}{2}$	$2\frac{1}{6}$	$6\frac{2}{3}$	$7\frac{1}{6}$	$20\frac{3}{4}$	$5\frac{1}{3}$
2.	$5\frac{1}{3}$	$4\frac{7}{16}$	$5\frac{1}{3}$	$3\frac{7}{12}$	$4\frac{1}{5}$	$1\frac{5}{6}$	$8\frac{1}{4}$	$2\frac{2}{9}$	$8\frac{1}{3}$
	$2\frac{1}{4}$	$3\frac{5}{8}$	$2\frac{3}{4}$	$4\frac{1}{3}$	$6\frac{1}{2}$	$7\frac{3}{4}$	$9\frac{3}{4}$	$3\frac{1}{3}$	$1\frac{2}{5}$
	$4\frac{1}{6}$	$2\frac{1}{4}$	$6\frac{5}{6}$	$3\frac{3}{4}$	$5\frac{7}{10}$	$3\frac{5}{12}$	$4\frac{3}{4}$	$12\frac{1}{9}$	$3\frac{1}{3}$

3. Jack caught a fish that weighed 2 pounds. Jim caught a fish that weighed $2\frac{1}{2}$ pounds. Joe caught a fish that weighed $1\frac{3}{4}$ pounds. How much do the 3 fish weigh?

4. Our troop of Boy Scouts took a long hike. We walked $3\frac{1}{2}$ miles the first hour, $3\frac{3}{8}$ miles the second hour, and $2\frac{3}{4}$ miles the third hour. How far did we walk in the three hours?

5. Mrs. Walters measured $3\frac{1}{4}$ pounds of brown sugar, $2\frac{3}{4}$ pounds of white sugar, and $\frac{5}{8}$ pound of powdered sugar. How many pounds of sugar was that?

6. Tom worked after school for these periods of time: $2\frac{1}{2}$ hours, $3\frac{2}{3}$ hours, and $6\frac{1}{4}$ hours. How long did he work altogether?

Problems

1. The F. A. S. Club girls made $7\frac{1}{2}$ pounds of fudge and $3\frac{3}{4}$ pounds of taffy for the candy sale. How many pounds of candy did they make?

2. They used $\frac{3}{4}$ of a pound of pecans, $\frac{3}{4}$ of a pound of walnuts, and $\frac{1}{2}$ of a pound of hickory nuts. Did they use more or less than 1 pound of nuts? How much more than a pound did they use?

3. They need $8\frac{2}{3}$ yards of curtain material for one window of their club room. For another window they need $8\frac{2}{3}$ yards of curtain material, and for the third window they need $9\frac{1}{4}$ yards. If they buy 28 yards of curtain material, will they have enough for the 3 windows?

Find the answers:

	(a)	(b)	(c)	(d)	(e)
4.	$3\frac{3}{4} + 6\frac{1}{8}$	$5\frac{7}{8} - 3\frac{1}{8}$	$12 - 8\frac{1}{3}$	$4 + 6\frac{2}{3}$	$5\frac{1}{5} - 1\frac{2}{3}$
5.	$8\frac{2}{5} - 5\frac{3}{5}$	$5\frac{1}{6} + 8\frac{1}{4}$	$7\frac{1}{4} - 6\frac{1}{2}$	$5\frac{2}{3} + 4\frac{1}{4}$	$6\frac{1}{7} - 2\frac{1}{2}$
6.	$8\frac{1}{2} - 6\frac{3}{4}$	$4\frac{7}{8} + 5\frac{1}{2}$	$10 - 5\frac{2}{3}$	$8\frac{3}{8} - 5\frac{7}{16}$	$7\frac{3}{4} - 5\frac{1}{3}$

A Test on Fractions

1. In a fraction the figure which tells the number of parts is written _____ the line and is called the _____.

2. In a fraction the figure which tells the size of each part is written _____ the line and is called the _____.

3. What figure in each of these fractions shows the size of the part? the number of parts?

a. $\frac{5}{8}$ of a cake   c. $\frac{1}{2}$ of a pound
b. $\frac{3}{4}$ of an inch   d. $\frac{1}{8}$ of a circle

4. Before we can add or subtract parts, the parts must be the _____ size.

5. Is the piece of paper divided into halves, thirds, or fourths?

6. What addition does Picture A show?

Picture A   Picture B

7. What subtraction does Picture B show?

8. When we add mixed numbers, we add the _____ first. Then we add the _____ numbers. When the sum of the fractions is 1 or more, we write the fraction and _____ the whole number.

9. Terry weighs $87\frac{1}{2}$ pounds with his overcoat off and $94\frac{1}{2}$ pounds with his overcoat on. His overcoat weighs _____ pounds.

10. Sue weighed $79\frac{3}{4}$ pounds at the beginning of her vacation and $83\frac{1}{2}$ pounds when her vacation was over. She gained _____ pounds during her vacation.

Test: Adding and Subtracting Fractions

Add	Study	Practice				
$\frac{2}{5}$ $\frac{2}{3}$ $\frac{1}{5}$ $\frac{1}{3}$	$\frac{2}{9}$ $\frac{1}{4}$ $\frac{2}{9}$ $\frac{3}{4}$ $\frac{4}{9}$ $\frac{4}{4}=1$	$\frac{1}{3}$ $\frac{1}{3}$	$\frac{5}{6}$ $\frac{1}{6}$	$\frac{1}{8}$ $\frac{3}{8}$	$2\frac{1}{2}$ $5\frac{1}{2}$	$4\frac{1}{8}$ $6\frac{3}{8}$
$\frac{1}{4}$ $\frac{1}{3}$ $\frac{1}{2}$ $\frac{1}{6}$	$\frac{1}{2}=\frac{4}{8}$ $\frac{7}{8}=\frac{7}{8}$ $\frac{11}{8}=1\frac{3}{8}$	$\frac{2}{3}$ $\frac{1}{6}$	$\frac{3}{4}$ $\frac{1}{8}$	$\frac{1}{2}$ $\frac{7}{8}$	$5\frac{1}{4}$ $3\frac{7}{8}$	$5\frac{2}{3}$ $3\frac{5}{6}$
$\frac{1}{4}$ $\frac{1}{2}$ $\frac{1}{3}$ $\frac{1}{3}$	$\frac{1}{4}=\frac{3}{12}$ $\frac{2}{3}=\frac{8}{12}$ $\frac{11}{12}$	$\frac{1}{2}$ $\frac{1}{5}$	$\frac{2}{3}$ $\frac{3}{8}$	$\frac{3}{4}$ $\frac{2}{3}$	$6\frac{1}{4}$ $4\frac{2}{3}$	$1\frac{1}{6}$ $4\frac{1}{4}$

Subtract	Study	Practice				
$\frac{5}{6}$ $\frac{5}{9}$ $\frac{1}{6}$ $\frac{4}{9}$	$\frac{7}{8}$ $\frac{1}{8}$ $\frac{6}{8}=\frac{3}{4}$	$\frac{3}{4}$ $\frac{1}{4}$	$\frac{7}{8}$ $\frac{3}{8}$	$\frac{7}{12}$ $\frac{5}{12}$	$6\frac{3}{8}$ $4\frac{1}{8}$	$7\frac{5}{16}$ $2\frac{1}{16}$
$\frac{7}{8}$ $\frac{3}{4}$ $\frac{1}{4}$ $\frac{1}{2}$	$\frac{7}{8}=\frac{7}{8}$ $\frac{1}{2}=\frac{4}{8}$ $\frac{3}{8}$	$\frac{5}{6}$ $\frac{1}{2}$	$\frac{5}{8}$ $\frac{1}{4}$	$\frac{2}{3}$ $\frac{7}{12}$	$9\frac{7}{16}$ $1\frac{1}{8}$	$3\frac{7}{10}$ $1\frac{1}{2}$
$\frac{3}{4}$ $\frac{3}{4}$ $\frac{2}{3}$ $\frac{1}{6}$	$\frac{2}{3}=\frac{8}{12}$ $\frac{1}{4}=\frac{3}{12}$ $\frac{5}{12}$	$\frac{2}{3}$ $\frac{1}{4}$	$\frac{1}{2}$ $\frac{1}{3}$	$\frac{2}{3}$ $\frac{5}{8}$	$8\frac{2}{3}$ $5\frac{1}{2}$	$4\frac{7}{8}$ $3\frac{1}{3}$

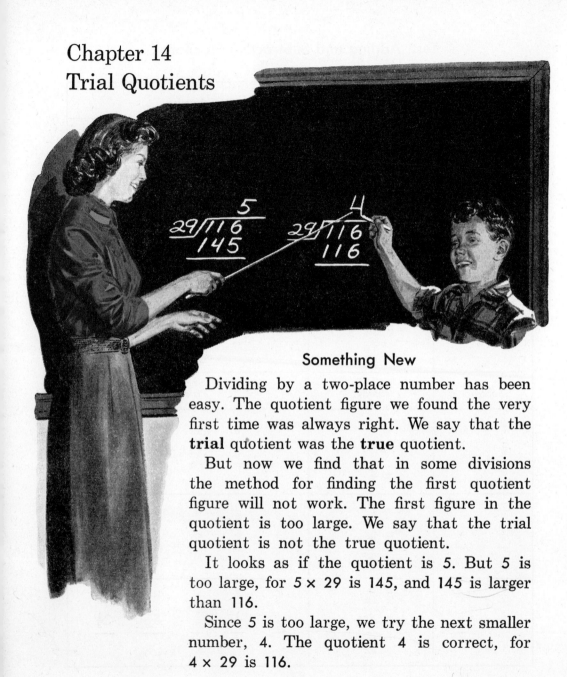

Chapter 14
Trial Quotients

Something New

Dividing by a two-place number has been easy. The quotient figure we found the very first time was always right. We say that the **trial** quotient was the **true** quotient.

But now we find that in some divisions the method for finding the first quotient figure will not work. The first figure in the quotient is too large. We say that the trial quotient is not the true quotient.

It looks as if the quotient is 5. But 5 is too large, for 5 × 29 is 145, and 145 is larger than 116.

Since 5 is too large, we try the next smaller number, 4. The quotient 4 is correct, for 4 × 29 is 116.

True Quotient Answers

In this example we wish to find how many 76's are in 4788. To divide, we think of the 7 (tens) as 7, and think, "Sevens in 47, 6." We write 6 in its proper place and multiply. We notice the product, 456, and see that it is less than 478; so we subtract. We now notice the remainder, 22, and see that it is less than the divisor, 76. So we bring down the next figure.

```
      6
76)4788
   456
    22
```

Again we think of the 7 (tens) as 7, and think, "Sevens in 22, 3." We write 3 in the answer and multiply. We notice the product, 228, and see that it is the same as the 228 above it. There is no remainder and there is nothing to bring down; so we have finished the example.

```
      63
76)4788
   456
   228
   228
```

At the beginning of the example when we think, "Sevens in 47, 6," we write 6 and **try it** to see if it is correct. We multiply and notice that the product is less than the number above it. We are now almost sure, but not quite, that 6 is the true quotient answer. We subtract and notice that the remainder is less than the divisor. We are now sure that 6 is the true quotient answer. We bring down the next figure and try for an answer here.

We think, "Sevens in 22, 3," and we try 3 as a quotient answer. We multiply and notice that the product is the same as the number above it. This makes us sure that the trial answer is also the true answer.

Remember: The product, if it is not the same as the number above it, must be less. The remainder, if there is one, must be less than the divisor.

Trial Quotient Answers

When we divide by tens and ones, it often happens that the trial quotient answer does not turn out to be the true quotient answer. When this happens, we have to keep on trying other answers until we find the true answer.

$$76)\overline{4940} \atop \begin{array}{r} 7 \\ \hline 4940 \\ 532 \end{array}$$

In this example we wish to find how many 76's there are in 4940. To divide, we think of the 7 (tens) as 7, and think, "Sevens in 49, 7." We write 7 in its proper place and multiply. After we multiply, we notice that the product, 532, is greater than the number, 494, above it. This makes us certain that our **trial** answer is not the **true** answer. Our trial quotient is too large. So we erase and try the next smaller number, 6, as a quotient answer.

$$\begin{array}{r} 6 \\ 76)\overline{4940} \\ 456 \\ \hline 38 \end{array}$$

We try 6 by multiplying, and we notice that the product, 456, is less than the number, 494, above it. We are almost sure that 6 is the true quotient answer, but not quite. We subtract and notice that the remainder, 38, is less than the divisor, 76. We are now sure that 6 is the true quotient answer; so we bring down the next number.

$$\begin{array}{r} 65 \\ 76)\overline{4940} \\ 456 \\ \hline 380 \\ 380 \end{array}$$

Again we think of 7 (tens) as 7, and think, "Sevens in 38, 5." We try 5 by multiplying, and we notice that the product, 380, is the same as the number, 380, above it. This makes us sure that 5 is the true quotient.

Check

$$\begin{array}{r} 76 \\ 65 \\ \hline 380 \\ 456 \\ \hline 4940 \end{array}$$

If we wish, we can check our answer by multiplying 76 by 65.

258

Testing Trial Quotients

1. Last summer Billy visited his grandfather on the farm. He helped pick the strawberries. His grandfather said, "We have now picked 168 quarts. A crate holds 24 quarts. Will you get the crates ready?"

How many crates should Billy get ready?

Trial Quotient	Too Large	True Quotient
8	8	7
24)168	24)168	24)168
	192 ☞	168 ☞

2. "You certainly sell a lot of berries," said Billy.

"Yes," answered his grandfather. "Last year we sold 1728 quarts. How many crates was that?"

Trial Quotient	Too Large	Not Too Large	True Quotient
8	8	7	7
24)1728	24)1728	24)1728	24)1728
	192 ☞	168 ☞	168
			4 ☞

3. "So far this year we have sold 1248 quarts," continued his grandfather. "That's over 50 crates."

How many crates will 1248 quart boxes fill?

Trial Quotient	Too Large	Not Too Large	True Quotient
6	6	5	5
24)1248	24)1248	24)1248	24)1248
	144 ☞	120 ☞	120
			4 ☞

Trial Quotient Answers

Are the trial answers the true answers?

1.
$$\begin{array}{r} 5 \\ 12\overline{)516} \\ \underline{60} \rightarrow \textit{too large} \end{array}$$

No. Why?

2.
$$\begin{array}{r} 3 \\ 12\overline{)372} \\ \underline{36} \rightarrow \textit{not too large} \\ 1 \rightarrow \textit{not too large} \end{array}$$

Yes. Why?

3.
$$\begin{array}{r} 9 \\ 75\overline{)6525} \\ \underline{675} \rightarrow \times \end{array}$$
$$\begin{array}{r} 8 \\ 75\overline{)6525} \\ 600 \rightarrow \checkmark \\ \underline{52} \rightarrow \checkmark \end{array}$$

Check these **trial** answers to tell which ones are **true**:

	(a)	(b)	(c)	(d)	(e)
4.	4 $54\overline{)2106}$	6 $45\overline{)2565}$	7 $24\overline{)1512}$	8 $23\overline{)1725}$	5 $97\overline{)4733}$
5.	7 $37\overline{)2331}$	5 $34\overline{)1768}$	4 $43\overline{)1978}$	2 $46\overline{)1058}$	8 $36\overline{)2586}$
6.	6 $43\overline{)2494}$	3 $44\overline{)1496}$	3 $51\overline{)1887}$	5 $57\overline{)2565}$	4 $55\overline{)2420}$
7.	2 $62\overline{)1488}$	9 $68\overline{)5644}$	4 $71\overline{)3266}$	7 $75\overline{)5025}$	8 $39\overline{)2613}$
8.	3 $72\overline{)2592}$	8 $74\overline{)5772}$	4 $92\overline{)3956}$	2 $91\overline{)2366}$	4 $97\overline{)4462}$
9.	2 $81\overline{)2187}$	7 $87\overline{)5829}$	7 $41\overline{)3157}$	5 $55\overline{)2530}$	7 $49\overline{)2891}$
10.	8 $43\overline{)3569}$	7 $53\overline{)3551}$	7 $63\overline{)4284}$	6 $68\overline{)3740}$	8 $83\overline{)6557}$
11.	8 $69\overline{)5074}$	4 $74\overline{)3034}$	6 $87\overline{)5394}$	9 $62\overline{)5828}$	5 $25\overline{)1125}$

Copy each example above and complete the division.

Trial Quotient Answers

Let us try another example. Suppose we wish to find how many 48's there are in 2736, or to find $\frac{1}{48}$ of 2736.

We think of the 4 (tens) as 4, and think, "Fours in 27, 6." We try 6 as a quotient answer by multiplying, and we notice that the product, 288, is greater than the number above it. This makes us certain that 6 is not the true answer. We erase and try the next smaller number, 5, as a quotient answer.

```
       6
48) 2736
    288
```

We try 5 by multiplying, and we notice that the product is less than the number above it. But we cannot be entirely sure of 5 until we subtract and notice that the remainder is less than the divisor. When we do that, we are sure that 5 is the true quotient answer. We bring down the next figure.

```
       5
48) 2736
    240
     33
```

We think of the 4 (tens) as 4, and think, "Fours in 33, 8." We try 8 by multiplying, and we see that the product is greater than the number above it. This makes us certain that 8 is not the true answer. We erase and try the next smaller number, 7, as a quotient answer.

```
      58
48) 2736
    240
    336
    384
```

We try 7 by multiplying, and we see that the product is the same as the number above it. This makes us sure that 7 is the true quotient answer.

```
      57
48) 2736
    240
    336
    336
```

There is no remainder, and there is nothing to bring down; so our example is finished. We can check our answer by multiplying 48 by 57.

261

Mental Trials

In the exercises that we have been working, we have been making our trials by actually working them out on paper. This causes us a lot of extra work in writing and in erasing. Let us see how such trials can be made mentally and without so much pencil work and erasing.

$$\begin{array}{r} 6 \\ 76\overline{)4788} \quad 456 \end{array}$$

We think of the 7 (tens) as 7, and think, "Sevens in 47, 6." Before writing 6, suppose we multiply in our heads: Six 6's are 36. Six 7's are 42, and 3 carried are 45. Our last product, 45, is less than 47; so we can be reasonably sure that 6 is the true quotient. If we cannot multiply mentally, we can write the trial answer and the product at the side of the example or on a separate piece of paper.

We can now write 6 in its proper place, multiply, notice the product, subtract, notice the remainder, and bring down the next figure.

$$\begin{array}{r} 7 \qquad 6 \\ 76\overline{)4940} \quad 532 \quad 456 \end{array}$$

In this example we think of the 7 (tens) as 7, and think, "Sevens in 49, 7." At the side of our example, on a piece of paper, or in our heads, we find the trial quotient and the product. Since 532 is more than 494, we know that our trial quotient is too large. We try the next smaller number, 6. Since 456 is less than 494, we write 6 in the answer, multiply, notice the product, subtract, and notice the remainder. Now we are sure that 6 is the true quotient. So we bring down the next figure.

This is how an example might look with the trial work at the side.

$$57$$
$$48\overline{)2736}$$
$$240$$
$$\overline{336}$$
$$336$$

6	5
288	240
8	7
384	336

This is how the same example might look when the trial work is done on another piece of paper or in our heads.

$$57$$
$$48\overline{)2736}$$
$$240$$
$$\overline{336}$$
$$336$$

The trial answer is not the true answer. Here is the way we find the true answer:

Trial 1

$$3$$
$$16\overline{)368}$$
$$48$$

Trial 2

$$2$$
$$16\overline{)368}$$
$$32$$
$$\overline{4}$$

Trial 1

$$24$$
$$16\overline{)368}$$
$$32$$
$$\overline{48}$$
$$64$$

Trial 2

$$23$$
$$16\overline{)368}$$
$$32$$
$$\overline{48}$$
$$48$$

The true answers are given. Complete the division.

1.
$$32$$
$$15\overline{)480}$$
$$45$$
$$\overline{30}$$

2.
$$57$$
$$24\overline{)1368}$$
$$120$$
$$\overline{168}$$

3.
$$36$$
$$24\overline{)864}$$
$$72$$
$$\overline{144}$$

4.
$$18$$
$$34\overline{)612}$$
$$34$$
$$\overline{272}$$

5.
$$18$$
$$45\overline{)810}$$
$$45$$

6.
$$24$$
$$13\overline{)312}$$
$$26$$

7.
$$36$$
$$36\overline{)1296}$$
$$108$$

8.
$$34$$
$$25\overline{)850}$$
$$75$$

9.
$$28$$
$$58\overline{)1624}$$

10.
$$28$$
$$46\overline{)1288}$$

11.
$$14$$
$$29\overline{)406}$$

12.
$$25$$
$$48\overline{)1200}$$

13.
$$34$$
$$14\overline{)476}$$

14.
$$23$$
$$15\overline{)345}$$

15.
$$34$$
$$13\overline{)442}$$

16.
$$48$$
$$26\overline{)1248}$$

Other Trial Quotient Answers

Sometimes we have to try more than one trial quotient before we can find the true one.

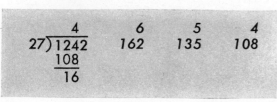

We think of the 2 (tens) as 2, and think, "Twos in 12, 6." We try 6 by multiplying, and we notice the product. Next we try 5 in the same way. But 5 is too large. So we try 4. We write 4 in the answer, multiply, notice the product, subtract, notice the remainder, and bring down the next figure.

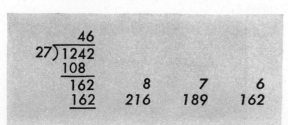

We think of the 2 (tens) as 2, and think, "Twos in 16, 8." We try 8 by multiplying, and we notice the product. Next we try 7. Then we try 6 in the same way. We write 6 in the answer, multiply, and notice the product.

In dividing by a two-place number, we think of the tens as ones and divide. We try the trial quotient by multiplying. If the product is larger than the number above it, we try the next smaller number as a quotient. We keep on trying the next smaller number until we get the true quotient answer. A quotient answer is the true one: (1) If, when we multiply the divisor by the trial quotient, the product is less than or the same as the number above it in the dividend; and (2) if, when we subtract, the remainder is less than the divisor.

Other Trial Quotient Answers

Notice, first, there are no 28's in 24. Then the question is "How many 28's in 243." Think of the 2 (tens) as 2, and think: "Twos in twenty-four." Of course,

$$28\overline{)2436} \quad \overset{9}{252}$$

the answer is 12. Since 9 is the largest quotient answer we can use at any one time, **do not try** 12, **then** 11, **then** 10. Use 9 as the first trial answer. In this case 9 is not the true answer, but 8 is.

Notice here there are no 17's in 15. Then the question is "How many 17's in 158." Think of the 1 (ten) as 1, and think, "Ones in fifteen." Since that answer is

$$17\overline{)1581} \quad \overset{9}{153}$$

larger than 9, use 9 as the first trial answer. In this case, 9 proves to be the true answer.

Never use a number larger than 9 as the first trial quotient answer.

1. A store has 58 employees. The weekly payroll is $5220. What is the average weekly salary?

2. A farmer planted 864 young apple trees in his orchard. He put 24 trees in each row. How many rows of apple trees did he plant?

Divide and check. **Remember: A trial quotient cannot be larger than 9.**

	(a)	(b)	(c)	(d)	(e)	(f)
3.	$15\overline{)135}$	$14\overline{)112}$	$13\overline{)117}$	$12\overline{)108}$	$15\overline{)105}$	$18\overline{)162}$
4.	$16\overline{)128}$	$19\overline{)114}$	$17\overline{)102}$	$18\overline{)144}$	$16\overline{)144}$	$18\overline{)126}$
5.	$19\overline{)171}$	$17\overline{)119}$	$16\overline{)112}$	$17\overline{)136}$	$24\overline{)216}$	$28\overline{)224}$

Exercises

Tell the number we should use as the first trial answer in each of the following examples. Tell why. Find the first true answer in the first example in each row.

	(a)	(b)	(c)	(d)	(e)
1.	15)1455	28)2604	36)3096	47)4183	18)1728
2.	25)2175	36)3456	47)4606	17)1581	29)2262
3.	37)3219	48)4707	16)1264	27)2538	37)3626
4.	48)4224	13)1027	26)2548	38)3002	49)4459
5.	17)1343	24)2352	38)3344	49)4263	14)1196
6.	23)2208	38)3686	52)5096	19)1653	27)2403
7.	42)4085	53)5247	18)1404	26)2548	44)4224
8.	56)5544	17)1275	33)3069	45)4005	57)5073
9.	16)1200	35)3255	46)4462	58)5104	58)5626
10.	72)7056	85)8075	59)5664	73)7081	86)8084

11. During an election campaign, a senator traveled 7328 miles in 32 days. How many miles did he average each day?

A Test

Copy the exercises in columns on your paper. Check (√) the trial quotient answers that are also the true quotient answers. Cross (✕) the trial quotient answers that are not the true ones.

$$\overset{6√}{32\overline{)2048}} \qquad \overset{7✕}{44\overline{)2948}} \qquad \overset{4✕}{53\overline{)2862}} \qquad \overset{7√}{67\overline{)4757}}$$

Find out which ones to check (√) and which ones to cross (✕) in this way:

$$\begin{array}{r} 6 \\ 32\overline{)2048} \\ 192√ \\ \hline 12√ \end{array} \qquad \begin{array}{r} 7 \\ 44\overline{)2948} \\ 308✕ \\ \hline \end{array} \qquad \begin{array}{r} 4 \\ 53\overline{)2862} \\ 212√ \\ \hline 74✕ \end{array} \qquad \begin{array}{r} 7 \\ 67\overline{)4757} \\ 469√ \\ \hline 6√ \end{array}$$

You do not need to finish working the examples.

	(a)	(b)	(c)	(d)	(e)
1.	$\overset{2}{14\overline{)294}}$	$\overset{3}{16\overline{)384}}$	$\overset{2}{13\overline{)299}}$	$\overset{7}{22\overline{)1584}}$	$\overset{9}{27\overline{)2349}}$
2.	$\overset{4}{24\overline{)984}}$	$\overset{6}{25\overline{)1375}}$	$\overset{8}{32\overline{)2592}}$	$\overset{7}{33\overline{)2376}}$	$\overset{9}{19\overline{)1444}}$
3.	$\overset{5}{46\overline{)2392}}$	$\overset{8}{46\overline{)3542}}$	$\overset{8}{44\overline{)3564}}$	$\overset{4}{57\overline{)2223}}$	$\overset{6}{38\overline{)1862}}$
4.	$\overset{4}{53\overline{)2226}}$	$\overset{4}{56\overline{)2408}}$	$\overset{7}{69\overline{)4692}}$	$\overset{7}{64\overline{)4672}}$	$\overset{9}{49\overline{)4320}}$
5.	$\overset{7}{63\overline{)4662}}$	$\overset{2}{77\overline{)2002}}$	$\overset{3}{78\overline{)2262}}$	$\overset{3}{71\overline{)2272}}$	$\overset{3}{52\overline{)1820}}$
6.	$\overset{5}{84\overline{)4284}}$	$\overset{7}{85\overline{)5695}}$	$\overset{8}{83\overline{)6889}}$	$\overset{4}{94\overline{)4042}}$	$\overset{7}{66\overline{)4686}}$
7.	$\overset{4}{97\overline{)4074}}$	$\overset{7}{94\overline{)6486}}$	$\overset{5}{63\overline{)3591}}$	$\overset{9}{47\overline{)3901}}$	$\overset{4}{74\overline{)3182}}$

A Mistake to Avoid

Sometimes in **trying** quotient answers, we make a mistake in multiplying. We think our trial quotient is wrong, and we try another answer. How can we tell when we make a mistake? Let us see.

```
      7        9      8      7
34)2788      306   (282)   238
   238               ?
```

In dividing 2788 by 34, we notice that there are no 34's in 27. Our first question is "How many 34's in 278?" We think of the 3 (tens) as 3, and think, "Threes in twenty-seven, nine." We try 9 by multiplying, as shown at the side of the example. Since 9 is too large, we try 8 by multiplying. Suppose we make a mistake in multiplying by 8, or for some other reason we try 7 by multiplying. Our product is 238. Since 238 is **less than the number above it**, we have some reason to think that 7 is the true quotient answer. But our trial is not complete until we subtract. Let us subtract, and then let us examine our work closely.

```
      7
34)2788
   238
    40
```

```
      8
34)2788
   272
     6
```

Look at the remainder. It is **greater** than the divisor, not **less**, as it should be; so we know that 7 is the wrong quotient answer. We must try a higher number than 7. We try 8, and this time we multiply carefully and correctly. Our product, 272, is less than the number above it. We subtract and notice that the remainder is less than the divisor. We now know that 8 is the true quotient answer; so we bring down the next figure and go ahead.

268

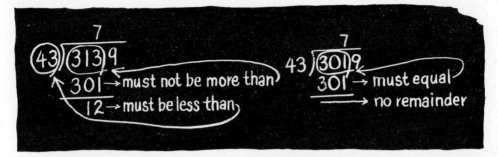

How to Try a Quotient Answer

1. Multiply the divisor by the trial quotient.
2. Notice the product.
   a. If the product is larger than the number above it, try the next smaller number as a quotient answer, and so on.
   b. If the product is the same as the number above it, the trial answer is the true answer.
3. Subtract.
4. Notice the remainder.
   a. If the remainder is larger than the divisor, the trial quotient answer is too small. Try the next larger number as a quotient answer.
   b. If there is no remainder, the trial answer is the true answer.
   c. If the remainder is less than the divisor, the trial answer is the true answer.

Summary

Notice the product and the remainder.
The product must be the same as the number divided and with no remainder, or the product must be less than the number divided and with a remainder which is less than the divisor.

Chapter 15
Trial Quotients in Division

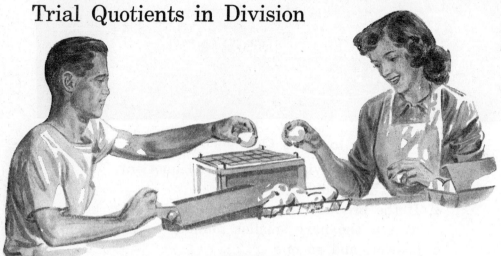

Dividing by Tens

1. During the month of April, Mr. Easton, the poultryman, packed 15,480 eggs for sale. Since there are 12 in a dozen, how many dozen eggs did he pack?

2. Mr. Easton packed 1290 dozen eggs in crates. In each crate he put 30 dozen eggs. How many crates did he pack?

Study the way Jim worked each of the above problems.

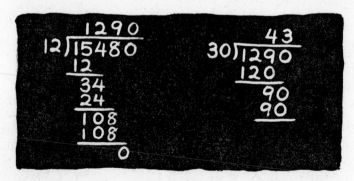

3. John had 1104 pennies saved that he wanted to put into rolls of 50 each before he took them to the bank. How many rolls of 50 pennies could he make? How many pennies would he have left over?

4. John had saved his nickels, too. He had 527 nickels. He put them into rolls of 40 each. How many rolls of 40 nickels did he have? Did he have any nickels left over? If so, how many?

5. John's brother Peter had saved dimes for a year. He had 785 dimes. He put them in rolls of 50 each. How many rolls of 50 dimes did he have? Were there any dimes left over? How many?

Keep an eye on the figure in ten's place in the divisor. Use it to find the trial quotient. Divide by tens and ones the way you divide by ones.

Copy and divide:

	(a)	(b)	(c)	(d)	(e)
6.	84⟌4536	21⟌1092	44⟌1056	61⟌4087	73⟌4015
7.	85⟌1020	42⟌1176	54⟌1458	71⟌6745	83⟌7553
8.	95⟌3515	43⟌2752	55⟌3960	72⟌3312	84⟌5460
9.	22⟌1386	37⟌1184	61⟌4575	73⟌3212	85⟌1955
✦ 10.	48⟌1488	45⟌3195	62⟌1364	74⟌6956	91⟌5915
11.	43⟌2365	55⟌4455	72⟌4032	84⟌6384	75⟌4575
12.	23⟌989	44⟌2376	61⟌5063	73⟌3312	85⟌2890
13.	32⟌1152	45⟌2385	62⟌2108	74⟌6142	91⟌6916
14.	33⟌2673	51⟌3978	63⟌3969	95⟌2945	76⟌3344

Dividing by Tens and Ones

1. Mr. West says that his car averages about 14 miles to a gallon of gasoline. Yesterday he drove his car 42 miles. About how many gallons of gasoline did he use?

First Trial

$$\begin{array}{r} 4 \\ 14\overline{)42} \\ 56 \end{array}$$

Second Trial

$$\begin{array}{r} 3 \\ 14\overline{)42} \\ 42 \end{array}$$

Check

$$\begin{array}{r} 14 \\ \underline{3} \\ 42 \end{array}$$

To answer the question that the problem asks, we divide 42 by 14.

We think, "How many 14's are in 42? There are about as many 14's in 42 as there are 1's in 4." We write 4 in our answer.

We try 4. We call it the trial quotient. We multiply 14 by 4 and get 56. We write 56 under 42. Now we compare 56 and 42. We see that 56 is larger than 42; so we know the trial quotient, 4, is too large.

We try 3. We multiply 14 by 3 and get 42. We see that 42 is not too large; so we know that 3 is the true quotient.

Mr. West used about 3 gallons of gasoline.

Sometimes when we divide, the first number that we try in the answer is too large. When this happens, we try the next smaller number.

---

2. Tell which trial quotients below are too large:

A	B	C	D	E
$\begin{array}{r} 5 \\ 13\overline{)52} \\ 65 \end{array}$	$\begin{array}{r} 6 \\ 15\overline{)60} \\ 90 \end{array}$	$\begin{array}{r} 4 \\ 23\overline{)96} \\ 92 \end{array}$	$\begin{array}{r} 5 \\ 14\overline{)56} \\ 70 \end{array}$	$\begin{array}{r} 4 \\ 13\overline{)42} \\ 52 \end{array}$

3. Jane has 150 pieces of candy to pack in boxes. She can pack 25 pieces in each box. How many boxes will she fill with candy?

4. Jim needs a car to drive to and from work. He can pay $35 a month on the car. He found a used car for $245. How many months will it take him to pay for the car?

5. Tom and his father sold a load of oats in town yesterday. The oats weighed 1504 pounds. A bushel of oats weighs 32 pounds. How many bushels did they sell?

```
        47
  32)1504
     128
     224
     224
```

6. There are 435 pupils in our school. The fifth-grade children are making programs for the play they are going to give. Each of the 29 pupils in the fifth grade plans to make the same number of programs. How many should each of them make?

7. Jack kept a record of the family car for 28 days. He found that the car was driven 1148 miles. How many miles was that per day on the average?

8. Jim and Joe planned to drive to California. They estimated the distance at about 600 miles. "If we drive day and night, we can make it in 1 day. We have to average only _____ miles per hour, and that's easy."

Copy and divide:

	(a)	(b)	(c)	(d)	(e)
9.	34)918	23)1794	72)2808	65)5460	22)1848
10.	25)1075	34)1292	23)1541	45)2025	34)1632
11.	62)2852	49)1813	81)1296	38)2052	52)4940

Two Trial Answers

1. Betty is planning to make curtains for her room. She finds that she needs 648 inches of curtain material. How many yards does she need? (36 in. = 1 yd.)

FIRST PART		SECOND PART	
First Trial	*Second Trial*	*First Trial*	*Second Trial*

$$
\begin{array}{r}
2 \\
36\overline{)648} \\
72 \\
\end{array}
\qquad
\begin{array}{r}
1 \\
36\overline{)648} \\
36 \\
\hline
28 \\
\end{array}
\qquad
\begin{array}{r}
19 \\
36\overline{)648} \\
36 \\
\hline
288 \\
324 \\
\hline
\end{array}
\qquad
\begin{array}{r}
18 \\
36\overline{)648} \\
36 \\
\hline
288 \\
288 \\
\hline
\end{array}
$$

2. The 36 pupils in our room sold 972 Christmas seals. What was the average number sold by a pupil?

3. There are 650 books in the room, and there are 25 children in the room. What is the average number of books for each pupil?

4. Jim raises rabbits and sells them. He has 512 rabbits in 16 pens. How many rabbits on the average are in each pen?

5. Jack read in the encyclopedia that a fast dog can run 795 feet in 15 seconds. How far is that in 1 second?

6. A milkman delivered 1704 quarts of milk to 24 customers in one month. What was the average number of quarts of milk delivered to each customer?

Copy and divide:

(a)	(b)	(c)	(d)	(e)	(f)

7. $13\overline{)481}$ $44\overline{)3872}$ $65\overline{)4810}$ $48\overline{)2016}$ $27\overline{)675}$ $24\overline{)912}$

8. $57\overline{)2736}$ $48\overline{)2736}$ $34\overline{)1836}$ $45\overline{)3960}$ $74\overline{)4958}$ $33\overline{)957}$

Two or More Trial Quotients

Notice the trial quotients that were tried before the true quotient was found in each example below:

True Quotients	Mental Trials		True Quotients	Mental Trials		
4	6	5	5	8	7	6
16)64	96	80	17)85	136	119	102
64			85			

45	6	5	64	8	7
27)1215	162	135	26)1664	208	182
108			156		
135	6		104	5	
135	162		104	130	

1. The Limited Express travels 1800 miles in 24 hours. How many miles per hour does it go on the average?

2. Mr. Wells has 1015 tulip bulbs. If he plants 29 bulbs in each row, how many full rows will he have?

Copy and divide:

	(a)	(b)	(c)	(d)	(e)
3.	19)437	38)1786	28)1288	35)2730	25)1400
4.	86)4042	25)1850	69)5482	29)174	27)189
5.	48)3744	37)2109	27)1053	16)1008	29)1044

Washington's Birthday

1. Our class is going to make 400 paper hats for the party on Washington's birthday. There are 25 of us in the class. How many hats should each of us make?

2. There are 25 of us to share equally the cost of the party. If the total cost is $8.50, how much should each of us pay as our share?

Copy and divide:

	(a)	(b)	(c)	(d)	(e)
3.	22)1408	38)1064	54)3456	70)4410	19)1368
4.	86)3784	64)4288	23)1679	55)3025	33)1551
5.	71)3479	87)2871	72)5616	24)1968	65)1625
6.	56)2576	72)2736	88)1848	25)2275	94)2444
7.	57)2109	73)1971	89)1068	93)6324	69)4899

The Largest Trial Quotient

1. There are 25 boys in the Bird Club. They have 225 cards for the children in their school to sign. When the children sign the cards, they promise to feed and water the birds during the long winter days. The members of the club decided to divide the cards equally. How many cards should each member take?

We notice there are no 25's in 22; so our first question is "How many 25's are in 225?"

We think, "Twos in 22, 11." But 9 is the largest trial quotient we can use. We try 9.

```
        9
25) 225
    225
```

A trial quotient cannot be larger than 9.

2. The 14 girls in our class want to divide equally 126 tickets to sell. How many should each girl take?

3. Study these examples. Tell how each is worked.

```
       93              98              90              92
23) 2139        37) 3626        17) 1530        28) 2576
    207             333             153             252
     69             296               0              56
     69             296                              56
```

Copy and divide:

	(a)	(b)	(c)	(d)	(e)
4.	23) 2001	28) 812	27) 783	48) 4368	23) 207
5.	59) 531	24) 2016	28) 2548	12) 1188	45) 4050
6.	33) 3036	51) 3672	87) 3045	63) 1008	75) 4275

Practicing Division

Keep an eye on the figure in ten's place in the divisor. Divide by tens and ones the way you would divide by ones.

Copy and divide:

	(a)	(b)	(c)	(d)	(e)
1.	10)9650	42)1176	74)1184	27)702	13)1274
2.	59)1121	91)4459	12)984	44)2024	47)1363
3.	76)5232	29)1334	61)3599	93)2511	75)2400
4.	14)896	46)2944	78)4992	31)1581	26)1248
5.	63)4851	95)9025	16)736	48)3936	89)6408
6.	80)3920	33)2409	65)6175	97)7081	34)1462
7.	18)504	50)2350	82)7216	35)3325	58)5088
8.	67)1876	20)5680	52)4264	84)5544	28)1512
9.	37)1369	69)2829	22)1408	54)3456	36)2268
10.	86)3784	39)741	71)3479	24)1968	94)4042
11.	88)1848	41)779	73)1971	56)2576	62)5828

12. There are 1190 cars parked in 14 rows in the parking lot. How many cars are in each row?

Using Zeros in Division

We know that zero is used to hold a place. In dividing, the zero will often help by **putting each part of the answer in its proper place**.

1. The first question is "How many 65's in 329?" Look at the 6 and at the 32, and think, "Sixes in thirty-two, five." Write 5, multiply, notice the product, subtract, and notice the remainder.

$$\begin{array}{r} 507 \\ 65\overline{)32955} \\ 325 \\ \hline 455 \\ 455 \\ \hline \end{array}$$

Bring down the next figure. 65's in 45? We can see that there are no 65's in 45. We know that we have no number to write in ten's place; so we write 0 in the answer to keep the place. The zero will keep the other parts of the answer in their proper places.

Bring down the next figure. 65's in 455? Look at the 6 and at the 45, and think, "Sixes in forty-five, seven." Write 7, and multiply.

2. The first question is "How many 65's in 370?" Look at the 6 and at the 37, and think, "Sixes in thirty-seven, six." Try 6. Since that is too much, try 5. Multiply, notice the product, subtract, and notice the remainder.

$$\begin{array}{r} 570 \\ 65\overline{)37050} \\ 325 \\ \hline 455 \\ 455 \\ \hline 0 \end{array}$$

Bring down the next figure. 65's in 455? Look at the 6 and at the 45, and think, "Sixes in forty-five, seven." Write 7, and multiply. Notice the product.

Since there is no remainder, bring down the next figure, which is zero. This means that there are no ones to be divided, that the answer is **hundreds** and **tens**, and that there are **no ones** in the answer. Write 0 in the answer to keep the rest of the answer in place.

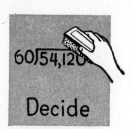

Practicing Division

Copy and divide:

	(a)	(b)	(c)
1.	60)54,120	50)7850	40)2680
2.	80)56,480	80)72,320	90)63,270
3.	26)15,756	34)30,838	41)16,646
4.	59)53,336	67)40,602	75)38,100
5.	91)73,164	95)48,260	86)34,830
6.	65)26,585	57)23,028	44)31,064
7.	65)18,915	57)35,454	44)41,316
8.	28)16,968	16)12,928	25)15,250
9.	28)21,560	16)14,720	25)11,775
10.	17)6460	33)24,156	49)44,737
11.	96)81,120	80)39,520	66)55,490
12.	70)42,280	90)72,540	56)22,904
13.	83)74,783	78)37,744	36)32,544
14.	88)32,648	38)23,142	38)25,042

15. An air pilot flew his plane 2916 miles in 27 hours. What was his average speed per hour?

16. How many busses, each seating 32 passengers, will be needed to take 640 pupils to the fair?

17. Mr. Thomas drove his car 3090 miles in 15 days. How many miles did he drive each day on the average?

280

Dividing Dollars and Cents

In dividing dollars and cents, we work the example as we would work any other example in division.

We place the point (.) in the quotient directly over the point in the dividend, and we write the dollar sign ($) before the first quotient figure.

Be sure to write each part of the answer **in its proper place** and to place the point correctly.

1. Henry's father received $175.50 as wages last month. He worked 26 days last month. How much was his wage each day?

Notice that we divide $175.50 by 26 the way we would divide 17550 by 26. Notice, also, that we are careful to put the point (.) in the answer just over the point (.) in the dividend.

```
        $6.75
26)$175.50
    156
     19 5
     18 2
      1 30
      1 30
```

Copy and divide:

	(a)	(b)	(c)	(d)
2.	15)$83.85	31)$160.89	47)$345.92	17)$163.54
3.	63)$489.51	79)$434.50	95)$907.25	68)$501.16
4.	16)$74.56	32)$200.96	48)$397.44	45)$413.55
5.	64)$554.24	80)$394.40	96)$810.24	39)$204.75
6.	56)$683.20	27)$789.75	72)$224.64 ·	26)$218.66
7.	83)$487.21	52)$294.32	29)$567.53	51)$140.25

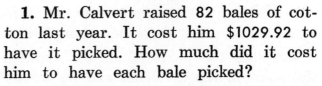

1. Mr. Calvert raised 82 bales of cotton last year. It cost him $1029.92 to have it picked. How much did it cost him to have each bale picked?

2. Mr. Johnson sold 48 bushels of seed corn. He was paid $84.00 for it. How much was Mr. Johnson paid for each bushel of seed corn?

3. Mrs. Jackson sold 79 dozen eggs for $35.55. For each dozen she was paid the same price. How much did she receive for each dozen?

4. The expenses of a football trip were $72.10. There were 14 boys on the trip, and they had agreed to share the expenses equally. What was each boy's share?

5. There were 15 rooms of pupils in the Adams School taking part in a school festival. After all expenses had been paid, it was found that $375 had been made. If each room got an equal share, how much did each room get?

6. A certain girls' club has 45 members. They collect $33.75 each year as dues. How much does each member pay as dues each year?

7. An automobile dealer bought 14 used cars at a total cost of $9450. How much was the cost of each car on the average?

8. The dealer bought 25 sets of seat covers at a total cost of $181.25. How much was the cost of each set of seat covers?

9. Bob earned $78.65 during his summer vacation, which was 13 weeks. How much did he earn each week on the average?

Problems

1. Mr. Henderson grew 456 bushels of wheat on 24 acres of land. How many bushels did he grow on each acre on the average?

2. A farmer had an apple orchard in which 1152 trees were planted in rows of 24 trees each. How many rows of trees are in his orchard?

3. There are 1440 trees in an apple orchard. In each row there are 32 trees. How many rows of trees are there in the orchard?

4. The boys on a 6-man football team weigh 113 lb., 121 lb., 146 lb., 109 lb., 115 lb., and 98 lb. What is the average weight of the boys on the team?

5. The distance by train from Bristol to Memphis is about 555 miles. At the rate of 37 miles an hour, how long will it take a train to make the trip?

6. The Lock family took a long automobile trip on their vacation. They traveled 4875 miles in 25 days. What was the average number of miles they traveled each day?

7. The principal of the Auburn School divided 2584 packages of seeds equally among the 17 classes in the school. How many packages did each class get?

8. Jack and his father loaded a wagon with oats. When it was weighed, they found that there were 1568 pounds on the wagon. If there are 32 pounds to the bushel, how many bushels of oats were on the wagon?

Practicing Division

Keep an eye on the figure in ten's place in the divisor. Divide by tens and ones the way you would divide by ones.

Copy and divide:

	(a)	(b)	(c)	(d)	(e)
1.	26)416	58)1624	90)5580	11)1001	27)2268
2.	43)1591	75)6825	28)1036	60)2280	35)2765
3.	92)3496	13)949	45)2475	77)5621	67)6231
4.	30)2520	62)4278	94)1504	15)1275	48)2640
5.	47)3431	79)4345	32)1984	64)5504	88)6248
6.	96)8064	17)1479	49)4459	81)8019	91)4277
7.	34)2856	66)1254	98)6076	19)361	52)3484
8.	51)4641	83)6391	99)5049	36)1656	16)1520
9.	68)2312	21)1155	53)3869	85)4675	37)3108
10.	38)1064	70)4410	23)1679	55)3025	40)3920
11.	87)2871	72)2736	25)2275	57)2109	73)2555

12. There are 1480 film slides in a box, divided into 20 rows. How many slides are there in each row?

How to Divide by Tens and Ones

1. Decide where to start writing the answer.

   a. Notice whether the first two figures in the dividend show a number which can be divided. The number can be divided when the first two figures show a number the same as the divisor or larger than the divisor.

   b. If the first two figures can be divided, write the first quotient answer above the second figure of the dividend.

   c. If the first two figures of the dividend show a number less than the divisor, write the first figure of the answer above the third figure of the dividend.

2. Divide. Think of the number to be divided as so many tens and of the divisor as so many tens. Think, "Threes in nine, three," and write 3 above the second figure of the dividend. Think, "Threes in twenty-two, seven," and write 7 above the third figure of the dividend.

3. Try the quotient answer that you get by multiplying, and notice the product. Do not try a quotient answer larger than 9.

4. Subtract and notice the remainder.

5. Bring down the next figure.

6. Divide again, as in 2.

7. Try the quotient answer, as in 3 and 4 until the example is finished.

$$36\overline{)97}^{\downarrow}$$

$$36\overline{)2268}^{\downarrow}$$

$$36\overline{)97}^{\,3}$$

$$36\overline{)2268}^{\,7}$$

$$36\overline{)\;97}^{\quad3}\;\underline{108}$$

$$36\overline{)2268}^{\quad7}\;\underline{252}$$

$$36\overline{)97}^{\quad2}\;\underline{72}\;25$$

$$36\overline{)2268}^{\quad63}\;\underline{216}\;\underline{108}\;108$$

Review Problems

1. During a certain week the four stores of the Reed Brothers Grocery Store sold the following amounts:

Store Number 1	$1382.76
Store Number 2	1061.04
Store Number 3	983.47
Store Number 4	1508.18

How much did all the stores sell that week?

2. On a certain day the company had $9704.68 in the bank. To pay a number of bills, the company drew out $3041.97. How much did the company have left in the bank?

3. The company ordered 100 dozen cans of tomatoes from a canning factory. The tomatoes came packed 24 cans in a box. How many boxes were there?

4. The company ordered 288 boxes of canned peas. The peas came packed in boxes with 4 dozen cans in each box. How many cans of peas were ordered?

5. During the canning season for peaches, the company sold 385 bushel baskets of peaches at an average price of $2.65 a bushel. How much did the company receive for the peaches?

Do You Need Practice?

Add and check:

	(a)	(b)	(c)	(d)	(e)	(f)	(g)	(h)	
1.	632		800	9	15	92	$17.25	24	(17)
	178	1962	1634	5	63	37	8.00	32	(18)
	409	5039	35	7	47	05	45.39	15	
	86	2004	204	3	90	16	2.15	89	
	300	670	9	8	26	29	.98	74	

2.

	(a)	(b)	(c)	(d)	(e)	(f)	(g)	(h)	
					$\frac{1}{2}$	$\frac{3}{4}$	$2\frac{1}{3}$	$1\frac{1}{2}$	(210)
	$\frac{1}{8}$	$\frac{11}{12}$	$4\frac{1}{6}$	$8\frac{2}{3}$	$\frac{1}{4}$	$\frac{5}{8}$	$4\frac{3}{4}$	$3\frac{3}{8}$	to
	$\frac{3}{8}$	$\frac{5}{6}$	$6\frac{3}{4}$	$5\frac{1}{4}$	$\frac{1}{8}$	$\frac{1}{2}$	$4\frac{1}{2}$	$4\frac{5}{6}$	(252)

Subtract and check:

	(a)	(b)	(c)	(d)	(e)	(f)	(g)	(h)	
3.	504	800	913	760	400	1509	$325.80	$.71	(21)
	162	45	216	183	174	890	75.92	.45	(22)

	(a)	(b)	(c)	(d)	(e)	(f)	(g)	(h)	
4.	5	$6\frac{1}{2}$	$8\frac{2}{3}$	$7\frac{5}{8}$	$2\frac{1}{2}$	$4\frac{1}{3}$	$9\frac{3}{8}$	$7\frac{5}{6}$	(212)
	$\frac{3}{4}$	2	$3\frac{2}{3}$	$\frac{3}{8}$	$1\frac{2}{3}$	$2\frac{5}{12}$	$5\frac{3}{4}$	$1\frac{1}{2}$	to (251)

Multiply and check:

	(a)	(b)	(c)	(d)	(e)	(f)	(g)	(h)	
5.	436	705	247	861	105	82	$40.27	$.35	(34)
	82	90	45	94	6	9	8	7	to (43)

	(a)	(b)	(c)	(d)	(e)	(f)	(g)	(h)
6.	500	600	580	509	958	347	197	25
	80	50	71	25	48	96	72	82

Divide and check:

	(a)	(b)	(c)	(d)	(e)	(f)	
7.	63)1575	19)893	27)18954	54)18360	35)2467	93)6310	(192) to (194)
8.	29)1102	8)736	9)1071	6)3642	7)672	8)6448	(60) to (62)

Chapter 16
Decimals as Measures

A Present for Bob

Bob's parents gave him a new bicycle on his birthday. He was so pleased with the gift that he wrote his uncle about it. His uncle wrote back that he was sending a **cyclometer** for Bob to attach to his bicycle.

"What is a cyclometer?" asked Bob.

His father said, "Wait until it comes. Then perhaps you can find out what it is and what it is used for."

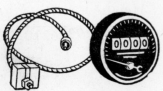

This is the way the cyclometer looked when it came and before Bob's father fastened it on the new bicycle.

What is a cyclometer? How is it used?

288

A New Way to Write Fractions

"A cyclometer," explained Bob's father, "is an instrument to measure the distance you travel on your bicycle. Now it registers zero miles. Get on your bicycle and ride down to the park entrance. Look at the cyclometer when you get there, and then ride back."

"What does the cyclometer register?" asked his father when Bob returned from his ride to the park entrance.

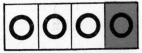

"It shows 10 miles," said Bob, "but I know that isn't correct. It is only a half mile to the park, and to the park and back would be just one mile and not ten miles."

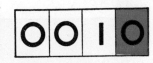

"When I got to the park entrance," continued Bob, "I looked at the cyclometer, and it showed 5 miles when it should have shown only a half mile."

Bob's father explained that the cyclometer was made to show not only miles but tenths of a mile. When the cyclometer reads ⊙⊙⊙ 5 , it shows 5 tenths of a mile. When it reads ⊙⊙ 1 ⊙ , it shows 1 and no tenth miles. The cyclometer is one of many modern instruments that measure in tenths. As it measures a tenth, it adds that tenth to what has already been measured.

Bob rode down to the park entrance and back. When he returned, the cyclometer read ⊙⊙ 2 ⊙ . After lunch Bob rode most of the afternoon. When he came home in the evening, the cyclometer read ⊙⊙ 9 6 .

How far did Bob ride that afternoon?

How far did he ride that day?

Writing Tenths in Tenth's Place

Just as we write **ones in one's place**,
tens in ten's place, and
hundreds in hundred's place,
so we write **tenths in tenth's place**.

In order to write tenths in tenth's place, we use a
decimal point (.) to show where we mean tenth's
place to be. Tenth's place is next to and just to the
right of the point.

In order to show:	We write:
Five tenths	.5
Eight tenths	.8
One tenth	.1
Nine tenths	.9
One and five tenths	1.5
Six and eight tenths	6.8
Fifteen and one tenth	15.1
Sixty-five and nine tenths	65.9

Write as decimals:

a. Six tenths
b. Thirty and six tenths
c. Fourteen and five tenths
d. One and two tenths
e. One tenth
f. Seven tenths
g. Ten and seven tenths
h. Eleven and one tenth
i. Three tenths
j. Fifty-two and two tenths

When we write tenths as decimals, we show both
number of parts and **size of parts**. Thus, when we
write **five tenths**, we write the figure 5 to show number, and we put it in tenth's place with the point (.5)
to show size.

Reading Decimal Fractions

One tenth may be written in two ways: $\frac{1}{10}$ or .1.

When we write one tenth as $\frac{1}{10}$, we call it a **common fraction**. When we write one tenth as .1, we call it a **decimal fraction**. Often we just say that $\frac{1}{10}$ is a **fraction**, and .1 is a **decimal**.

We read $2\frac{3}{10}$ as two and three tenths, and we read 2.3 as two and three tenths. We say that $2\frac{3}{10}$ is a **mixed number,** and we say that 2.3 is a **mixed decimal**.

Read these decimals:

.1   .4   .3   .8   .5   .7   .2   .6   .9

Read these mixed decimals. Remember the decimal point is always read **and**.

4.2   5.6   10.2   15.8   7.9   8.5   11.7   9.9

Write these decimals and mixed decimals as some boy or girl reads them. When he reads, "Five and six tenths," you write 5.6. The **and** tells you where to put the point. It tells where the whole number ends and the decimal begins.

10.8   9.5   6.4   85.5   6.1   75.3   84.6   99.9

TEMPERATURE CHART	
8 a.m.	100.3
Noon	99.9
4 p.m.	101.5
8 p.m.	99.4
Midnight	98.6

Railroad Mileage Chart	
Chicago	0.0
Evanston	12.1
Winnetka	16.7
Highland Park	23.2
Waukegan	35.9
Kenosha	51.6
Racine	61.9
Milwaukee	85.0

GAS
26.4¢

THIS SALE
3 8 9

GALLONS
1 4 $\frac{7}{10}$

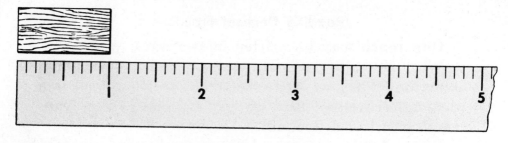

Measuring in Tenths

The picture shows part of a foot ruler, 12 inches long. Each inch is marked off into **10 tenths** of an inch. The picture shows how the ruler is used to measure the width of the block of wood in **tenths** of an inch.

How wide is the block? Count the tenths: one tenth, two tenths, and so on. The block is 10 tenths of an inch wide. Of course, 10 tenths ($\frac{10}{10}$) of an inch make 1 inch. But instead of writing the width as 1 inch, we write it as 1.0 inch. 1.0 means 1 inch, but it also means that the inch width was measured in tenths.

To write the width as 1 inch means that the width was measured as accurately as possible in **whole inches**. To write the width as 1.0 inch means that it was measured as accurately as possible in **tenths** of an inch.

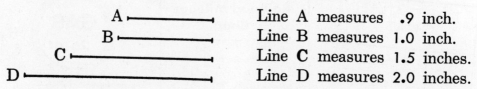

Line A measures .9 inch.
Line B measures 1.0 inch.
Line C measures 1.5 inches.
Line D measures 2.0 inches.

Thus, we know that the four lines were measured as accurately as possible in tenths of an inch. Line D is 2 inches long, but it does not tell us how accurately it was measured. Line D is 2.0 inches long. This tells that it was measured very carefully in tenths.

Decimals as Measures

A surveyor measured four lots near Bob's house. The lots were valuable; so he measured the widths and lengths of them very carefully and tried to get each measurement accurate to a tenth of a foot.

The surveyor used a steel tape measure marked off in feet and tenths of a foot.

These are the widths of the four lots as the surveyor recorded them in his book:

First lot	40.3 ft.
Second lot	60.0 ft.
Third lot	44.5 ft.
Fourth lot	51.0 ft.

The width of the first lot was recorded as 40.3 feet because the width was closer to 40.3 feet than it was to 40.2 feet or 40.4 feet. The width of the second lot was 60 feet. The surveyor wrote the width as 60.0 feet to show that he had measured it to the nearest tenths. Actually, the width was just a tiny bit less than 60 feet, but since it was more than half a tenth wider than 59.9 feet, he recorded its width as 60.0 feet. The third lot was slightly more than 44.5 feet, but it was closer to 44.5 than it was to 44.4 or 44.6 feet. The fourth lot was exactly 51 feet wide, as near as the surveyor could measure it. To show that he was measuring in tenths, he recorded the width as 51.0 feet.

Adding and Subtracting Tenths

1. The cyclometer on Bob's bicycle registered 2.0 miles at noon and 9.6 miles in the evening. How many miles did Bob ride in the afternoon?

2. The speedometer on Mr. Bell's car registered 7651.8 when the family started on their vacation trip and 8365.3 when they returned. How many miles was the car driven on the trip?

9.6
2.0
――――
7.6 miles

8365.3
7651.8
――――
713.5 miles

We subtract whole numbers and tenths the way we subtract whole numbers. We write **tenths** under **tenths** and subtract.

3. A surveyor measured the widths of four lots near Bob's house. He found the widths were: 40.3 ft., 60.0 ft., 44.5 ft. and 51.0 ft. What was the total width of the four lots?

40.3
60.0
44.5
51.0
――――
195.8 ft.

We add whole numbers and tenths the way we add whole numbers. We write **tenths** under **tenths** and add.

4. Add:

25.6 ft.
31.2 ft.
28.4 ft.

5. Add:

40.8 ft.
39.6 ft.
45.0 ft.

6. Subtract:

98.6 mi.
73.4 mi.

7. Subtract:

195.8 ft.
76.9 ft.

Adding and Subtracting Tenths

Tenths are added and subtracted the way **ones, tens,** and **hundreds** are added and subtracted. But we must be careful to write each number **in its proper place—tenths** under **tenths, ones** under **ones, tens** under **tens,** and so on.

Add:

	(a)	(b)	(c)	(d)	(e)	(f)
1.	47.6	8.6	.4	108.3	27.5	18.2
	82.4	7.2	.8	74.6	110.4	73.5
	31.0	9.0	1.0	95.0	72.0	6.3
	57.2	12.5	.7	82.1	18.7	41.0
2.	28.5	15.4	.9	35.6	40.8	13.8
	17.9	10.8	1.2	28.9	18.6	14.9
	24.7	9.5	1.0	32.3	20.4	11.2
	20.3	11.0	1.5	30.7	18.8	12.5

Subtract:

	(a)	(b)	(c)	(d)	(e)	(f)
3.	57.9	28.5	46.8	124.5	106.3	138.2
	42.6	24.3	35.0	95.5	82.8	91.9
4.	97.0	478.3	129.0	96.3	80.2	76.8
	65.3	283.5	57.6	62.7	57.6	9.9
5.	28.3	1.5	1.0	7.2	72.5	64.5
	20.5	.8	.4	.6	18.6	35.7

6. The school nurse used the scales that weigh in tenths of a pound. Jane weighed 75.4 lb., Alice weighed 80.5 lb., Susan weighed 76.3 lb., and Beth weighed 82.8 lb. What is the total weight of the girls?

Multiplying and Dividing Tenths

1. Last Saturday Bob had to make 3 trips to the store. The distance there and back is 2.4 miles. How many miles did Bob ride in going to and from the store?

```
 2.4
   3
 7.2
```
Multiply the way you would multiply a whole number. In the answer, place the point to show **tenths**. Bob rode 7.2 miles.

2. The total width of the 4 lots Mr. Horner bought measured 211.2 feet. What is the average width?

```
     52.8
4)211.2
  20
  11
   8
   3 2
   3 2
```
Divide the way you would divide a whole number. In the answer, place the point over the point in the dividend.
The answer is 52.8 feet.

Multiply:

	(a)	(b)	(c)	(d)	(e)	(f)
3.	24.7	92.1	8.5	17.4	20.5	42.3
	2	4	6	8	7	43
4.	15.7	35.2	61.6	28.4	14.6	91.6
	31	25	7	9	12	5

Divide:

	(a)	(b)	(c)	(d)	(e)
5.	5)289.0	6)44.4	9)264.6	8)281.6	4)168.4
6.	7)59.5	4)106.8	25)437.5	12)631.2	5)210.5

More Accurate Measurement

In 1 foot there are 12 inches; so 1 inch is $\frac{1}{12}$ of a foot. One tenth (.1) of a foot is slightly longer than $\frac{1}{12}$ of a foot, or 1 inch.

1 inch

The .1 foot, shown here, is divided into ten equal parts. Each of the ten equal parts of the .1 foot is one tenth of one tenth foot long, or one hundredth foot long. When we measure in hundredths, we measure more accurately than when we measure in tenths.

10ths

One tenth foot

We measure valuable city lots in hundredths of a foot. To measure in hundredths of a foot, the surveyor uses a steel tape. On this tape each foot is marked off in tenths, and each tenth is marked off in tenths. Thus, the tape is marked off in tenths and tenths of tenths, or hundredths.

surveyor's tape

The weatherman catches the rain as it falls in a special container. He tells us in hundredths of an inch how much rain has fallen.

rain gauge

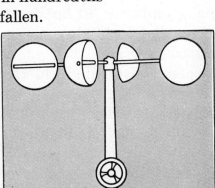
wind gauge

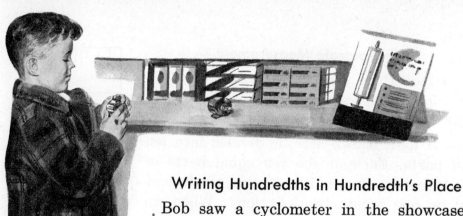

Writing Hundredths in Hundredth's Place

Bob saw a cyclometer in the showcase at the bicycle shop. It was slightly different from the one he had. This one registered distance not only in miles and tenths of a mile, but also in hundredths of a mile.

A boy rode the bicycle with this cyclometer on it. When he had ridden a short distance, it read:

The cyclometer showed that the bicycle had gone 1 hundredth of a mile.

0	0	0	0	1

When the bicycle had gone 10 hundredths of a mile, the cyclometer read:

The cyclometer showed that the bicycle had gone 1 tenth, or 10 hundredths, of a mile.

0	0	0	1	0

Then Bob rode the bicycle for a while. He stopped now and then to see what the cyclometer registered. Read the distances.

0	0	0	9	6

We write the distances shown on the cyclometer like this:

0	0	1	3	4

.01   One hundredth

.10   Ten hundredths

0	0	2	4	0

.96   Ninety-six hundredths

1.34   One and thirty-four hundredths

0	0	3	6	7

2.40   Two and forty hundredths

3.67   Three and sixty-seven hundredths

The Meaning of Numbers

Each figure in a number tells both number and value. Let us look at **276**. The **6** is in the first place. The value of this place is one. So our number, **276**, has **6** ones. What is the value of the second place? How many tens does our number have? What is the value of the third place? How many hundreds does our number have? What does the number **276** mean?

The value of each place is how many times as much as the place to its right? The value of each place is what part of the place to its left?

Our number system is a system of tens.

One's place is the center of our number system. For each place to the left of one's place, there is a place to the right, whose name is about the same. The place to the left of ones is tens, and the place to the right of ones is tenths. Two places to the left of ones is hundreds, and two places to the right of ones is hundredths.

We read **.6** as six tenths.

We read **.58** as fifty-eight hundredths.

We read **3.45** as three **and** forty-five hundredths.

We read **14.605** as fourteen **and** six hundred five thousandths.

.6

.58

3.45

14.605

Kinds of Fractions

Fractions are parts of a whole.

The denominator tells the size of the parts.

The numerator tells the number of parts.

Common fractions are the fractions of common everyday use. We speak of, and write, $\frac{1}{2}$ pound butter, $\frac{7}{8}$ inch thickness of a board, and so on.

The ruler the carpenter uses to measure lengths, widths, and thicknesses of board is marked off in whole inches, and in halves, fourths, eighths, and sixteenths. He may wish to saw off a piece of board 4 ft. $3\frac{1}{4}$ in. long. With his ruler he measures 4 ft. and 3 in. and $\frac{1}{4}$ in. more.

If the size of the parts is in tenths or hundredths, we need to write only the numerator to tell the number of parts. We show the denominator by position, as .1 and .01.

When we write the denominator, we call the fraction a **common fraction**. Fractions like $\frac{1}{2}$, $\frac{2}{3}$, $\frac{3}{4}$, and $\frac{7}{8}$ are common fractions.

When we show the denominator by the position of the numerator, the fraction is a **decimal fraction**. We usually call it a decimal. Fractions like .1, .5, .08, and .20 are decimals.

$$\frac{3}{10}$$

$$.3$$

$$\frac{3}{100}$$

$$.03$$

Three hundredths
- as a common fraction is $\frac{3}{100}$.
- as a decimal fraction is .03.

Decimal fractions are the fractions of accurate measurement. Thus, an inch is marked off in tenths or in hundredths so that we can measure to the nearest tenth or to the nearest hundredth.

300

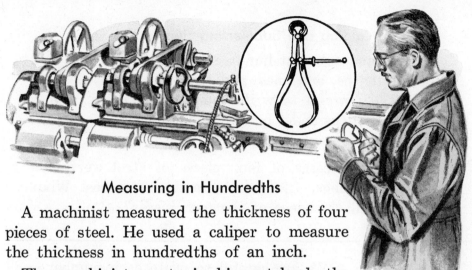

Measuring in Hundredths

A machinist measured the thickness of four pieces of steel. He used a caliper to measure the thickness in hundredths of an inch.

The machinist wrote in his notebook the four thicknesses as shown. Each thickness was measured accurately to a hundredth of an inch. The first thickness was just a shade less than one and five hundredths inches, but since it was nearer one and five hundredths than one and four hundredths, he wrote the thickness as 1.05.

1.05 in.
.92 in.
1.20 in.
.80 in.

The second thickness was nearer ninety-two hundredths than ninety-three hundredths.

The third thickness was almost exactly one and twenty hundredths. Instead of writing 1.2 inches, he wrote 1.20 inches to show that he had measured in hundredths and not in tenths.

The fourth thickness was more than halfway between seventy-nine hundredths and eighty hundredths. The machinist wrote the thickness as .80 instead of .8 to show that the measurement was accurate to a hundredth of an inch.

Adding and Subtracting Hundredths

We add and subtract hundredths the way we add and subtract tenths, and ones, and tens, and hundreds. But we must be careful to write each answer in its proper place: hundredths under hundredths, tenths under tenths, ones under ones, and so on.

1. The thicknesses of four pieces of steel were 1.05 inches, .92 inches, 1.20 inches, and .80 inches. What was the total thickness of the four pieces?

1.05 .92 1.20 .80 —— 3.97 in.	We are careful to write each number in its proper place—hundredths under hundredths, tenths under tenths, and ones under ones. Then we add the way we add whole numbers.

2. The owner of the bicycle shop loaned Bob for a week's trial a cyclometer that registered in hundredths. At the beginning of the week the cyclometer registered 3.67 miles, and at the end of the week it registered 18.82 miles. How many miles did Bob ride his bicycle that week?

18.82 3.67 ——— 15.15 miles	We are careful to write each number in its proper place. Then we subtract the way we subtract whole numbers.

Adding and Subtracting Hundredths

In adding and subtracting hundredths, or tenths and hundredths, be sure to write each number in its proper place.

Add:

	(a)	(b)	(c)	(d)	(e)	(f)
1.	.87	2.67	2.28	5.07	.86	57.36
	.92	3.04	.40	4.80	2.43	9.87
	1.07	2.90	.37	5.23	1.05	20.02
	.90	3.28	.32	4.96	4·17	5.08
2.	32.40	.73	2.85	5.18	41.37	1.10
	36.09	.60	3.40	6.74	167.25	14.75
	35.00	.84	3.04	4.90	8.60	20.50
	30.68	.69	2.91	5.20	25.90	38.85

Subtract:

	(a)	(b)	(c)	(d)	(e)	(f)
3.	7.68	.97	.68	1.46	63.50	100.25
	4.25	.30	.48	.82	32.98	46.75
4.	6.50	5.09	8.00	16.24	81.06	121.02
	2.36	4.21	2.07	8.36	24.65	53.64
5.	38.40	.84	2.91	6.74	135.60	42.50
	23.75	.28	1.76	4.87	92.50	27.65
6.	67.20	9.71	8.64	19.23	123.54	37.45
	18.59	7.88	3.25	10.79	91.99	16.82

7. The heaviest rainfall in twenty-four hours in New York City in the last seventy years was 9.40 inches on October 8, 1903. The next heaviest was 6.17 inches on September 23, 1882. How much more was the rainfall on October 8, 1903, than on September 23, 1882?

Multiplying Tenths and Hundredths

1. Bob's father owns 3 lots in the new addition to the city. Each lot, when it was surveyed, measured 62.5 feet in width. How wide were the lots altogether?

<table>
<tr><td>62.5 ft.
3
—————
187.5 ft.</td><td>We multiply tenths the way we multiply whole numbers. We are very careful to put the point (.) so that the answer will have each number in its proper place.</td></tr>
</table>

2. A machinist measured the thickness of 5 pieces of steel. The thickness of each piece was .28 inches. What was the combined thickness of all the pieces?

<table>
<tr><td>.28 in.
5
—————
1.40 in.</td><td>We multiply hundredths the way we multiply whole numbers. We are very careful to write each part of our answer in its proper place.</td></tr>
</table>

When we multiply tenths by a whole number, we must place the point in our answer to show tenths. When we multiply hundredths by a whole number, we must place the point in our answer to show hundredths.

3. Copy and multiply:

(a)	(b)	(c)	(d)	(e)	(f)	(g)
2.03	89.04	1.82	50.17	6.91	46.85	40.36
7	4	8	6	3	5	6

Dividing Tenths and Hundredths

1. Mr. Jackson drove his car **92.5** miles on 5 gallons of gas. How many miles did he get per gallon?

We divide tenths the way we divide whole numbers. We write each part of the answer in its proper place. We put the point in the answer just above the point in the dividend.

$$\begin{array}{r} 18.5 \\ 5\overline{)92.5} \\ 5 \\ \hline 42 \\ 40 \\ \hline 25 \\ 25 \\ \hline \end{array}$$

2. During a week of rainy weather the rainfall in a certain town was **18.76** inches. What was the average number of inches of rainfall per day?

We divide hundredths the way we divide whole numbers. We write each part of the answer in its proper place. We put the point in the answer just above the point in the dividend.

$$\begin{array}{r} 2.68 \\ 7\overline{)18.76} \\ 14 \\ \hline 47 \\ 42 \\ \hline 56 \\ 56 \\ \hline \end{array}$$

Copy and divide:

	(a)	(b)	(c)	(d)	(e)	(f)
3.	4)38.04	5)41.45	7)6.86	5)68.75	6)39.12	4)109.96
4.	9)22.32	4)14.24	8)6.72	9)81.45	7)14.42	8)20.48

Dollars and Cents

For a long time we have been writing decimals. We have added, subtracted, multiplied, and divided decimals. When we have worked with dollars and cents, we have worked with decimals. When we write $3.75, we write 3 and 75 hundredths dollars, although we call it 3 dollars and 75 cents.

Add:

	(a)	(b)	(c)	(d)	(e)
1.	$7.50	$ .75	$17.80	$1.85	$50.00
	8.75	.50	25.63	.48	14.86
	6.48	1.25	19.82	.63	5.10
	3.57	2.60	20.07	2.05	68.37

Subtract:

2.	$ .93	$46.50	$75.00	$168.50	$100.00
	.65	24.75	28.63	76.25	86.14
3.	$200.00	$26.42	$65.08	$217.00	$137.40
	76.48	17.28	26.14	28.75	84.86

Multiply:

4.	$ .75	$4.65	$18.36	$7.28	$17.65
	36	18	45	19	16
5.	$ .27	$9.15	$82.26	$9.95	$45.82
	55	23	15	35	76

Divide:

6.	6)$34.50	25)$18.75	25)$208.50	7)$120.96	2)$10.04
7.	9)$78.48	32)$15.68	71)$104.15	5)$460.75	8)$18.16
8.	7)$72.38	53)$12.19	47)$241.11	4)$159.68	9)$17.28

Tom's Trip

1. One Saturday Tom went on a trip with his father. When they started, the speedometer showed 3437.2. When they got back home, it showed 3606.8. How many miles did they travel?

2. As they started out, Mr. Clark bought 12 gallons of gasoline at 21¢ a gallon and 2 quarts of oil at 37¢ a quart. How much was Mr. Clark's bill at the filling station?

3. With the car that Mr. Clark now owns, he averages 15 miles to a gallon of gasoline. Did he have to stop on the trip to buy more gasoline?

4. Their lunch bill was $1.20, and their dinner cost $2.25. During the afternoon each had a 15¢ ice-cream soda. How much did they pay for food that day?

5. Mr. Clark's errand to the city was to talk to a car salesman about trading his old car for a new one. The car he wanted cost $1585. The salesman would allow Mr. Clark $565 for his old car. Then if he would pay $420 in cash, he could take the car and pay the rest of the amount in one year. If Mr. Clark paid the same amount each month, what would his monthly payments be?

Are You a Good Thinker?

1. John has a little instrument, called a pedometer, that shows how far he walks. One week he kept a record of the number of miles he walked each day. The record showed the following distances: Monday, 3.0 mi.; Tuesday, 3.4 mi.; Wednesday, 4.7 mi.; Thursday, 2.9 mi.; Friday, 4.2 mi.; Saturday, 5.6 mi.; Sunday, 4.9 mi. What was the average distance that he walked each day?

2. John's pedometer shows that he lives .7 miles from school. If he goes home for lunch, how many miles does he walk going to and from school each day? each school week?

3. Ellen has a Saturday job that pays 35¢ an hour. She usually works 4 hours a day. She wants to use one half of the money she earns each Saturday to pay for her own schoolbooks, which cost $5.38 this year. Can she finish paying for the books after working 7 Saturdays? 8 Saturdays?

4. Ben earns 25¢ an hour taking care of little Billy Adams on evenings that his parents go out. One evening Ben stayed from 5:30 p.m. until 11:30 p.m. How much did he earn that evening?

5. Allen helped Mr. West pick up his 80 bushels of potatoes. Mr. West agreed to pay Allen by giving him $\frac{1}{10}$ of the potatoes he picked up. Allen sold his share of the potatoes for $2.10 a bushel. How much money did he get for the job?

6. Ronnie gets 75¢ an evening helping Mr. Olds at the picture show. There are shows 6 days a week. How much does Ronnie make each week?

Practice with Decimals

Copy and multiply:

	(a)	(b)	(c)	(d)	(e)	(f)
1.	3.75	4.82	16.7	24.8	25.05	30.01
	5	6	4	9	6	9
2.	62.4	8.17	2.58	46.3	36.10	40.40
	3	7	8	2	8	12
3.	27.6	49.7	60.3	5.08	10.75	12.45
	27	35	96	48	8	6
4.	6.18	.78	7.8	3.04	13.82	27.05
	91	54	67	38	8	29

Copy and divide:

	(a)	(b)	(c)	(d)	(e)
5.	5)40.85	6)100.2	4)19.28	9)119.34	45)247.5
6.	3)82.8	7)5.46	8)206.4	2)75.36	58)74.24
7.	43)27.52	24)196.8	16)258.88	73)197.1	24)43.68
8.	37)225.7	53)143.1	69)164.91	14)606.2	86)31.82

Copy and add:

9. $27.80 + $90.69 + $148.20 + $400.75 + $74.09

10. $495.10 + $.82 + $11.14 + $66.85 + $10.00

11. $13.09 + $265.70 + $29.95 + $44.98 + $70.03

Copy and subtract:

12. $91.81 from $100.00; $73.84 from $210.66

13. From $80.00 subtract $78.05

14. From $893.72 subtract $785.95

Chapter 17
Measuring by Squares

Bob and Betty's New Home

Bob and Betty had just moved into their new home. Betty was pleased with her own room. It was light and airy and was, she thought, a nice large room for a girl her size.

Bob liked his room, too. He thought that his room was just as big as Betty's. Sometimes he thought that it was just a little larger, but he was not sure.

They had a little playground in the back yard next to the vegetable garden. Here they had a trapeze, wickets for croquet, and three holes for golf.

Their Rooms

Betty spoke up, "I am sure my room must be larger than Bob's."

Bob answered, "No, I think my room is just as large as yours and maybe larger. Let's measure our rooms."

The children went inside and measured their rooms with the yardstick. Betty's room measured 12 feet long and 9 feet wide, and Bob's room measured 10 feet long and 10 feet wide.

Then they drew the floor plans of their rooms from the measurements.

"You are right," said Bob to Betty. "My room is wider than yours, but it is not as big as yours."

How could they tell which room was larger?

BETTY'S ROOM

BOB'S ROOM

In trying to answer this question, let us review what we know about how to measure lengths and distances.

12 inches	= 1 foot	36 inches	= 1 yard
3 feet	= 1 yard	5280 feet	= 1 mile
$5\frac{1}{2}$ yards	= 1 rod	1760 yards	= 1 mile
$16\frac{1}{2}$ feet	= 1 rod	320 rods	= 1 mile

We know that the way to measure the amount of a certain thing is to take the right unit of measure and apply it to the thing to be measured. The way to measure liquids is to take the pint, quart, or gallon measure and **apply it** (count the times the liquid fills the pint, quart, or gallon measure). The way to measure lengths is to take the **inch, foot, yard,** or **rod measure** and to **apply it** (count the times the inch, foot, yard, or rod measure covers the length being measured).

How to Measure Lengths

To measure lengths, we must have the right unit of measure: the inch, foot, yard, rod. Next, we must **apply the measure** to the length, and count the times the measure has to be applied to cover the length. Let us see how we measure height:

Jack stood with his back to the wall. Jim made a mark on the wall level with the top of Jack's head. Then Jack took a foot ruler, **applied it** to the length from the floor to the mark on the wall, and **counted the feet** as he covered the distance: one, two, three, four, and a half—4½ feet. Or he **counted the inches** as he covered the distance: 12, 24, 36, 48, and 6 are 54 inches.

To measure the width of the vegetable garden, Bob took the yardstick, applied it to the distance from corner stake to corner stake, and **counted the yards**, or the **feet**, as he covered the distance: 1, 2, 3, 4, 5, 6, 7, 8, **9 yards**, or 3, 6, 9, 12, 15, 18, 21, 24, **27 feet**.

This is the way in which people always measure lengths or distances: **Take a measure and apply it.** Long ago the measures used were not as exact as the ones we use now. Yet our modern measures and the method of applying them have come from the measures and the method of former times.

Early Measures of Length

In olden times to measure a short length or distance, a person would use the length of his **foot** or his **feet** as a measure. He applied this measure by placing his feet heel to toe from one end of the length to the other, and by counting the times (feet) he set his feet down to cover the distance.

To measure longer distances, people used a **pole** or **rod** and applied it to the distance. Sometimes they used a **stick** of shorter length which they called a **yard**. The old meaning of yard is stick, rod, or measure. We still use the yardstick. The thing to remember is that people applied the rod, pole, yard, or foot just as we apply our measures today.

We can understand how the use of such measures led to many disputes about lengths and distances. The poles, rods, and sticks used were of different lengths. Two persons using different length sticks to measure a piece of land could easily get into a dispute about the size of the land. People's feet differed in size then as they do today so that two people could hardly settle a dispute about distance by stepping off the distance. Such disputes could not be avoided until the exact lengths of various measures (standards) were decided upon.

Measuring in Ancient Times

This ancient man has just traded some fish for a new fishing line. How long is the new line? To tell, he wraps it around his waist and measures its length as so many **girths**. A girth corresponds closely to our yard in length.

The **span** was used to measure short lengths. The span is the length from the tip of the thumb to the tip of the little finger of the outstretched hand.

The Roman soldier measured distances in **steps** and **paces**. The step of the soldier was about 30 inches or $2\frac{1}{2}$ feet. The pace was 2 steps or about 5 feet. The Roman mile was the distance marching troops would go in 1000 paces. Their mile was about 5000 feet, and our mile is 5280 feet.

Long before the foot ruler or the yardstick came into use, people used other methods of measurement. The length of some part of the body was often used as the unit of measure.

Measuring in Ancient Times

This ancient workman wants to saw off a block that is a **cubit** in length. He is measuring the length with his cubit. A cubit is the length from the point of the elbow to the tip of the middle finger.

This man wants to replace a log in his cabin. He wants to know how long the new log will have to be. He is measuring the length of his cabin in **fathoms**. A fathom is the length from finger tip to finger tip when the arms are outstretched.

From the tip of the middle finger of the outstretched arm to the middle of the chest is an **ell**, or a yard. An ell is one-half fathom.

This bowman is trying out his arrow to see if it is an ell in length.

Present Measures of Length

The **yard** of length, as we use it today, is the distance between two gold plugs in a certain bronze bar kept at Westminster in England. It is also the exact length of a metal bar kept at Washington, D.C. **All yard** measures are marked off from one of these so that the yard as we use it today is always the same length. Our other measures of length are related to the yard length. Five and one-half such lengths make one **rod**. One third of a yard is our **foot**, and a twelfth part of a foot is our **inch**. The word inch comes from a Latin word meaning *twelfth part*.

An old English law declared that the length of the inch must be that of "three grains of barley dry and round placed end to end." In early times they used to say, "3 barleycorns make one inch; 12 inches make one foot." It is interesting to notice that the old English law stated that grains of barley had to be placed end to end. It **applied** a grain of barley as a measure to tell how long an inch should be.

It took the people of former days a long time to agree on their use of measures of length so that they could have exact measures, such as we use today. They had to work out, or decide upon, a **measure of length** before they could measure length exactly. After they decided upon a measure, they **applied it**. Let us remember these two important steps which must be done in order to measure anything:

1. Decide upon a **measure**.
2. **Apply** the measure.

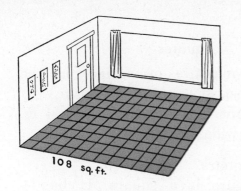

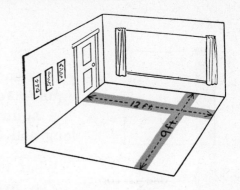

108 sq. ft.

Surfaces

Bob and Betty were interested in the sizes of the whole vegetable garden, the whole playground, and all the space in their rooms, not just the lengths and widths of them. How big is Betty's room? Betty knew, when she had measured the room, that it was 12 feet long and 9 feet wide. What she really wanted to know was how big the **whole surface** of the floor is, not merely how big it is along two sides.

In measuring the garden, Bob measured first along one edge of it, then along another edge. But Bob wanted to know how big the **whole garden** is, not merely how big it is along its edges.

The garden, the playground, and the floors in the two children's rooms are **surfaces**, not lengths. A surface has length just as a piece of thread has length, but the **surface** of a garden is quite different from the **length** of a thread.

We must learn how to **measure surfaces**. In order to tell how big a **surface** is, we must do two things:

1. Decide upon a **measure of surfaces**.
2. **Apply** the measure.

Let us now do each of these in turn.

317

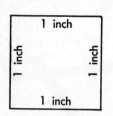

1 inch

1 inch | 1 inch

1 inch

Squares

A common measure of surface is the **square foot** (sq. ft.).

A **square foot** is a **square** that is 1 ft. long and 1 ft. wide.

What is a square?

The first figure is a square. It has **4 sides**. The sides are all the **same length**. It has **square corners**. This square is a **square inch** in size.

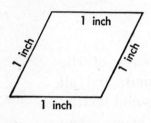

1 inch

1 inch | 1 inch

1 inch

The second figure is *not a square*. It has 4 sides, and the sides are all the same length. But it does not have square corners.

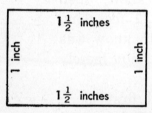

1½ inches

1 inch | 1 inch

1½ inches

A figure may have square corners and not be a square. Look at the next figure. It is *not a square*. It has 4 square corners, but the 4 sides are not the same length.

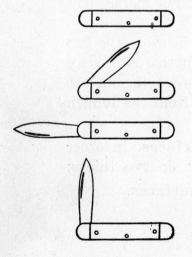

When Bobby's knife is **closed**, it looks like the picture at the left.

Here is his knife **partly opened**. Between the blade and the handle there is a **small opening**.

Here is his knife **wide open**.

And here is Bobby's knife **half opened**. The opening between the blade and the handle is half of what it is when the knife is wide open.

318

Learning about Angles

Between the lines in A, the opening is small. In B, it is larger, and in C the opening is still larger.

The opening between lines is called an **angle**. An opening, or an angle, as large as the one in B is called a **right angle**. The corner is square. The corners in A and C are not square; so the openings are angles but not right angles.

A right angle is an opening as large as that in a half-opened knife. Here are some right angles:

Draw a right angle on your paper.
Draw a right angle on the board.
Point to the right angle and the square corner.

Name some objects that have square corners. The pictures on this page may help you.

319

The Square Foot

Draw a square foot on a piece of cardboard.

Use a square corner of your tablet to draw a right angle as shown in A. Take your ruler and draw a straight line 1 foot long to B. At B, place the square corner of your tablet with one edge along line AB, and draw a right angle with the line pointing to C. Draw line BC 1 foot long. Then draw a right angle at C as shown.

Now you have a square. It has 4 sides. The sides are the same length. The 4 corners are square, and the 4 angles are right angles.

You have a **square foot**, a square whose sides are each 1 foot long. You can use the square foot to measure the sizes of surfaces.

Which is nearest in size to a square foot, a Savings Stamp, a page of your book, the cover of your geography, a man's handkerchief, or the top of your desk?

The sidewalk in the picture is made of stone. Each stone is 1 foot on a side. This means that each stone covers exactly 1 square foot of surface. Six stones cover 6 square feet of surface. How many square feet of surface will 10 stones cover?

320

Applying the Square Foot Measure

A 4-sided figure with square corners is called a **rectangle**. A square is a rectangle. A square is a 4-sided figure with square corners, but in a square the sides are equal. So a square is a special kind of rectangle.

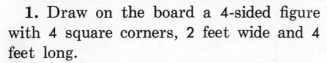

rectangle

1. Draw on the board a 4-sided figure with 4 square corners, 2 feet wide and 4 feet long.

How large is the rectangle you have drawn? How many square feet in size is it? We can measure it and see.

square

Place your square foot measure in one of the corners, as at **a**, and carefully mark the space it covers, or 1 square foot. Next, measure in the same way another square foot at **b**, and mark it.

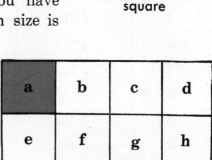

Do the same at **c**, then at **d**, **e**, **f**, **g**, and **h**. Now count the square feet you have measured in the rectangle that is 4 feet long and 2 feet wide.

There are 8 square feet in the rectangle.

2. Draw other rectangles on the board and on the floor, and measure the square feet in each:

    a. 3 feet long and 3 feet wide
    b. 4 feet long and 3 feet wide
    c. 5 feet long and 2 feet wide
    d. 4 feet long and 4 feet wide

321

Applying the Square Foot Measure

Make a table like the one below to show the sizes of the rectangles you have measured.

Number	Lengths of Sides		Size of Rectangle in Square Feet
	Feet Long	Feet Wide	
1.	4 ft.	2 ft.	8 sq. ft.
2.	3 ft.	3 ft.	9 sq. ft.
3.	4 ft.	3 ft.	12 sq. ft.
4.	6 ft.	2 ft.	12 sq. ft.
5.	4 ft.	4 ft.	16 sq. ft.
6.	5 ft.	2 ft.	10 sq. ft.
7.	5 ft.	3 ft.	15 sq. ft.
8.	5 ft.	4 ft.	
9.	6 ft.	3 ft.	
10.	6 ft.	4 ft.	

When Ned Barton was making his table, he had an idea. He said, "Really, you don't have to measure the square feet in a rectangle with your square foot measure. If you multiply the number of feet long by the number of feet wide, you will always get the number of square feet there are in the rectangle." Look at numbers 1 to 7 in your table. Was Ned correct?

Can you tell the sizes of rectangles 8 to 10 without measuring? Find the size of each, and record it in the table you have made.

Finding Sizes without Measuring

To find the size of a rectangle in square feet, multiply the number of feet long by the number of feet wide.

To find the size of a rectangle in square inches, multiply the number of inches long by the number of inches wide.

To find the size of a rectangle in square yards, multiply the number of yards long by the number of yards wide.

To find the size of a rectangle in square rods, multiply the number of rods long by the number of rods wide.

1. The back of Edna's tablet is 6 inches wide and 8 inches long. How big is it in square inches?

```
    8  number of inches long
   x6  number of inches wide
   48  number of square inches
```

Edna found that the tablet back is 48 square inches in size.

Just to check, she marked off the back in square inches, as shown in the diagram, and counted the square inches. Is 48 square inches the correct answer?

2. The back of Elmer's tablet is 8 inches wide and 10 inches long. How big is the back of his tablet in square inches?

3. Betty's room is 12 feet long and 9 feet wide. How big is her room in square feet?

4. Bob's room is 10 feet long and 10 feet wide. How big is his room?

The size of a surface is called its **area**. We find the areas of surfaces in square inches, square feet, square yards, square rods, and so on.

1. The kitchen in Bob's and Betty's house is 12 feet long and 9 feet wide. The linoleum the workman put on the floor is in foot squares, a red square, a black square, and so on. How many square feet of linoleum did it take to cover the floor?

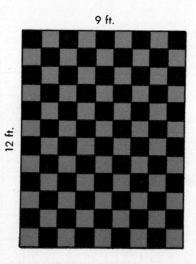

9 ft.

12 ft.

2. How many square yards of linoleum did it take?

Draw a square yard on the board. Find the number of square feet in a square that is 1 yard or 3 feet long, and 1 yard or 3 feet wide.

9 square feet = 1 square yard.

12 ft. ×9 ft. 108 sq. ft.	12 9)108 9 18 18	In 9 sq. ft. there is 1 sq. yd. In 108 sq. ft. there are 12 sq. yd.

4 yd.
×3 yd.
12 sq. yd.

Wilma said, "I know another way of finding the area of the linoleum in square yards. 12 feet long and 9 feet wide in yards would be 4 yards long and 3 yards wide. So 4 times 3 gives 12 square yards." Is she right?

Finding Areas

1. The playground at Bob and Betty's home is 30 feet wide and 50 feet long. How large is it in square feet?

2. The vegetable garden is 60 feet long and 27 feet wide. How large is it?

3. Which is larger, the garden or the playground? how much larger?

4. The lot on which the house is built is 60 feet wide and 180 feet long. How large is the lot in square feet?

5. How large is the lot in square yards?

6. Mr. Veasey bought a big roll of chicken wire to go around his chicken yard. The wire was 60 yards long and 2 yards wide. How many square yards of wire did he buy? How many square feet of wire did he buy?

7. Mr. Veasey owns a large lot at the edge of town. It is in the shape of a rectangle, 20 rods long and 16 rods wide. How large is the lot in square rods?

8. The floor of the fifth-grade room in the Webster School measures 33 feet long and 24 feet wide. How large is it in square feet? How large is it in square yards?

9. Measure the length and width of your school room in feet. Find how large it is in square feet.

10. The size of the Webster School lot is 300 feet wide and 360 feet from front to back. What is its area in square feet?

11. Measure the length and width of your school lot. Find its area in square feet.

12. Mr. Bell wants to lay a new sidewalk 4 feet wide and 54 feet long. Find the cost at $3.25 a square yard.

Distance Around and Size

1. Steve and his father marked off a space for a chicken yard by driving stakes at the four corners.

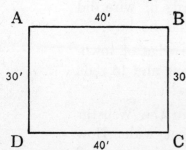

They staked off a space 40 feet long and 30 feet wide. Steve's father asked him two questions:

a. How big is the chicken yard in square feet?

b. How long must the fence be to go around the chicken yard?

This is the way Steve found the area:	This is the way Steve found the distance around it:	
40	From A to B	40 ft.
30	From B to C	30 ft.
1200 sq. ft.	From C to D	40 ft.
	From D to A	30 ft.
		140 ft.

2. Here is another way to find the distance around it:

40 ft.	30 ft.	80 ft.
2	2	60 ft.
80 ft.	60 ft.	140 ft.

3. Can you think of another way?

Distance Around and Size

1. Steve was papering his room which is 14 feet long and 12 feet wide. He needed a strip of border to go around the walls at the edges next to the ceiling. How long a strip did he need?

2. How large is Steve's room in square feet?

3. Mr. Leach built a fence around his garden to keep the rabbits out. His garden is 100 feet long and 75 feet wide. How long is the fence? How large is the garden?

4. A farmer had a field that was 40 rods long and 40 rods wide. How large was his field in square rods? How long was the fence around it?

5. For exercise Sue and Martha walked around their block 4 times. Their block is 420 feet long and 350 feet wide. How far did they walk?

420'

350'

6. James was building a pen for his rabbits. He was putting up a fence of chicken wire. He wanted the pen to be 20 feet long and 12 feet wide. How many feet of chicken wire did he need?

Square Inches in a Square Foot

1. How many square inches are there in 1 square foot?

A square foot is a square 1 foot long and 1 foot wide, or 12 inches long and 12 inches wide.

12 → number of inches long
12 → number of inches wide
───
24
12
───
144 → number of square inches

12 in. = 1 ft.   **144 sq. in. = 1 sq. ft.**

2. How many square feet are there in 1 square yard?

3 ft. = 1 yd.   **9 sq. ft. = 1 sq. yd.**

3. How many square inches are there in 9 square feet? How many square inches are there in 1 square yard?

4. Find the area of a window whose shape is a rectangle, 36 inches long and 12 inches wide.

5. Measure the length and the width of the top of your desk to the nearest inch and find its area.

Study these tables. Is the table of square measure correct? How can you tell?

Length		Square Measure	
12 in.	= 1 ft.	144 sq. in.	= 1 sq. ft.
3 ft.	= 1 yd.	9 sq. ft.	= 1 sq. yd.
$5\frac{1}{2}$ yd.	= 1 rd.	$30\frac{1}{4}$ sq. yd.	= 1 sq. rd.
$16\frac{1}{2}$ ft.	= 1 rd.	$272\frac{1}{4}$ sq. ft.	= 1 sq. rd.

Area and Perimeter

1. Jack has a garden 18 ft. long and 15 ft. wide. Henry's garden is 20 ft. long and 12 ft. wide. Which garden has the greater area? How many more square feet are in the larger garden than in the smaller one?

2. Dan wants to put a fence around his garden, which is 14 ft. long and 14 ft. wide. The wire for the fence costs 27¢ a foot. How much must Dan pay for the wire?

3. The floor of Mary's room is 10 ft. long and 9 ft. wide. She wants a rug that will be 6 in. from each wall. What will be the area of the rug?

4. Mr. Jones wants to have a new cement floor put in his garage. At 25¢ a square foot what will the floor cost if it is 16 ft. long and 12 ft. wide?

5. Which room has the larger area, one 12 ft. long and 8 ft. wide, or one 16 ft. long and 6 ft. wide?

6. Mrs. Elder wants to have her 9′ × 12′ rug cleaned. What will it cost if the cleaners charge 15¢ a square foot?

7. The boys' club room is 14 ft. long and 11 ft. wide. What is the perimeter of the floor? What is its area?

8. Susan made a rug that is 6 ft. long and $4\frac{1}{2}$ ft. wide. She wants to buy fringe to put all around it. How much fringe will she have to buy?

9. Mr. Walters plants his rosebushes so that each bush has 4 sq. ft. of ground. His rose bed is 15 ft. long and 3 ft. wide. Is the bed large enough for 9 bushes?

10. Martha's room is 14 ft. long and 8 ft. wide. What is the perimeter of her room? the area?

Problem Test

1. Martha bought 24 tulip bulbs. If she plants 6 bulbs in each flowerpot, how many flowerpots will she need?

2. At 75¢ each, what should Mrs. West pay for 3 violet plants?

3. Jane had 63 books in her library. She gave 19 of them to her cousin. How many books were in Jane's library then?

4. Bill went fishing four days last week. He caught 8 fish one day, 6, 10, and 4 on other days. In all how many fish did Bill catch last week?

5. One Saturday the Scouts walked 8 mi. On other Saturdays they walked 5 mi., 4 mi., and 7 mi. What was the average distance that the Scouts hiked?

6. Jim picked 36 lb. of walnuts. He sold one third of them and kept the rest. How many pounds did he keep?

7. Jack had $3.56. He bought a bucket for 85¢ and a sponge for 39¢ so that he could start a business of car washing. How much money had he left?

8. Ted picked 32 qt. of strawberries one day and sold all but 7 qt. of them. How much did he get for the berries if he sold them at 24¢ a quart?

9. Helen has 12 boxes, all the same size, to wrap for the grab bag at the carnival. She plans to use about 10 feet of ribbon to tie up each box. At 3¢ a yard, how much will the ribbon cost?

10. Twelve of the fifth-grade pupils had a party for the class. For refreshments they bought 36 ice-cream cups at 5¢ each. If the 12 pupils shared this expense equally, what did each one pay?

Test on Fundamentals

Watch what you are told to do. Check each example.

1. Add:
269
377
486

2. Subtract:
837
105

3. Multiply:
48
65

4. Subtract:
1000
460

5. Add:
$8\frac{2}{3}$
$2\frac{1}{6}$

6. 372
×84

7. 50.4
−29.8

8. $4\frac{5}{8}$
$-2\frac{1}{8}$

9. 43.72
+19.56

10. $36\overline{)1224}$

11. $\frac{3}{5}$
$+\frac{1}{2}$

12. $6.95
×34

13. 7.8
×8

14. Add $\frac{2}{3}$
$\frac{1}{4}$
$\frac{5}{6}$

15. $17\overline{)816}$

16. $5\frac{1}{3}$
$-1\frac{3}{4}$

17. 109
×83

18. $67\overline{)\$270.01}$

19. $45\overline{)4095}$

20. $9\overline{)37.8}$

21. 12.8
×7

22. 9
$-3\frac{3}{5}$

23. $15.04
−7.98

24. 24.3
×36

25. $.64
.08
.73

Test on Vocabulary

1. $12\overline{)84}$ quotient 7

2. 37
×4
148

3. 18
+43
61

4. $3.45
−1.27
$2.18

5. $\frac{4}{8}$

6. $\frac{6}{5}$

7. $3\frac{1}{2}$

8. 8.02

9. .9

Match a number from these examples with one of the words below:

a. Sum
b. Difference
c. Product
d. Quotient
e. Divisor
f. Fraction
g. Numerator
h. Denominator
i. Decimal
j. Tenths
k. Mixed number
l. Improper fraction

331

TABLES OF MEASURES

Liquid Measure

2 cups = 1 pint (pt.)
2 pints = 1 quart (qt.)
4 quarts = 1 gallon (gal.)

Dry Measure

2 pints = 1 quart (qt.)
8 quarts = 1 peck (pk.)
4 pecks = 1 bushel (bu.)

Measures of Weight

16 ounces (oz.) = 1 pound (lb.)
2000 pounds = 1 ton (T.)
2240 pounds = 1 long ton

Measures in Counting

12 things = 1 dozen (doz.)
12 dozen = 1 gross
144 things = 1 gross

Measures of Length

12 inches (in.) = 1 foot (ft.)
3 feet = 1 yard (yd.)
36 inches = 1 yard
$5\frac{1}{2}$ yards = 1 rod (rd.)
$16\frac{1}{2}$ feet = 1 rod
5280 feet = 1 mile (mi.)
1760 yards = 1 mile
320 rods = 1 mile

Measures of Time

60 seconds (sec.) = 1 minute (min.)
60 minutes = 1 hour (hr.)
24 hours = 1 day
7 days = 1 week
52 weeks = 1 year (yr.)
12 months = 1 year
365 days = 1 year
366 days = 1 leap year
10 years = 1 decade
100 years = 1 century

Square Measure

144 square inches (sq. in.) = 1 square foot (sq. ft.)
9 square feet = 1 square yard (sq. yd.)
$30\frac{1}{4}$ square yards = 1 square rod (sq. rd.)
$272\frac{1}{4}$ square feet = 1 square rod

change unlike denominators to like de
usually you change to the larger one when
they are both even numbers as 2, 4, 6, 8 etc.
When one is uneven multiply the to togethe
to get a common denominator $\frac{2}{3} + \frac{3}{4}$ the
common denominator = 12